RADIOS BY

hallicrafters ™

WITH PRICE GUIDE

Chuck Dachis

Schiffer Publishing Ltd

77 Lower Valley Road, Atglen, PA 19310

Dedication

To the memory of Timothy Dachis,
my lover, without whose steadfast
support and encouragement over the years
this collection would not be what it is today

and to my parents
Hannah Lea and Irving Dachis.

Acknowledgments

I wish to thank the hundreds of people who have provided me with information and equipment for this collection over the past twenty years. Special thanks to the following: Phil Beautrow, John Bryant, H. L. "Chad" Chadbourne, Tony Dambrauskas, Robert Dambrauskas, Fritz Franke, William J. Halligan, Stan J. Jurczuk, Tom Lott, John Nagle, Robert J. Orwin, Robert E. Samuelson, George Watkins, Bill Ross, Richard M. Shappee, William I. Orr, Berry Wiseman, Fred W. Bonavita, Ferdinand Schor, Joseph Schroeder, Raymond S. Moore, Durrell Roth, Candy Drake of Howard W. Sams & Co. in Indianapolis, IN, and Richard "Dick" Chambers of Hillandale TV & Appliance in Silver Spring, Maryland.

Library of Congress Cataloging-in-Publication Data

Dachis, Chuck, 1942-
      Radios by Hallicrafters / Chuck Dachis.
           p.   cm.
      ISBN 0-88740-929-6 (soft)
        1. Amateur radio stations – Equipment and supplies – History.
2. Hallicrafters, Inc. – History. 3. Shortwave radio – Receivers and reception – Collectors and collecting. 4. Shortwave radios – Transmitters and transmission – Collectors and collecting.
    I. Title.
TK9956.D24   1995
621.384'13 – dc20   95-45247
                                      CIP

Printed in China
ISBN: 0-88740-929-6

Publisher's note: During production, this wonderful book gre well beyond its original scope with information and phot graphs. Because of this, combined with the tremendous i crease in paper prices and increased cost of color printin the publisher has printed many photographs in black a white instead of color as originally planned.

Published by Schiffer Publishing, Ltd.
77 Lower Valley Road
Atglen, PA 19310
Please write for a free catalog.
This book may be purchased from the publisher.
Please include $2.95 postage.
Try your bookstore first.

We are interested in hearing from authors
with book ideas on related subjects.

Contents

SX-122R

Preface

My involvement with electro-mechanical devices extends back to my early childhood. As a toddler I had no interest in playing with toys designed for children of my age, but rather with our neighbors' discarded toasters, burned-out electric fans, or old carburetors! My mother saw no problem with this until a friend admonished her for letting me play with this 'junk' instead of buying me proper toys. In an effort to persuade me to play with more ordinary toys, Mother told me that since all these old things were dirty and could "cause germs," it would be a good idea not to play with them anymore.

I was always very logical, with a thought pattern approaching that of the scientific process even at age of 3 or 4. My logical response to this problem of germs was simple. I took all my junk, threw it in the bathtub and washed it!

After that, Mother told her friend to mind her own business.

I have always had an affinity for mechanical and electronic devices, and wanted to know what made them work. My dad wouldn't let me take apart the family radio because, as he said, "It works fine, and if it works—,don't fix it!" So at age 8 I found an old Philco 'cathedral', plugged it in, and watched it smoke and blow a fuse. (No, I hadn't washed it in the tub.) I excitedly rounded up some of my dad's tools and started an autopsy, completely disassembling the set and studying all the weird little parts it yielded. During the next few years I dissected about two hundred radios, most of which collectors would give their eye teeth for

today. By the age of twelve I was quite familiar with the mechanical principles of radio construction, and could identify parts and understand their function.

One of the radios I purchased at the local Goodwill store for one dollar (a half-week's allowance) was an RCA 816K. It was scheduled for major surgery so it would fit in my 'rocket ship' control panel (Tom Corbet and Captain Video were my heroes). I had it out of the cabinet and on the bench when its grandeur suddenly hit me — I couldn't cut it up. I decided I would get it working, and I did! Ever since, the 816K has been very special to me. Though I sold that model a year later and haven't seen one since, I have had many dreams about it. Fixing it was a real triumph, and marked a turning point in my relationship with radio.

I was no longer interested in just taking them apart; instead I wanted to fix and use them. The more frequency bands, tubes, dials and knobs they had, the better I liked them. I called these sets 'super radios'. My first Hallicrafters was the SX-28, which certainly fit the 'super radio' classification. It was also my first communications receiver. I became an avid AM and shortwave DX listener. Whenever my family took cross-country trips, my dad would be amazed; no matter what city we were in, I knew the call letters and frequencies of the stations.

During the next thirteen years I looked for bigger and better radios and found few. I always hoped I'd find a 'dream store' with wall-to-wall, floor-to-ceiling 'super radios' at prices I could afford. I never found that

store! My interest in radio waned for a decade or so, and most of what I had acquired was given away or sold.

In 1973, I decided (again) to start a collection of 'super radios' of all brands. The first radio I wanted, for nostalgic reasons, was the SX-28. Since I did not know where to look, it took over six months of advertising in the local newspaper to find one. This radio had been in a flood, was full of mud, and was in awful condition. It had taken me so long to find it that I considered it rare, and proceeded with my first 'modern' restoration.

While looking for the SX-28, I had come across an S-36. Until then, I hadn't known that Hallicrafters made anything other than SX-28s. I realized if there were 28 and 36 models, there must also be 29 and 37. With almost no documentation available, finding products, technical data, advertising and promotional items from Hallicrafters would be a challenging and exciting project. It quickly became apparent that I would need to specialize. My collection currently contains over four hundred different pieces of major equipment, displayed on wall-to-wall and floor-to-ceiling shelves, with hundreds of original technical manuals, advertising brochures, and smaller accessory units. Sitting in my collection room one day, admiring all the Hallicrafters radios I have accumulated, I came to a realization — I have *created* my dream store!

My new dream—actually a necessity—is to open a Hallicrafters museum to properly display the products and memorabilia of the company, so this wonderful and unusual collection can be enjoyed by anyone who is interested.

One might ask me, "How is it that you have more duplicate Hallicrafters units than most other collectors have items in their collections?" Well, there is no simple answer. These poor things just seem to find me, and say "Please take me home and take care of me." I can't stand the thought of forgotten, dirty and decrepit radios living in someone's shed or barn — or worse yet, about to go to the city dump! Whenever I see a Hallicrafters item at a garage sale, flea market, or swap meet, the 'motherly' instinct comes over me; if I can afford it, I buy it even if I have a dozen others of the same model.

Sometimes these radios actually appear on my doorstep, with a note that says "Give me a good home." Still others are given to me in various conditions by people who can no longer take care of them and want to insure that they will continue to be useful and appreciated by someone. My doors are always open to new arrivals; no Hallicrafters will ever be turned away!

So, you ask, what do I do with them? If the radio is one that I need for the collection, it goes to the emergency room (my electronic work area in the garage), where it is immediately resuscitated and given emergency restoration treatment according to the diagnosis. If it is a duplicate, I stabilize its condition and put it aside for future restoration. If there is no possibility of economical restoration, it will usually give me permission to donate its major organs so that a more rare brother or sister in the collection may come back to life. If none of my units are in need of major organ transplants, these parts are held in reserve for national distribution to bring life to other units living in different parts of the country.

As time permits, I restore the duplicate units as near as is possible to their original condition, and then use them as trading material with other collectors. (See the chapter on Radio Restoration for further discussion.) They may be sold to people who want a specific model and have not been able to locate one after years of searching.

One of the most gratifying things for me is being able to help someone else fulfill a childhood fantasy. One gentleman wrote me a letter about a Hallicrafter radio a high school friend had owned in the mid-1930s. This radio, for some reason, had made a great impression on him. He explained that he could not afford such a radio back then, when they were available at the local radio store, and by the time he could afford one they were no longer in production, and could not be found for love or money! Not knowing the model of the radio, he gave me a 'picture' from memory, and asked my assistance in finding one. After some thought, I determined that the radio he wanted was a SX-9. I sent a photo of the SX-9, and he immediately recognized it. I had a spare unit, so I restored it and sold it to him. I know that it will have a good home, and will give pleasure for many more years.

A Note To Collectors

When most of us think of Hallicrafters we remember the SX and HT lines of Ham and SWL sets. If you had told me in 1974 (when I started collecting in earnest) that I would still be searching for Hallicrafters models more than twenty years later, I would have said you were nuts! I thought there had only been a dozen or so radio models manufactured! Actually, the SX and HT lines are only a small portion of what was produced. To date I have found over thirty different major product series, each containing up to two hundred models — not including World War II military gear! There is an extensive line of home entertainment equipment, including hi-fi and stereo models, clock radios, televisions, portable radios, and even electronic organs. There is no doubt in my mind that if Hallicrafters were still in business, I would have written this book on a Hallicrafters computer!

Finding documentation has become as important to me as acquiring the products. Most of the original company records were either lost or destroyed years ago, and until I published the first edition of my comprehensive product list, *The Hallicrafters Company: 1932-1982, A Partial Product Listing Covering Fifty Years of Production* in 1983, no one knew just what the company had made. This first list consisted of over thirty pages of condensed type, and contained the model numbers, names, production dates, original prices, and a brief technical description of as many Hallicrafters products as I was aware of, along with some historical information on the company and comments on some of the equipment.

I published four more editions before 1994, as I constantly found new models and product lines I hadn't known existed. This book is based on those product lists, and contains all of the Hallicrafters known to exist today, and even some that have only been found in advertisements!

There are several books available that give a good cross section of information on many different radio brands, including Hallicrafters. Two that I recommend are *A Flick Of The Switch 1930-1950* by Morgan E. McMahon, published by Vintage Radio (Box 1331, North Highlands, CA 95660), and *Communication Receivers, The Golden Years* by Raymond S. Moore (RSM Communications, P.O. Box 218, Norwood, MA 02062).

What can the beginning collector expect as the 21st century approaches? In the early 1970s there were only a handful of serious radio collectors. Most had no interest in communication gear, but rather in the grand old Scotts, Midwests, Atwater Kents, and Zeniths, among others. This left the field of collecting vintage communication equipment wide open, and relatively inexpensive. There was little demand for radios like Hallicrafter's, and I was able to buy many models in the $5 to $20 range; as often as not was told I could have it if I would just haul it off! Unfortunately, this is not the case today.

In the past few years there has been a tremendous resurgence of interest in antiques and collectible items of every description, especially vintage radios of all types. This has driven the price of most of these items to levels where only the well-off can contemplate a collection of considerable size. Today most radios are are bought by what I call 'mini-collectors', who want from one to a dozen sets. For most, the emphasis is on simply owning these radios, not restoring them. Don't despair—there are still some good deals out there. About eighty percent of the radios I buy are acquired through my continuous ads in the national radio magazines, like *QST, Antique Radio Classified*, and *Electric Radio*. The remainder I find by attending radio swap meets.

Because these radios are from twenty to sixty years old, they will almost certainly need considerable work to bring them back to their original glory. Once properly restored, however, they will usually provide many more years of good service. For those of you who are not technically inclined but want to own and operate one of these radios, good news! One of the 'spin-offs' of the antique radio boom is the re-emergence of technicians who know how to work on these sets. Several advertise in the magazines mentioned previously, and any large city is likely to have one or more vintage radio repair shops listed in the phone book. Be careful — it is not be unusual to spend $300 to $400 to have the SX-28 or other vintage 'super radio' restored! For those who want a refresher course in radio repair so they can do their own restorations, I recommend *Practical Radio Servicing* by William Marcos and Alex Levy, published by McGraw Hill in 1953. Also see the chapter on Radio Restoration in this book.

The author and Bill Halligan at the Hallicrafters Old Timers Reunion party in Chicago in September, 1983.

List of Technical Abbreviations

AVC	automatic volume control
AFC	automatic frequency control
AGC	automatic gain control
IF	intermediate frequency
RF	radio frequency
AF	audio frequency
TRF	tuned radio frequency
AMP	amplifier
DET	detector
BFO	beat frequency oscillator
Hz	Hertz
KHz	kiloHertz
MHz	megaHertz
XTAL	crystal
S-meter	signal strength or tuning meter
BAND	a range of frequencies
AM	amplitude modulation
FM	frequency modulation
AC	alternating current
DC	direct current
CRT	cathode ray tube
UHF	ultra high frequency
VHF	very high frequency
PM	permement magnet
VOX	voice operated transmission & reception
PTT	push to talk
CW	continuous wave
SSB	single sideband
NBFM	narrow band frequency modulation
PEP	peak envelope power
CB	citizens' band
FINAL	usually refers to the last stage of amplification in a device and could be either audio or radio frequency.
PLL	phase lock loop

Bill Halligan and Fritz Franke, a former chief engineer of the company, at the Old Timers Reunion in 1983. Sadly, Fritz passed away in December 1994 at age 86, and Bill Halligan passed away in July 1992 at age 93.

The History of Hallicrafters

How It All Began

In Boston, Massachusetts, during the spring of 1899, Hallicrafters' founder William J. Halligan was born. It would be another thirty-two years before he or anyone else new how crucial a role he would play in the development of radio technology. As a youngster, Bill was fascinated with the new technology of radio telegraphy, anxiously gleaning information on the subject from the latest scientific journals and the few books that were available. His first real job, when he was sixteen, was as a wireless operator on a excursion boat in the Boston area. Bill spent the next several years as a wireless operator on a number of ships, serving sea duty on a mine-layer off the coast of Scotland during World War I.

After the war Bill attended electrical engineering school at Tufts College and then at West Point, leaving West Point in 1922 to marry Kate Fletcher. He took a job as a reporter on a Boston newspaper, and also wrote articles for the 'new' American Radio Relay League. In 1924 he became sales manager for his old friend Toby Deutschmann, who was distributing imported radio parts to American radio manufacturers. By 1928, Toby's business was booming. Bill decided to strike out on his own as a manufacturers' representative, selling parts directly to the radio makers. In 1928, this decision led Bill to Chicago; most of the radio manufacturers were located there, so it was the logical place to set up shop. For three years his business did well, but in 1931 his clients were hit hard by the Depression, going bankrupt faster than the wind was blowing off the lake!

The First Hallicrafters Radios

Continuously active in building and operating his own Ham radio station, but unable to sell enough parts to pay the bills, Bill was inspired to build handcrafted Ham radio receivers, which had not existed previously in any commercial inventory. He made just a few at a time, using the highest quality parts, with no mass production.

He called his new business "The Hallicrafters." The name was chosen as a composite of two words: "Halligan" and "handcrafted." Bill adopted the creed "Handcraft Makes Perfect," and it was used in the first logo of the new enterprise in late 1932. A few sets were built, the S-1 through the S-3, at an old manufacturing plant at 417 North State Street.

Immediately the young Hallicrafters company was beset with problems. Most of the "Hams" these new radios were designed for hadn't yet recovered from the Depression, and didn't have the money to buy them. As if this wasn't enough, RCA came down hard on Hallicrafters for patent infringements, inisting that no more radios could be built until they granted Bill a license — which they had no intention of doing!

Bill didn't give up. Procuring as many orders for his radios as possible, he contracted with a licensed manufacturer to build them in small production runs of fifty or a hundred sets. He had to use the orders themselves for collateral, an arrangement that at best was very limiting.

What Hallicrafters needed was a license to build under RCA patents. In 1933 Silver-Marshall Inc. went into bankruptcy, and Bill saw an opportunity to get his coveted licence. A deal was engineered; Bill and Hallicrafters took over Silver-Marshall Inc., re-naming it the "Silver-Marshall Manufacturing Company" and operating it from the State Street address. This relationship was also plagued with financial problems, and ended in late 1934. Bill was released from his obligations to Silver-Marshall with the help of Ray Durst, a customer credit manager for the Echophone Radio Company.

Echophone was also in financial trouble, for all practical purposes out of business. They had a 50,000 square foot plant at 2611 Indiana Avenue, and a good license. Bill struck a deal with the owner of Echophone and the two companies merged, with Hallicrafters being the dominant partner. Ray Durst became vice president of Hallicrafters.

During the first few months the company did contract work for other radio manufacturers and large mail-order houses in order to build its cash reserves. In late 1935 they started producing their own line of communications receivers, which we are all familiar with. The SX-9 "Super Skyrider" was the first model to be produced in significant quantities. The company logo was changed.

Hallicrafters in the Late '30s

Hallicrafters' policy was to build a quality product with all the state-of-the-art advances and features, at a price that was affordable. With this policy and good management, they pulled themselves up by their bootstraps. By 1938 Hallicrafters was the most popular manufacturer of communications receivers in the US, and were doing business in eighty-nine other countries.

Bill decided on another policy: that as new features and technical advances were made, Hallicrafters would bring out new models, rather than just upgrade the same basic model. This explains the profusion of different models, which in the three-year period from 1936 to 1938 had reached twenty-three.

Until 1938 the production was limited to receivers and associated accessories; it was time to produce transmitters. The job of designing the new product line belonged to the newly hired Bob Samuelson, who was responsible for the designs of the HT-1 through the HT-14, and would shortly become the company's chief engineer.

Hallicrafters & World War II

The onslaught of World War II took the U.S. by surprise. There was a shortage of military radio equipment and tremendous government demand for electronic equipment of all types. Many of the existing Hallicrafters products and designs were pressed into military service. The company geared up for wartime production, and was responsible for many new designs and innovations. Probably the best-known of these were the HT-4 (BC-610) and related equipment used in the SCR-299. Production of Ham radio gear and related items was all but suspended until 1945.

Post-War Hallicrafters

By August of 1945, the war was over, and so were wartime production and most government contracts. It was time again to produce ham radio equipment. A new line of consumer electronics was needed to satisfy a public hungry for products they had gone without for over five years.

The old plant at 2611 Indiana Ave. had served Hallicrafters well during the war years, but the company needed a modern image for their facility and product line in the postwar period. A new plant was designed and built at 4401 West 5th Avenue (5th and Kostner) that would be the company's home for the next twenty years. The products were given a 'modern' look with the help of Raymond Loewy, a well-known industrial designer of the time. One of the first postwar sets produced in the new facility was the S-38. The logo was again changed, this time to the familiar "Circle H."

Production also began on the new line of consumer electronics, including radio phonograph units of all shapes and sizes, AM/FM receivers, clock radios in brightly colored Bakelite cases, and television receivers (the first being the T-54). Many of the consumer products bore the name "Echophone," which had been all but forgotten by that time. Competition was stiff in the consumer electronics field, and this Hallicrafters line never really took hold, although stayed in production until the late 1950s. Even so, the company was doing better than ever, was employing 2,500 people by 1952.

The 1950s were very successful for the company. Bill's son, Bill Jr., and possibly other family members were involved in the operation. The United States' focus during the 'fifties was civil defense, so many Hallicrafters products from this period bore names like "Civic Patrol" and "Defender." Some of the Ham radio products became classics, like the HT-32 and SX-101 (1957). Much of this equipment is still in use today and is sought after by nostalgia buffs and collectors.

By 1958 Bill, Sr. wanted to retire, and the company was sold. Little was known about this transaction, but it apparently failed and the Halligans resumed control a short time later. In 1963 Hallicrafters purchased Radio Industries, Inc. of Kansas City, running it as a subsidiary. Radio Industries produced many of the Ham radio accessories and some major equipment like the HT-45 "Loudenboomer." The Halligans continued operations until about 1966, when the company was sold to the Northrop Corporation. This ended forever the Halligans' involvement in Hallicrafters.

The End of Hallicrafters

Northrop moved the company to a new plant at 600 Hicks Road in Rolling Meadows, IL, and modified the logo again. While a subsidiary of Northrop, Hallicrafters produced Ham radio products for a few more years, but the main function was producing para-military equipment in Northrop's defense systems division, much of it in El Paso, TX. For all practical purposes the last Ham radio item produced was the FPM-300 in 1972, and a few accessories through 1974. There were also some CB units and portable 'jam box' type AM/FM/SW sets of Japanese origin released under the Hallicrafters name. At this point, Northrop turned Hallicrafters over to its partner, Wilcox.

The annual sales of Hallicrafters had been falling off sharply since 1970. On December 4, 1975, Wilcox sold the company to the Braker Corporation of Dallas, Texas, represented by Darrell Fletcher. Braker packed up fourteen semi-trailer loads of Hallicrafters records and parts and moved the company to Grand Prairie, Texas. They set up shop there, with several former Hallicrafters employees of the late '60s and '70s who relocated to Texas. A few more CB's and various portable radios of Japanese and Taiwanese origin were released, but Braker began to suffer severe financial difficulties.

Around 1980 Braker ceased doing business, and Hallicrafters along with it.

On August 24th 1979 Clarence E. Long (a business acquaintance of Fletcher's from Miami) engineered a purchase of the name, logos and what was left of the company. A new corporation, called Hallicrafters International, was set up in Miami; it also had international trademarks.

Long set up shop and hired a large staff in anticipation of receiving large government contracts to build paramilitary radios for the armed forces. The new Hallicrafters International had to prove to the government they could handle the contracts as well as the old firm had. Something went wrong, however; Long's plans failed to be approved, and Hallicrafters lost the contracts.

In the early 1980s Long set up a plant somewhere in the New England States, and also had convinced several well-known people in other parts of the country to join the company. Among them was Tom Lott, who had worked for Bell Laboratories for many years and was responsible for research and development of some of the first transistors in the early 1950s.

Despite all this activity, Long was in serious financial and legal trouble. He declared bankruptcy on June 1, 1988 in San Antonio Texas. All of his property—including the Hallicrafters name, logos, and whatever records were saved—were made property of a court-appointed trustee.

Since this time, the Hallicrafters name has not been used, and, for all practical purposes, is non-existent.

Though the Hallicrafters Company of old is no more, the 'old' Hallicrafter Company will always be alive, a large part of my life and the lives of those who love the radios they made for so many years.

A typical mid- and late 1940s company letterhead.

Bill Halligan, the founder of Hallicrafters, taken from the 1934 Silver Marshall/Hallicrafters catalogue.

A typical mid- and late 1960s company letterhead.

Kendall Clough, chief engineer of Silver Marshall Inc. and designer of the Z-Deluxe receiver, taken from the 1934 Silver Marshall/Hallicrafters catalogue.

Bill Halligan in his office at 2611 Indiana Avenue, sitting at his Ham radio station. Bill's call sign at this time was W9WZE. This photo is from late 1938 or early 1939 and was given to me by Bob Samuelson

The management and engineering staff gathered around the DD-1 receiver in Bill Halligan's office in 1939, at the 2611 Indiana Avenue plant. There appear to be Christmas decorations on the blinds, suggesting that the photograph was taken in December 1938. This print was given to me by Bob Samuelson who was the chief engineer of Hallicrafters at that time. According to Mr. Samuelson, this same photograph was published in the March 1939 issue of QST magazine as part of a advertisement introducing the SX-23. It was also used in a 12-page advertising brochure on the SX-23 published by the company in March 1939. From left to right are Fred Strowatt (the engineer who designed the SX-32); Royal Higgeons (sales); Ed Caroran (purchasing); Bill Halligan; Loren Toogood (production engineer); Ray Durst (vice president and former consumer credit manager of the Echophone Radio Company); Joe Frendreis (controller); Herb Hartley (production manager); Bob Samuelson (chief engineer); J.L.A. McLaughlin (receiver engineer who designed the dual diversity receiver DD-1). Fred Schor, the lead receiver engineer, is missing from the photo.

INTERESTING AND PERHAPS LITTLE KNOWN FACTS ABOUT HALLICRAFTERS

Over the years the Hallicrafters Company has been responsible for pioneering many innovations in communications equipment and related electronics. What follows is a chronicle of some of them.

In 1936 they introduced the first commercially-built VHF receiver, the SX-10 Ultra Sky Rider.

In 1937 they introduced the first calibrated S-meter, used in the SX-16.

In 1939-40 They built and marketed the first commercial AM/FM Receiver, the S-31.

In 1939-40 they made one of the first battery-powered "all-wave" portable receivers, the S-29 Sky Traveler.

In 1946 they built and marketed the first continuous tuning "all-wave" receiver covering 535KHz to 110MHz, the SX-42.

In 1952 they pioneered the use of printed circuit technology, used in the ATCL series clock radios and displayed in the CPCR-1* dealer display.

In 1955 they introduced one of the first receivers having swith-selectable choice of upper or lower sideband, the SX-96.

In 1957 they introduced the first SSB transmitter using the quarts filter sideband system (the HT-32), perfected differential temperature compensation for variable frequency oscillators, and patented the "bridge tee" sideband modulator.

In 1959 they pioneered one of the first transistorized HF transceivers with the introduction of the FPM-200.

In 1960 they patented one of the first electronic code keyers using digital techniques, the HA-1 "T.O. Keyer."

In 1961 they introduced two of the first "transverters" for the VHF bands (the HA-2 and the HA-6), and in 1961-62 they introduced Receiver Incremental Tuning (R.I.T.) inthe amateur transceiver line, with the SR-150.

In 1963 Hallicrafters established the Citizens' Band Radio Club devoted to highway safety and emergency, with a program called "REACT" — "Radio Emergency Associated Citizens Team."

The following photographs are of the Hallicrafters staff of the mid-1940s during the "war effort."

They were all taken from *The HT-4 Goes To War*, a book produced by Hallicrafters in 1944.

These distinguished members of the Clearing cast are: M. J. Pannell, Tony Grossi, A. Boettcher, Wally Burandt, Ray Reynolds, William Racek, H. Schwenker, J. Herman, E. E. Harrison and K. Holmgren.

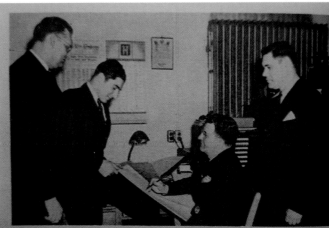

These are some of the key men in the Wabash Avenue setup: A. Harvey, P. Skarpho, A. Apih, A. Dziencolowski.

Production and shipping of the HO-17 shelter is handled by this Clearing task force. Shop foreman is Earl Barnes, seated center. He is backed up by Harold De Bonis, Oliver Newman, Walter Malona, Willis Johnson, Buck Rogers, George Hjelkrem, Mike Perri, James Maxey, B. Flowers, Fred Porter, William Conway, and D. C. McCann.

These main cogs in the big Hallicrafters war machine include, left to right: E. A. LaBelle, traffic manager; Rex Briselden, production planning manager; Clete Wiot, manager, contract division; Joe Thompson, assistant sales manager; Bob Russell, administrative assistant.

The 299's and 399's owe some of their fame to these three who handle repairs and testing on this world renowned equipment. They are Ted Cassell, Ray Polkinghon, Melvin Malley. Dave Healy is now in charge of this important operation.

The vital job of backing up the equipment with spare parts, on time and in good shape, is handled by this 29th street crew: Tom Caprio, August Fisher, Henry Baker, Lulu Dimitz, Frank Oslakovich, Mike Jakubczak.

Notice the SCR-299 in the background.

This quintet includes Evelyn Van Cura, Hazel Mehler, Matt Heinz, Flo Dershem and Florence Snyder.

Department heads and their assistants in the general engineering department: left to right, Corwin Livenick, Myrtle Willner, Milton Wullenweber, Ed Keyes, Harry McCarty, Jay Dawson, Jules Leonhardi, Ed Voznak, Wally Hildebrand, Ann Fremiarek and Florence Lindahl.

Notice the HT-11 transmitter (right center).

The highly important operations of purchasing and expediting fall into these capable hands: Bob Campbell, Hans Sauer, John Butler, Stewart Nelson, Dave Katznelson, Roman Possley, Jack Bentkower, Ed McNulty.

The people that pile up the production records: Carl McConkey, general foreman, W. Carlson, Ben Timms, Eleanor Foster and J. Smith, who does such a good job on protection and maintenance.

The SX-25 appears here.

And here are Ken McClelland's staff assistants in personnel: William Meyer who heads up the training program, Frank Peplowski, Ern Armbruester, and George Snider.

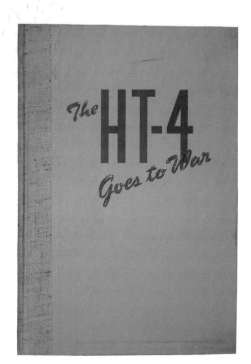

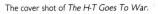

The cover shot of *The H-T Goes To War.*

These pictures were taken from the technical manual for the SCR-299 communications truck.

THE HALLICRAFTERS LOGO

Over the years, the logo and signature of the Hallicrafters Company has changed a number of times. Most of us are familiar with the circle containing the large lower-case 'h'. This is perhaps the best-known and most common, but there were others. Most of these signatures and logos overlapped in sequence, and may even have been used out of sequence. The chronology that follows is aproximate.

The first signature was "By The Hallicrafters," usually prefaced by "Sky Rider" or "Super Sky Rider." This was used (generally without a logo) on the S-1 through the S-7 models, and dates to the start of the company in 1933. It was used through 1939 on models running from the S-9 to the S-22, along with two different logos.

Another signature was "The Hallicrafters," used on the Super Seven, S-8A, and probably others in 1935.

"The Hallicrafters Inc." was used on the S-20 through the SX-28 from 1938 to 1941.

"The Hallicrafters Co." was used on most of the postwar equipment through the SX-115 in 1961.

After Northrup purchased the company the signature was abreviated to "Hallicrafters," which was used until the company's demise in the late 1970s.

The Hallicrafters signature of the 1930s.

The Hallicrafters logo from the early 1930s, during the association with Silver Marshall Mfg.Co.

The mid-1930s logo.

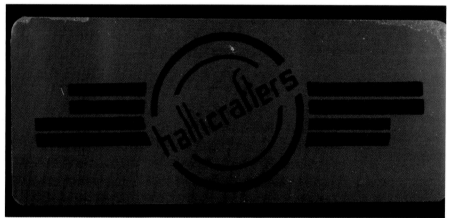

The best-known of the Hallicrafters logos. This design was used from aproximately 1939 through 1960.

The logo and signature of the company in the late 1960s and early 1970s, when the company was a part of Wilcox.

The logo and signature of the company during the mid- and late 1960s, when the company was a part of Northrup.

THE EARLY HALLICRAFTERS PLANTS

Over the years, Hallicrafters has occupied three major sites in Chicago for the company's headquarters and production facility. The first was 417 North State Street, used during 1933 and 1934 during Hallicrafters association with Silver Marshall. I have no photographs of this plant, which was torn down years ago to make room for high-rises and other downtown commercial development.

The second plant was at 2611 Indiana Avenue, the site of the old Echophone plant, which Hallicrafters occupied from late 1934 until 1945. Hallicrafters used the top four floors of the building, while other tenants used the rest of it. This plant was only a few blocks from the Old Lexington Hotel, Al Capone's headquarters.

The plant at 4401 West 5th Avenue (5th and Kostner) was designed and built especially for Hallicrafters, and was used from approximately 1945 through 1965. This plant is still in existence and is being used as a warehouse.

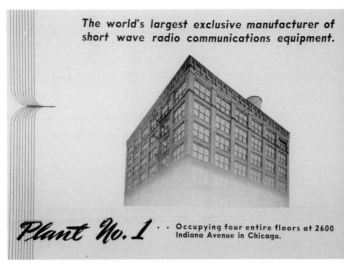

The world's largest exclusive manufacturer of short wave radio communications equipment.

Plant No. 1 · · Occupying four entire floors at 2600 Indiana Avenue in Chicago.

The second Hallicrafters site, at 2611 Indiana Avenue. This picture was taken from a Hallicrafters advertising brochure. Today, the site is a residential complex.

HALLICRAFTERS NEW HOME, efficiently designed to house the main plant, research laboratories and general offices

This ariel shot of the 5th and Kostner plant was taken from a Hallicrafters advertising brochure.

The Plant

This office section of the 5th and Kostner plant was also taken from a Hallicrafters brochure.

The main entrance to the 5th and Kostner plant, as it appears today.

These photos show the 5th and Kostner plant as it is today. *Photographs courtesy of Ken Schroeder, Rock Island, IL.*

THE GATTI/HALLICRAFTERS EXPEDITION

In 1948, Hallicrafters teamed up with world-renowned traveler and author Attilio Gatti, to make a scientific safari expedition to Africa. The main purpose of the expedition was to test Hallicrafters radio equipment and to study radio phenomena under the adverse conditions found in the African jungles. The expedition had regularly scheduled radio transmission and contacts with Ham radio operators all over the world. The equipment used on the trip was the HT-4E, SX-42, SX-43, S-38, and the HT-18, all of which was installed in a specially designed trucks. The transmitting antenna was a prefabricated rhombic for 10, 20, and 40 meters, and could be assembled and disassembled in short order. Outboard diesel and gas generators were used to power the equipment. Some of the other people involved in the expedition were Weldon King (a former Army photographer at Corregidor), Ham radio operators William Snyder (WOLHS from Fargo, ND) and Robert Leo (W6PBV) of San Mateo, CA). The official photographers were Keith Sisk of Cumberland, MD and Erroll C. Prince of Milwaukee, WI. The official correspondent was James D. Powers, who was with the International News Service. The expedition's official USA radio contact station was W9CGC, which was the 5th Avenue Radio Club located in the Hallicrafters plant at 4401 West 5th Avenue in Chicago.

A paper machete safari hat promoting the expedition. *Photograph by Jim Sargent of Sherwood, AK.*

Portable power genera[...] accompany the Expedit[...] enabling the Hallicraf[...] transmitters to put out [...] nals that hams around [...] world can pick up.

Radio Restoration

"This radio has been completely restored"—How many times have you heard that statement? What does it mean? 'Restored' means different things to different people.

I have seen 'restored' radios in which nothing but a tube or two and a capacitor were replaced to get them to work, and the dust was wiped off.

I have also seen radios that have been completely disassembled, all metal parts refinished to exact paint or plating formulas, new lettering silk-screened on the new finish, all components and wiring replaced with 'new' components of the same type and vintage, and new plastic parts molded from old formulas. Should this radio be considered 'restored', or is it new?

To me the answer lies somewhere between these two examples. Each restoration is judged on its own merits, dictated by the condition of the raw material.

Beginning the Restoration

The process of restoration begins with a preliminary physical cleaning and assessment of the radio's general condition. Any physical or mechanical problems or modifications that would impede the electrical restoration are handled first.

Extra non-original switches, 'magic tuning eyes', or meters must be removed, and the resulting holes in the front panel filled. Filling the holes can be tricky. Depending on the location of the hole, the panel may have to be removed to effect repairs. Generally I use a backing of metal duct tape, then fill the hole with automotive Bondo. Sometimes several thin coats are necessary, with a light sanding between each. Once they are dry and sanded smooth, I spot-paint the repaired area(s) with matching paint, usually with an air brush, blending it to the existing finish.

If any original controls or switches are broken, bad, or missing, they will be replaced or added at this time.

Electrical Restoration

Proceeding to the electrical restoration, all modifications are removed, sloppy former repairs reworked, and all circuitry returned to the original factory schematic. Next check the small individual components, paper and wax bypass capacitors. To check these capacitors, carefully de-solder the terminal holding one of the leads, and remove the lead. Then check the capacitors for leakage resistance on the high range of a good analog VOM (it must be analog; the digital units do not work well for this test).

It has been my experience that most of these capacitors are bad, typically having a leakage resistance of 100 K ohm to 10 megohm, and

I will generally replace all of them. The reason leaky capacitors are replaced is three-fold. First, a circuit will not operate properly when a capacitor is acting more like a resistor. Second, the leakage current through a dozen or so capacitors can create enough additional 'load' on the power supply to cause failure of the power transformer and other power supply components. And last, when I restore a set I want it to work for a long time. If all these capacitors aren't replaced, sooner or later (usually sooner), they will fail.

The mica and ceramic capacitors are almost always good and will not generally need to be replaced or even checked.

Any resistors connected to the terminals that were de-soldered (while the capacitors were being checked and replaced) must also be checked at this time, and replaced if necessary. Resistors are the next biggest culprit in degrading the performance of the equipment. It is typical for many of them to look perfectly good, but to nonetheless be any where from 10% to 200% higher in resistance than the marked value. This causes a serious voltage deficiency in a given circuit, preventing it from functioning properly. Any resistor that is more than 10% out of tolerance (high or low) will be replaced.

Now I get brave, and apply power—to see if it works or smokes! Usually it works, though not always well; there is still more to do. Check and replace any bad tubes, and any major component that may be bad (transformers, IF cans, and electrolytic capacitors). Clean the controls and switches with control cleaner, and finish the physical cleaning of the chassis and major components. Next do a complete IF (intermediate frequency) and RF (radio frequency) alignment, in that order, following the factory instructions.

Major Components

In replacing small components I use state-of-the-art mylar capacitors to insure continued long-lasting performance, and new resistors of proper type and values.

But what about large components such as power, audio, and IF transformers? Sometimes repair to the damaged or worn components is unavoidable; for example, if I am restoring a rare model that needs a power transformer, and the chance of finding another in better condition is slim, I will have the transformer re-wound. (One company doing transformer re-winding is The Peter Dahl Co. of El Paso, Texas.) But my philosophy is to use only original parts in good working condition, gleaned from other radios, whenever possible.

There is no commercial source for these parts, so where do you find them? The answer is simple, although somewhat costly. I will sometimes purchase as many as five radios of the same or similar model to get enough parts to restore one. Many of the Hallicrafters models from a given time period used the same or very similar components.

This gives me a choice of models to scavenge from, making the acquisition of parts easier.

It is my policy to buy any Hallicrafters product whenever it is offered if the price is right, regardless of how many of the same model I already have. After twenty years of doing this, I have built quite a stock of parts radios. This stock of parts makes restoration much faster than would otherwise be possible. If a front panel, dial, or power transformer is needed, it's off to my 'parts department', get one, and continue the restoration without waiting weeks or months to locate and obtain the part. I usually purchase tubes, and sometimes capacitors, resistors, power cords, and small items like rubber grommets, at swap meets. I have bought many hundreds of 'new' military surplus tubes, usually in lots of a hundred or more for a few dollars. Admittedly, this is getting harder to do as most people are now selling by the tube for a much higher price.

Purchasing radios and parts in these quantities is probably not a good idea for everyone. There are commercial sources where most tubes, manuals, and some components can be purchased in small quantities. One such source is Antique Electronic Supply in Tempe, Arizona. I can usually supply collectors with photocopies of Hallicrafters manuals. For other brands I recommend "HI Inc." in Counsel Bluffs, Iowa. To see advertisements for these and other companies supplying antique radio parts, get a current issue of the *Antique Radio Classified.*

Other Points to Check

Lead 'dress' on the replaced components is very important from an electrical point of view, and also from an esthetic one. Keep the leads as short as possible. The new component should be installed in the same space from which the old one was removed, and all terminals to which the component is connected should be de-soldered and old lead material completely removed prior to installing the new component. Some of these components are in places that seem nearly impossible to reach. It helps if you have training as a brain surgeon, and a lot of patience!

When working with the series-strung filament sets of the mid-1960s that use a 'glow bar' (S-120, SW-500, WR-700, etc) be sure the pilot lamps are good. They are in series with a voltage dropping resistor that is in series with the tube filaments and glow bar. If the lamps are burned out, the tubes do not get enough filament voltage and will not light up. Replacing the lamps corrects the problem, and the glow bar is not usually bad.

Useful Tools

In addition to the usual tools I find surgical and dental tools such as hemostats and tweezers very useful. A magnifier light is essential for those of us with failing eyesight! The only electronic tool really essential for most restorations is a good analogue VOM. Oscilloscopes, frequency meters, and signal tracers can make the job easier but are not necessary. For RF alignment I do recommend using a signal generator, but it can be accomplished without one by using broadcast stations of known frequencies on the standard broadcast band and WWV on the short wave bands. IF alignment can be done by ear, but again I do recommend a signal generator for accuracy and maximum performance.

After you've been through all these steps, the set should work as well or better than it did new!

Cosmetic Restoration

What can be done about paint and lettering on the case and front panel? Most of the time the paint and lettering can be restored to its original brilliance by using various cleaners and rubbing compounds available for that purpose. Caution should be exercised with some cleaners on some surfaces. Test it on a small inconspicuous area first. There is nothing more disheartening than "cleaning" all the numbers or lettering off the surface of a dial or panel! A mild dishwashing detergent will usually remove most of the dirt and grime with no damage to paint or lettering. Extreme caution should be used in cleaning the numbered side of glass or plastic dials. Start with plain water and a soft cloth; do not rub hard.

Using Windex or other glass cleaners can be disastrous. They contain ammonia, which can dissolve the lettering.

After cleaning, any paint scratches can be touched up, and a missing or faint letter here and there can be replaced quickly by using dry-transfer lettering. The lettering I use is "MarKit JR." made by Russell Industries Inc. It is available at most electronic supply houses.

Matching Paint

Matching paint for cabinets and panels can be a challenge. To solve this problem I took clean examples of the dozen or so shades of Hallicrafters gray and black to a local automotive lacquer company and had them special-mix a quart of each. If a panel or cabinet is in very bad condition, I will acquire another (unless rare) rather than do a complete repaint or re-lettering job.

Chuck in his lab.

THE GENEOLOGY OF THE S-38:1935-1961

1935? Wait just a minute!

Everyone knows the S-38 wasn't produced until 1946!

However, Hallicrafter's idea of producing an inexpensive, introductory general-coverage receiver began in late 1935, with the 5-T Sky Buddy.

Other communications receiver manufacturers of the time were producing high-quality receivers that were very expensive, designed for serious (and wealthy) Hams. Hallicrafters had a share of this market, with top-end units such as the SX-9, SX-10, SX-11, and SX-12.

Bill Halligan realized that this practice was excluding many Hams and other people interested in short-wave radio who were still reeling from the effects of the Depression, and were unable to afford a $100 radio. Hallicrafters decided to produce a radio for $29.50—the 5-T Sky Buddy. If you didn't have the entire sum, you could buy it with time payments, sending in just $2.50 each month. At the end of twelve months, your new Sky Buddy would arrive.

The 5-T was sold at cost, so Hallicrafters realized no immediate profit from this inexpensive introductory radio. Still, the price sold a lot of radios and got many people hooked on short-wave radio. In this way, Hallicrafters created future customers for their more profitable high-end units.

The 5-T Sky Buddy: (1935-1936)

The first production run of the 5-T had a picture of a boy sitting at a desk, wearing a set of headphones and with his hand on a telegraph key, as part of the artwork on the celluloid dial. According to Hallicrafters legend, Bill Halligan's neighbor had a young son named Buddy who was very interested in short-wave radio, but couldn't afford an expensive commercial set. Bill dedicated this first introductory radio to the boy, naming it "Sky Buddy." The 5-T was produced just before Hallicrafters obtained its license to build radios under RCA patents, and may actually may have been manufactured by The Howard Radio Company.

The S-19 & 19R Sky Buddy

Those of us who got started in ham radio just prior to World War II may remember the S-19 Sky Buddy, which was a repackaging of the 5-T using octal tubes. The S-19 was produced for a short time in late 1938 and is quite rare today. More will likely remember the S-19R which was introduced in 1939. Similar in appearance to the S-19, it was a totally re-designed radio with expanded frequency coverage and band spread, and is what most of us think of when talking about the Sky Buddy. It had a large production run, kept a lot of us in tune with world events during the war, and is still common today. The original selling price of the S-19 and the S-19R was $29.50, just like the original Sky Buddy.

Echophones: EC & EC-1

Hallicrafters had a secondary line of beginner's radios produced under the Echophone name. The EC (Echophone Commercial EC-1) and the EC-1 (a and b) series were produced from 1941 through 1946. These sets were aimed at getting inexpensive short-wave radios to the general population during the war years. The S-41G and S-41W (Sky Rider Jr.) were the same radio as the EC-1a and EC-1b and were produced in 1945 (just prior to the introduction of the S-38). The EC line became known as "The Poor Mans Hallicrafters." Even though they were produced on the same assembly line, their price was lower because they bore the relatively unknown name of Echophone Radio Co. Between 1941 and 1946 the price rose from $19.50 to $29.50. In 1951 the consumer electronics division of Hallicrafters produced another spin-off of the S-38 series for the general public. It was the 5R10, and 5R100. These radios are almost identical to the S-38D in appearance except for a chrome dial escutcheon, a black case, and no BFO, stand-by or speaker-phones switches and related circuitry.

The S-38

After the war was over, a new product line with modern design was needed to compete with the glut of war surplus electronics. Bill enlisted the services of Raymond Loewy to give the Hallicrafters product line its new look. The first Loewy-designed radio was the S-38, produced in 1946. It was specifically designed to replace the Sky Buddy and take its place as the beginner's radio, selling for $47.50. The S-38 series was produced from 1946 through 1961 starting with the S-38 and culminating with the S-38E. The price went from $47.50 to $59.95 in keeping with inflation. Most of us younger radio buffs got our start on one of the S-38 series. For me it was the S-38C in 1955.

The Sky Buddy II

In 1961, the model number next in line for production use was S-119. Perhaps because this number was the hundredth model since the S-19, the S-119 was termed a commemorative radio and was given the name of Sky Buddy II. It sold as a kit for $39.95, or wired for $49.95. Production also began in 1961 on the S-120, a direct replacement for the S-38 series which sold for $69.95.

This ends the genealogy of the S-38.

THE S-38 SERIES: THE TECHNICAL STORY

For those of you who are thrilled by tube functions, the following is a list of tubes used in the S-38 models, their functions, and type of construction.

Tube construction has changed numerous times since they were first invented. From 1935 to 1961 there were three basic styles.

The first was the prong type. These tubes had hollow 'prongs' ranging from 1/16" to 1/8" in diameter and 5/8" in length, mounted in a Bakelite base. Each prong was connected to a separate element inside the tube. Depending on the number of elements in the tube they may have from four to eight prongs. The tube sockets had the exact number of holes of proper diameters to accept a particular tube in only one orientation. You could not put a four-prong tube in a six-hole socket, and you could not install the tube so that the wrong prongs were in the wrong holes.

The second style was the octal type. These tubes had hollow pins of smaller diameter than the prong type. Each was the same diameter, and they were mounted around the periphery of a Bakelite base with a 1/4" diameter 'key' in the center. Again the number of pins was determined by the number of elements. The tube sockets were all uniform, having eight equally spaced holes of the same diameter, and a 1/4" diameter center hole that was keyed to accept the key of the tube for proper orientation.

The third style was the miniature type, which had either seven or nine solid pins of smaller diameter then the octal type. These pins extend directly from the glass envelope of the tube in a circular arrangement, with one pin missing to form a flat spot in the circle for orientation. There was no Bakelite or plastic base. The sockets were either seven-hole or nine-hole in the same arrangement.

Tubes used in the 5-T through the S-120 models

P = Prong, O = Octal, and M = Miniature

TUBE TYPE	FUNCTION	CONSTRUCTION
6A7,6K8,12SA7, 6BE6,12BE6	Oscillator/Mixer/1st Detector	P, O, O, M, M
6F7,6L7	IF Amp/BFO	P, O
6K7,12SK7, 6BA6,12BA6	IF Amp	O, O, M, M
6CM8	IF AMP/DET/AUDIO	M
75,6Q7,6SQ7, 12SQ7,12AV6	2nd Det/AVC/1st Audio	P, O, O, O, M
76	BFO	P
41,42,6K6,35L6, 50L6,50C5	Audio power output	P, P, O, O, O, M
80,35Z5,35W4	Rectifier	P, O, M

The 5-T Sky Buddy (1935)

The model number 5-T was probably derived from this being a five-tube set. It was produced just before the "S" line of numbers was firmly in place. It had a BFO (Beat Frequency Oscillator for code reception), built-in speaker, and "airplane" dial. The frequency coverage was .55 Mhz to 16 Mhz in three bands. Its tube compliment was a 6A7, 6F7, 75, 42, and 80, all prong type tubes.

The S-19 Sky Buddy (1938)

There were a number of significant differences in the S-19, but it was basically a repackaged 5-T. The S-19 also had five tubes, the same frequency coverage as the 5-T, with BFO and built-in speaker. The significant differences were the use of octal tubes rather than prong type (except for the 80), a different chassis layout, and a new cabinet design with the exterior 'silver' dial. The tube complement was a 6K8, 6L7, 6Q7, 6K6, and 80. The cabinet design was the first of a new appearance that would be used on several models over the next few years.

The S-19-R Sky Buddy (1939)

The S-19R was a completely different radio, with six tubes, a frequency coverage of .55 Mhz to 46 Mhz in four bands, and an electrical band spread. The cabinet style and dial were the same as the S-19, but the chassis was painted black and was an integral part of the cabinet, not separate as with the 5-T, S-19 and most other models. The 'unitized' painted chassis, panel and cabinet were used on only one other Hallicrafters model, the SX-23.

There were two production runs of the S-19R, using different tubes. The first run used a 6K8, 6K7, 6Q7, 76, 41, and 80. The second run used a 6SK7 in-place of the 6K7 and a 6SQ7 in-place of the 6Q7. Both runs had the strange mixture of prong and octal style tubes. The mixture of prong and octal tubes seems a step backwards, but is understandable. The octal tubes (introduced in 1935) were the latest advance in tube construction; the prong type were being phased out and were much less expensive. I theorize that the prong tubes were used to keep the ever-increasing cost of production down, enabling the end price to remain lower.

The S-38 (1946)

The S-38 was a six-tube radio with a variable pitch BFO, audio noise limiter (ANL), electrical band spread, and built-in speaker. Its frequency coverage was .55 Mhz to 30.0 Mhz in four bands. To cut costs it had an AC-DC power supply rather than the familiar transformer-operated AC supplies of the 5-T, S-19, and S-19R. The tube complement was a 12SA7, 12SK7, two 12SQ7s, 35L6, and 35Z5. The tube filaments were series wired. The smooth finish charcoal gray cabinet was smaller than the earlier Sky Buddy's and aesthetically pleasing. The two green 'half-moon' dials with black lettering and red dial pointers and the well balanced control panel were impressive and would set the style for the next several years.

The S-38A (1946-1947) was a five-tube radio with fixed frequency BFO and no ANL. Its other features and appearance were the same as the S-38 except it had no BFO pitch control or ANL switch. The tube complement was a 12SA7, 12SK7, 12SQ7, 50L6, and 35Z5. Varying the pitch of an incoming CW signal was accomplished by de-tuning the set to one side or the other of the incoming signal rather than varying the frequency of the BFO as in the S-38.

S-38 SKY BUDDY (1935)

S-19 SKY BUDDY (1938)

S-19 R SKY BUDDY (1939)

S-38 (1946)

The S-38B (1947-53) was virtually the same radio as the S-38A with exception of the cabinet finish, which was a grainy-textured flat black. There were also some minor electrical differences including an interlock on the AC line cord.

The S-38C (1953-55) was again the same radio as the S-38A with a 'hammertone' gray finish and a black dial with white lettering rather than the green with black lettering. It was also the last of the traditional styling of the S-38. The S-38D would have many changes.

The S-38D (1955-57) was again electrically the same radio as the A through C models but had a totally different front panel, dial, and control design. Its slide-rule dial behind glass covering about 80% of the front panel, listed many of the countries, cites, and uses of frequencies such as Ham, police, etc. above the frequencies. The controls were across the bottom of the panel with the exception of the speaker-phones switch, which was moved to an inconvenient location on the back apron of the chassis. The finish of the cabinet was 'hammertone' gray, and its size was the same as the A through C models. The styling of the S-38D was taken from the 5R10 mentioned earlier.

The S-38E (1957-61) was the last of the S-38 series. It incorporated several electrical changes over the earlier models, but its features were the same. It used miniature rather than octal tubes, and had a BFO 'injection' control on the back apron of the chassis. This control was used to set the strength of the BFO signal input. The tube complement was a 12BE6, 12BA6, 12AV6, 50C5, and a 35W4. The front panel design was similar to the D model, but had a larger slide-rule dial covering about 90% of the panel. The controls were again across the bottom of the panel, and the speaker-phones switch was returned to the front panel (where it belongs!). There were three cabinet finishes to choose from; 'hammertone' gray, beige, and mahogany wood grain. Each of these finishes had a different model designation: the S-38E was 'hammertone' gray, the EB was beige, and the EM was mahogany.

The S-120 (1961-1964)

The S-120 replaced the S-38 series. It was a totally different radio, although its features were the same as the S-38 series with BFO, band spread, and a frequency coverage of .55 Mhz to 30 Mhz in four bands. It was a four-tube set with a selenium rectifier. The tubes used were 12BE6, 12BA6, 12AV6, and 50C5. The chassis and cabinet were sleek and of a smaller stature than the S-38 series. It had a telescoping whip antenna mounted with clips on the back panel for use on short-wave, and a built-in ferrite loop for standard broadcast. These antennas were a real improvement in convenience of operation, as was the use of a standard 'shorting' phone jack on the front panel which eliminated the need for the speaker-phones switch, and an improvement over the two hole pin type phone jack of the S-38s.

The S-119 Sky Buddy II (1961)

The S-119 was a three-tube set with a selenium rectifier. The frequency coverage was the same as the 5-T and S-19 (.55 to 16 Mhz) in three bands. The tubes used were a 6BE6, 6BA6, and 6CM8, and it had a AC-operated transformer power supply. It was smaller in size than any of the other beginner's radios, and its appearance was unique. It is interesting to note that the dial of this radio was similar to the S-19, which had a rotating circular silver dial and a stationary clear plastic pointer. The S-119 had a stationary circular dial with a rotating clear plastic pointer! The set also had a BFO and provision for use of ear phones. This set did not sell well, had a limited production run and is difficult to find today.

The S-38 Series: Performance

Even though the 5-T through the S-120 were beginner's radios, their performance has never failed to amaze me, considering the minimal parts used and type of construction. Hallicrafters always produced radios that did exactly what they were advertised to do (and did it well) at a nominal cost.

I have had the opportunity to use all of these models in restored condition. What I find is they are very sensitive on the lower frequencies (.55 to 16 Mhz) receiving hundreds of stations with just a twelve foot 'long wire' antenna. From 16 to 30 Mhz the sensitivity tends to drop off, and there can be "images" of local high power broadcast stations, but I have been able to listen to CB'ers on 11 meters and amateurs on 10 meters! The audio quality is exceptional for speakers of this size, and volume is ample. On CW reception the BFOs tend to be a bit unstable, but work well. The calibration of the dials is good and it is possible to guess the frequency of a station on the standard broadcast band with good accuracy. On the short-wave bands it is more difficult, because the width of the pointer can be a couple hundred KC depending on the frequency band. The band spread not being calibrated also makes frequency identification more difficult.

But who cares? You can hear the world!

The Radios

S AND SX SERIES RECEIVERS

MODEL	NAME	DATE	ORIGINAL PRICE
S-1	SKYRIDER	1933	$39.95

A 5-TUBE 4-BAND TUNED RADIO FREQUENCY REGENERATIVE SET COVERING 1.5MHz TO 22MHz. THE DIAL IS HEAVY PAPER WITH ROOM FOR OPERATOR NOTATIONS. BUILT-IN SPEAKER, NO BAND SPREAD, BFO, OR SEND-RECEIVE SWITCH. THE FRONT PANEL IS SOLID TIN. THE SET SHOWN HERE HAD AN EXTRA HOLE IN THE PANEL WHICH I PATCHED. THE PANEL TARNISHED AND THE PATCH DIDN'T! THERE MAY HAVE BEEN A BATTERY OPER-ATED VERSION OF THIS RADIO BUT I HAVE NEVER SEEN ONE. THERE IS NO MODEL NUM-BER AND THE NAME "SKYRIDER" DOES NOT APPEAR ANYWHERE ON THE RADIO. THE ONLY IDENTIFICATION IS THE METAL TAG IN THE CENTER OF THE PANEL INDICATING IT IS A HALLICRAFTERS RADIO MANUFACTURED BY SILVER-MARSHALL MFG. CO. TUBES USED: 80 RECTIFIER, 42 AUDIO OUTPUT, 6D6 RADIO FREQUENCY AMPLIFIER, 6D6 DETECTOR, AND 6C6 FIRST AUDIO. POWER SOURCE IS 120 VOLTS AC.

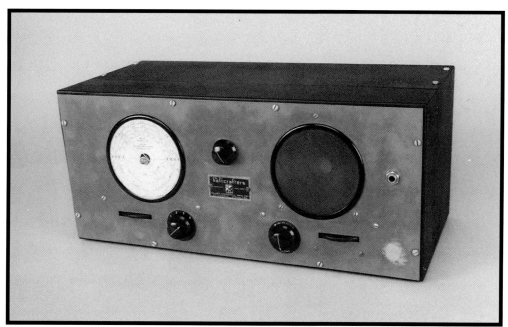

S-1 SKYRIDER

S-2   **SKYRIDER**   **1933-34**   **$39.95**

THE S-2 IS BASICALLY THE SAME RADIO AS THE S-1, HAVING THE SAME FREQUENCY COV-
ERAGE AND USING THE SAME LAYOUT AND TUBES. IT DIFFERS FROM THE S-1 IN THAT IT
HAS BANDSPREAD AND A SEND-RECEIVE SWITCH. THE FRONT PANEL ON THE RADIO
SHOWN IS STEEL, PAINTED SILVER. SOME COLLECTORS HAVE REFERRED TO THIS SET AS
THE "S-1 SPECIAL," BUT TO ME IT HAS ALWAYS BEEN THE S-2. POWER SOURCE IS 120 VOLTS
AC. *From the Collection of William H. Ross of Winnetka, IL.*

S-2 SKYRIDER

S-3   **SKYRIDER**   **1933-34**   **$49.95**

A 5-TUBE 5-BAND TUNED RADIO FREQUENCY REGENERATIVE SET COVERING 1.6MHz TO
23MHz AND THE STANDARD BROADCAST BAND. WITH BANDSPREAD BUILT-IN SPEAKER,
AND SEND-RECEIVE SWITCH, NO BFO. POWER SOURCE IS 120 VOLTS AC. USES THE SAME
TUBES AND BASIC LAYOUT AS THE S-1 IN A LARGER CABINET. THE FRONT PANEL IS SOLID
TIN. THE DIALS ARE CELLULOID AND ALTHOUGH THERE IS NO MODEL NUMBER ON THE
RADIO THE NAME "SKYRIDER" APPEARS ON THE BANDSPREAD DIAL. THERE IS NO REFER-
ENCE TO SILVER-MARSHALL MFG. CO.

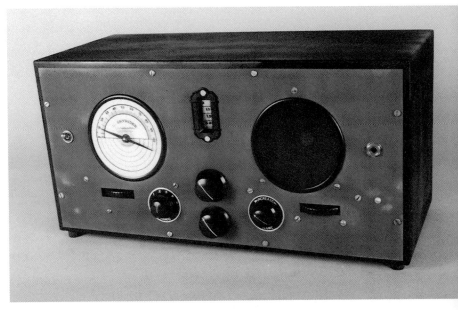

S-3 SKYRIDER

S-4, 5, 6   SUPER SKYRIDER   1934-35 $59.95

SX-4, 5, 6

THESE THREE RADIOS ARE 7-TUBE SUPERHETERODYNES WITH THE ONLY DIFFERENCE BEING THE FREQUENCY COVERAGE OF THE "X" BAND. THE FREQUENCY COVERAGE OF THE S-4 IS 1.3MHz TO 21MHz IN 4 BANDS WITH NO "X" BAND. THE FREQUENCY COVERAGE OF THE S-5 IS 1.3MHz TO 21MHz IN 4 BANDS WITH THE 5TH OR "X" BAND COVERING STANDARD BROADCAST. THE FREQUENCY COVERAGE OF THE S-6 IS 1.3MHz TO 21MHz IN 4 BANDS WITH THE 5TH OR "X" BAND COVERING FROM 28MHz TO 30MHz. OTHER FEATURES INCLUDE A BUILT-IN SPEAKER, A BFO, BANDSPREAD, AND OPTIONAL CRYSTAL FILTER. IF THE CRYSTAL FILTER WAS INCLUDED, THE MODEL NUMBER CHANGED TO "SX."

THE "X" IN THE MODEL NUMBER MEANT THE INCLUSION OF THE CRYSTAL FILTER. THIS DESIGNATION WILL CONTINUE THROUGH THE REST OF PRODUCT LINE. THE INTERMEDIATE FREQUENCY OF ALL THREE OF THESE RADIOS IS 465KHz. THESE SETS WERE THE FIRST SUPERHETERODYNES PRODUCED BY THE COMPANY. THE POWER SOURCE IS 120 VOLTS AC. TUBES USED: 80 RECTIFIER 42 AUDIO OUTPUT, 6D6 RADIO FREQUENCY AMPLIFIER, 6A7 OSCILLATOR AND FIRST DETECTOR, 6D6 FIRST INTERMEDIATE FREQUENCY AMPLIFIER, 6D6 SECOND INTERMEDIATE FREQUENCY AMPLIFIER, AND 6F7 SECOND DETECTOR AND BEAT FREQUENCY OSCILLATOR. THE FRONT PANEL IS TIN PLATED STEEL.

S-5 SUPER SKYRIDER

5-T SKYBUDDY (NO BOY)

5-T SKYBUDDY (WITH BOY)

5-T SKYBUDDY DIAL

S-7   SUPER SKYRIDER   1935 $89.50 with crystal

SX-7 $79.50 without crystal

A 9-TUBE 5-BAND SUPERHETERODYNE COVERING .54MHz TO 48MHz, WITH BFO, BUILT-IN SPEAKER, BANDSPREAD, AND OPTIONAL CRYSTAL FILTER. THIS SET MADE FIRST USE OF THE EXTERNAL ENGRAVED "SILVER" METAL DIAL. IT WAS VERY SIMILAR IN APPEARANCE AND LAYOUT TO THE S-9, AND I BELIEVE IT WAS A FORERUNNER OF THE S-9 THAT NEVER WENT INTO PRODUCTION. THE I.F. WAS 465KHz AND WAS THE FIRST OF THE RADIOS SO FAR TO MAKE USE OF THE NEWLY DESIGNED OCTAL TUBES WITH EXCEPTION OF THE RECTIFIER. TUBES USED: 5Z3 RECTIFIER, 6F6 AUDIO OUTPUT, 6K7 R.F. AMPLIFIER, 6L7 FIRST DETECTOR AND MIXER, 6C5 OSCILLATOR, 6K7 I.F. AMPLIFIER, 6H6 SECOND DETECTOR AND A.V.C, 6F5 FIRST AUDIO, AND 6K7 B.F.O. POWER SOURCE 120 VOLTS AC. SORRY, NO PHOTO AVAILABLE.

5-T   SKYBUDDY   1935-36 $29.50

A 5-TUBE 3-BAND SUPERHETERODYNE COVERING .54MHz TO 18MHz, WITH SPEAKER AND B.F.O. THE I.F. FREQUENCY IS 465KHz. THIS RADIO IS THE FIRST OF THE THREE DIFFERENT SKY BUDDY MODELS. THERE ARE TWO VERSIONS, DIFFERING ONLY IN THE ARTWORK OF THE CELLULOID DIAL. ONE VERSION HAS A CARICATURE OF A BOY WITH HEADPHONES AND FINGER ON A TELEGRAPH KEY, THE OTHER DID NOT. BOTH VERSIONS ARE SHOWN HERE WITH A CLOSE-UP OF THE DIAL. TUBES USED: 80 RECTIFIER, 42 AUDIO OUTPUT, 6A7 FIRST DETECTOR AND MIXER, 6F7 B.F.O. AND I.F. AMPLIFIER, 76 SECOND DETECTOR, A.V.C., AND FIRST AUDIO. POWER SOURCE IS 120 VOLTS AC. FOR MORE INFORMATION, SEE THE SKY BUDDY SECTION ON PAGE 22.

NONE   SUPER SEVEN   1935 $49.50

A 7-TUBE 3-BAND SUPERHETERODYNE COVERING .54MHz TO 18MHz THE I.F. FREQUENCY IS 465KHz, WITH SPEAKER, AND B.F.O. NO BANDSPREAD. HAS A VERNIER TUNING CONTROL FOR EASIER SHORT-WAVE TUNING. TUBES USED: 80 RECTIFIER, 42 AUDIO AMPLIFIER, 78 B.F.O., 75 SECOND DETECTOR, A.V.C., AND FIRST AUDIO, 78 I.F. AMPLIFIER, 6A7 FIRST DETECTOR AND OSCILLATOR, 78 R.F. AMPLIFIER. THERE MAY HAVE BEEN ANOTHER VERSION OF THIS RADIO WITH A PUSH-PULL AUDIO OUTPUT USING TWO 42 TUBES. SOME PEOPLE MAY ALSO REFER TO THIS SET AS THE S-7 OR S-7A, BUT IT IS TOTALLY DIFFERENT THAN WHAT I LIST AS THE S-7. POWER SOURCE IS 120 VOLTS AC. THE FRONT PANEL IS AN INTEGRAL PART OF THE CASE AND IS PAINTED STEEL. THE ONLY INDICATION THIS IS A HALLICRAFTERS RADIO IS THE GLUED-ON METAL TAG BETWEEN THE SPEAKER AND DIAL.

S-8A   NONE   1935 $49.50

A 7-TUBE 3-BAND RADIO VERY SIMILAR IN APPEARANCE TO THE SUPER SEVEN. THERE ARE SLIGHT DIFFERENCES IN FREQUENCY COVERAGE, TUBES USED, AND CONTROL LAYOUT.

THE I.F. FREQUENCY IS 465KHz, AND THE FREQUENCY COVERAGE IS .54MHz TO 17MHz. TUBES USED: 80 RECTIFIER, 6B5 AUDIO AMPLIFIER, 6K7 B.F.O., 75 SECOND DETECTOR, A.V.C., AND FIRST AUDIO, 78 I.F. AMPLIFIER, 6A7 FIRST DETECTOR AND OSCILLATOR, 78 R.F. AMPLIFIER. I BELIEVE BOTH THE SUPER SEVEN AND S-8A WERE PROBABLY BUILT BY THE HOWARD RADIO CO.

S-9   SUPER SKYRIDER   1936 $89.50 with plug-in crystal

SX-9 $79.50 without plug-in crystal

A 9-TUBE 5-BAND SUPERHET COVERING .54MHz TO 42MHz. WITH BUILT-IN SPEAKER, B.F.O., BANDSPREAD AND OPTIONAL CRYSTAL FILTER. THERE WAS FRONT PANEL CONTROL OF A.V.C., CRYSTAL PHASING, SEND-RECEIVE, R.F. GAIN, AND B.F.O. PITCH. THE FRONT PANEL WAS NICKEL-PLATED STEEL AND ALL NOMENCLATURE WAS ENGRAVED. THERE WERE TWO VERSIONS PRODUCED, WHAT I CALL THE EARLY AND THE LATE. THE EARLY HAD THE COMPANY LOGO ENGRAVED IN THE UPPER RIGHT HAND CORNER OF THE PANEL. THE LATE HAD NO LOGO. SHOWN HERE ARE BOTH VERSIONS AND THE WORKING ENGINEERING MODEL SHOP HAND BUILT PROTOTYPE WITH A CHROME PLATED PANEL. ALL FEATURED THE ENGRAVED "SILVER" DIAL. THE S-9 WAS THE FIRST TO BE PRODUCED IN SIGNIFICANT QUANTITIES. TUBES USED: 5Z4 RECTIFIER, TWO 6F6 IN PUSH-PULL FOR AUDIO OUTPUT, 6K7 B.F.O., 6F5 FIRST AUDIO, 6H6 SECOND DETECTOR AND A.V.C., 6K7 I.F. AMPLIFIER 6C5 OSCILLATOR, 6L7 FIRST DETECTOR AND MIXER, AND 6K7 R.F. AMPLIFIER. NOTE THAT ALL OF THESE TUBES WERE "METAL" OCTAL TYPES. 465KHz I.F. POWER SOURCE IS 120 VOLTS AC.

The S-9

I have noticed significant physical and electrical differences between radios of the same model number in the early days of production (1934-1940). For example, the S-9 (which was the first unit that Hallicrafters mass-produced) had two different front panels. The first production had the company logo in the upper right corner of the panel, the second run had no logo. There were also some minor circuit changes in the form of diferent value parts and parts location. It appears that whatever parts were on hand at the time of production of a particular radio are what were used. The same model produced two weeks later may not have exactly the same parts.

SUPER SEVEN

S-8A

S-9, SX-9 SUPER SKYRIDER (PROTOTYPE)

S-9, SX-9 SUPER SKYRIDER (EARLY)

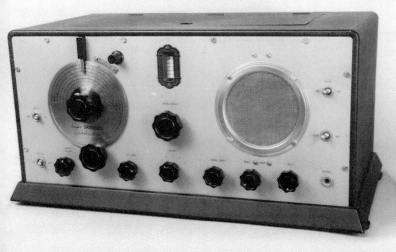

S-9, SX-9 SUPER SKYRIDER (LATE)

| S-10 | ULTRA SKYRIDER | 1936 | $114.50 with crystal |
| SX-10 | | | $99.50 without crystal |

A 10-TUBE 4-BAND SUPERHET COVERING 5.6MHz TO 79.5MHz. 1600KHz I.F. WITH VARIABLE INJECTION B.F.O, BANDSPREAD, VARIABLE I.F. SELECTIVITY, VARIABLE NOISE LIMITER, OPTIONAL CRYSTAL FILTER. EXTERNAL SPEAKER. ENGRAVED "SILVER" DIAL, FRONT PANEL IS 1/8" THICK BRASS PAINTED BLACK WITH EMBOSSED NOMENCLATURE. THE STANDARD "CABINET" WAS A CLOSE-FITTING METAL DUST COVER, AND THERE WAS AN OPTIONAL MAHOGANY CASE THE ENTIRE UNIT SLIPPED INTO (ALTHOUGH I HAVE NEVER SEEN ONE). TWO SPEAKERS WERE AVAILABLE FOR THIS RADIO, BOTH 12" PERMANENT MAGNET TYPES. FOR THE STEEL CASE RADIO THE PM-12 AND FOR THE WOOD CASE THE PM-12M (SEE SPEAKER SECTION). POWER SOURCE IS 120 VOLTS AC. TUBES USED: 5Z4 RECTIFIER, 6F6 AUDIO OUTPUT, 6Q7 FIRST AUDIO AND NOISE LIMITER, 6J7 NOISE LIMITER AMPLIFIER, 6R7 SECOND DETECTOR, A.V.C., AND B.F.O., 6L7 SECOND I.F. AMPLIFIER, 6K7 FIRST I.F. AMPLIFIER, 6C5 OSCILLATOR 6L7 FIRST DETECTOR AND MIXER, 6K7 R.F. AMPLIFIER. THE RADIO PICTURED HERE WAS PURCHASED FROM BILL ORR AND WAS FEATURED IN HIS ARTICLE "THE 1936 RECEIVER OF THE YEAR."

| S-11 | SUPER SKYRIDER | 1936 | $99.50 with crystal |
| SX-11 | | | $89.50 without crystal |

AN 11-TUBE 5-BAND SUPERHET COVERING .54MHz TO 38.1MHz. 465KHz I.F., WITH VARIABLE INJECTION B.F.O., BANDSPREAD, OPTIONAL CRYSTAL FILTER, AND A "MAGIC EYE" SIGNAL STRENGTH INDICATOR. EXTERNAL SPEAKER. 1/8" BRASS PANEL PAINTED BLACK WITH EMBOSSED NOMENCLATURE, ENGRAVED "SILVER" DIAL. THE SAME CABINET AND SPEAKER TYPES WERE AVAILABLE AS USED ON THE S-10. POWER SOURCE IS 120 VOLTS AC. TUBES USED: 5Z3 RECTIFIER, TWO 6L6 IN PUSH-PULL FOR AUDIO OUTPUT, 6G5 SIGNAL STRENGTH AND TUNING INDICATOR, 6K7 B.F.O., 6R7 SECOND DETECTOR, A.V.C., AND FIRST AUDIO, 6K7 SECOND I.F. AMPLIFIER, 6K7 FIRST I.F. AMPLIFIER, 6C5 OSCILLATOR, 6L7 FIRST DETECTOR AND MIXER, 6K7 R.F. AMPLIFIER.

The SX-11

There is an error on the SX-11 schematic. The value of R-9 is shown to be 50 Kohm, but should be changed to 100 Kohm.

S-10, SX-10 ULTRA SKYRIDER

S-11, SX-11 SUPER SKYRIDER

S-12   SKYRIDER COMMERCIAL   1936 $114.50 with crystal

SX-12 $99.50 without crystal

AN 11-TUBE 5-BAND SUPERHET COVERING 110KHz TO 11.5MHz. 1600KHz
I.F., WITH VARIABLE INJECTION B.F.O., BAND SPREAD, "MAGIC EYE" TUN-
ING AND SIGNAL STRENGTH INDICATOR, OPTIONAL CRYSTAL FILTER,
AND EXTERNAL SPEAKER. EXCEPT FOR THE DIFFERENT FREQUENCY
COVERAGE THIS RADIO USES THE SAME TUBES, CHASSIS LAYOUT AND
ACCESSORIES AS THE S-11. POWER SOURCE IS 120 VOLTS AC.

The SX-10, 11, and 12

There was an optional wood cabinet for the
SX-10, 11, 12.

S-12, SX-12 SKYRIDER COMMERCIAL

S-14 SKYCHIEF

S-14   SKYCHIEF   1936 $44.50

A 7-TUBE 3-BAND SUPERHET COVERING .54MHz TO 18MHz. 465KHz I.F.,
WITH B.F.O., BUILT-IN SPEAKER, AND "MAGIC EYE" TUNING AND SIG-
NAL STRENGTH INDICATOR. THIS SET USED A VERNIER TUNING UNIT
WITH "AIRPLANE" DIAL. THE FRONT PANEL IS STEEL AND IS AN INTE-
GRAL PART OF THE CASE. TUBES USED: 80 RECTIFIER, 6B6 AUDIO OUT-
PUT, 6G5 TUNING AND SIGNAL STRENGTH INDICATOR, 75 SECOND
DETECTOR AND FIRST AUDIO, 6F7 I.F. AMPLIFIER AND B.F.O., 6A7 FIRST
DETECTOR AND OSCILLATOR, AND 6D6 R.F AMPLIFIER. POWER SOURCE
IS 120 VOLTS AC. THE RADIO PICTURED HERE HAD TO HAVE THE FRONT
PANEL REPAINTED WHICH WIPED OUT WHAT WAS LEFT OF THE ORIGI-
NAL SILK-SCREENED NOMENCLATURE. I RE-LETTERED USING "DRY
TRANSFER" LETTERING WHICH IS CLOSE TO THE ORIGINAL IN SIZE AND
COLOR. I COULD NOT REPRODUCE THE LOGO WHICH WOULD HAVE
BEEN IN THE UPPER RIGHT HAND CORNER OF THE PANEL.

S-15   SKY CHALLENGER   1936 $81.95 with crystal

SX-15 $69.50 without crystal

A 9-TUBE 5-BAND SUPERHET COVERING .54MHz TO 38.1MHz. 465KHz
I.F., WITH BANDSPREAD, AND B.F.O. OPTIONS INCLUDED AN EXTER-
NAL SPEAKER AND PLUG-IN CRYSTAL FILTER. POWER SOURCE IS 120
VOLTS AC. THE FRONT PANEL IS STEEL PAINTED BLACK WITH THE NO-
MENCLATURE ON SEPARATE METAL TAGS RIVETED TO THE PANEL. I HAVE
SEEN TWO VERSIONS OF THIS RADIO: ONE WHOSE PANEL IS SEPARATE
FROM THE CASE, THE OTHER WITH THE PANEL AN INTEGRAL PART OF
THE CASE. THE SET PICTURED HERE HAS THE SEPARATE PANEL. TUBES
USED: 80 RECTIFIER, 6F6 AUDIO OUTPUT, 6K7 B.F.O., 6Q7 SECOND DE-
TECTOR, A.V.C., AND FIRST AUDIO, 6K7 FIRST I.F. AMPLIFIER, 6K7 SEC-
OND I.F. AMPLIFIER, 6C5 OSCILLATOR, 6L7 FIRST DETECTOR AND MIXER,
AND 6K7 R.F. AMPLIFIER.

S-15, SX-15 SKY CHALLENGER

The S-15

There were two different cabinets produced with the S-15. The most common has a one-piece top, back, and sides, with the front panel and
bottom cover as separate parts. The other style has the same one-piece top, back, and sides, but the front panel and bottom cover are also one
piece, L-shaped, making access to the underside of the chassis impossible without removing the front panel. Most inconvenient!

S-16   SUPER SKYRIDER   1937 $111.00 with crystal
SX-16 $99.00 without crystal

A 11-TUBE 6-BAND SUPERHET COVERING .54MHz TO 62MHz. 465KHz I.F. WITH B.F.O., BANDSPREAD, FLYWHEEL DRIVE FOR BANDSPREAD AND MAIN TUNING, S-METER, AND I.F. SELECTIVITY SWITCH (SHARP OR BROAD). THIS IS THE FIRST SET PRODUCED BY THE COMPANY TO EMPLOYE FLYWHEEL TUNING AND S-METER. THE PANEL IS STEEL PAINTED BLACK WITH EMBOSSED NOMENCLATURE. I HAVE ALSO SEEN TWO VERSIONS OF THIS SET. ONE HAS THE BAND SWITCH SHAFT EXTENDING TO THE REAR APRON OF THE CHASSIS, THE OTHER HAS THE BAND SWITCH SHAFT STOP AT THE REAR OF THE R.F. DECK WHICH IS SEVERAL INCHES SHORT OF THE REAR APRON. BOTH HAVE PORCELAIN TUBE SOCKETS FOR THE OSCILLATOR, MIXER, AND R.F. AMPLIFIER FOR LOWER SIGNAL LOSS AT HIGHER FREQUENCIES. OPTIONS INCLUDE AN EXTERNAL SPEAKER, AND A PLUG-IN CRYSTAL FILTER. POWER SOURCE IS 120 VOLTS AC. TUBES USED: 5Z3 RECTIFIER, TWO 6V6 IN PUSH-PULL AUDIO OUTPUT, 6J7 S-METER AMPLIFIER, 6J7 B.F.O., 6R7 SECOND DETECTOR, A.V.C., AND FIRST AUDIO, 6K7 SECOND I.F. AMPLIFIER, 6K7 FIRST I.F. AMPLIFIER, 6J5 OSCILLATOR, 6L7 FIRST DETECTOR AND MIXER, 6K7 R.F. AMPLIFIER.

S-16, SX-16 SUPER SKYRIDER

SX-16

Many of the schematics and parts lists on the older models like the S-20-R and SX-16 had missing parts or errors. For example, "R-34" of the SX-16 schematic is not listed on the parts list. It is a 100K ohm 1/2 watt, and decreasing its value will help zero the S-meter if you are having trouble in that area.

The SX-16

The SX-16 had two different production runs. In the early run the band switch stopped at the rear of the RF section, and the antenna terminals were centered on the rear apron of the chassis. The shaft that connected the variable capacitor (main tuning gang) to the dial was solid, and porcelain tube sockets were used for the osc, mixer, and rf tubes. In the later run the band switch shaft went clear through to the rear apron and was anchored there. The antenna terminals were off-center to accomodate this change. The shaft of the main tuning capacitor was split into two sections with a universal joint as a coupler, and the osc, mixer, and rf tube sockets were made of clear plastic. The RF section was also different in that there were no rf or mixer trimmers for band six at either the low or high end.

S-17   SUPER SKYRIDER   1937 $137.50 with crystal
SX-17 $125.50 without crystal

A 13-TUBE 6-BAND SUPERHET COVERING .54MHz TO 62MHz. 465KHz I.F. IT HAS ALL THE FEATURES OF THE SX-16 PLUS AN EXTRA STAGE OF R.F. AMPLIFICATION AND A NOISE LIMITER. THE CHASSIS IS DEEPER THAN THE SX-16 AND THE PANEL IS VERY SIMILAR IN LAYOUT WITH THE ADDITION OF A NOISE LIMITER SWITCH. IF ONE IS NOT FAMILIAR WITH THE TWO RADIOS IT IS EASY TO CONFUSE THEM. TUBES USED: 5Z3 RECTIFIER, TWO 6V6 IN PUSH-PULL AUDIO OUTPUT, 6H6 NOISE LIMITER, 6J7 S-METER AMPLIFIER, 6J7 B.F.O., 6R7 SECOND DETECTOR, A.V.C., AND FIRST AUDIO, 6K7 FIRST I.F. AMPLIFIER, 6K7 SECOND I.F. AMPLIFIER, 6J5 OSCILLATOR, 6L7 FIRST DETECTOR AND MIXER, 6K7 FIRST R.F. AMPLIFIER, AND 6K7 SECOND R.F. AMPLIFIER. POWER SOURCE IS 120 VOLTS AC.

S-17, SX-17 SUPER SKYRIDER

SX-17-F   SUPER SKYRIDER   1937   UNKNOWN

A 12-TUBE SET WITH ALL THE FEATURES AND SPECIFICATIONS OF THE SX-17 WITH EXCEPTION OF A SINGLE 6V6 IN THE AUDIO OUTPUT. THE FRONT PANEL HAS A SLIGHTLY DIFFERENT CONTROL LAYOUT WITH THE ADDITION OF A 117 VOLT AC OR 6 VOLT DC POWER SELECTION SWITCH AND THE S-METER ZERO ADJUSTMENT CONTROL ON THE FRONT PANEL THESE SETS WERE USED AS MOBILE AND BASE STATION MONITORS BY THE FCC. AN OPTIONAL 6 VOLT DC VIBRAPACK WAS AVAILABLE FOR MOBILE USE. I HAVE NO PRICE DATA ON THIS SET BUT SUSPECT IT WAS SOMEWHAT MORE EXPENSIVE THAN THE REGULAR SX-17.

SX-17-F SUPER SKYRIDER

DD-1	SKYRIDER DIVERSITY	1937-38	$550.00 with all options
DD-A	AUDIO POWER AMPLIFIER		
DD-P	TUNER POWER SUPPLY		

TO ME THIS IS THE MOST EXOTIC RADIO EVER PRODUCED BY THE COMPANY, WITH ITS THREE CHASSIS, TWENTY-FIVE TUBES, CAST ALUMINUM CENTER PANEL WITH PRECISION TUNING GEARS AND FLYWHEELS FOR MAIN TUNING AND BAND SPREAD, NOT TO MENTION THE CHROME WORK, FOUR METERS AND THE OPTIONAL JENSEN FIFTEEN INCH SPEAKER IN A WOOD CONSOLE CABINET WITH A PULL-OUT WRITING DESK. THIS SET WAS SOLD IN TWO CONFIGURATIONS, THE TABLE TOP VERSION, AND THE CONSOLE VERSION. IN THE CONSOLE THE AMPLIFIER AND POWER SUPPLY FIT INTO SHELVES IN THE REAR OF THE SPEAKER CABINET. THE TABLE TOP UNIT SHOWN HERE IS MISSING THE DIVERSITY METERS WHICH WOULD BE IN A SMALL SLANT FRONT METAL CASE AND PLACED IN FRONT OF THE SPEAKER ON TOP OF THE TUNER SECTION. THE CONSOLE UNIT HAS THE DIVERSITY METERS IN THE WOOD BONNET SITTING ON TOP OF THE TUNER. THERE WERE BETWEEN 250 AND 500 OF THESE UNITS PRODUCED. ON THE TECHNICAL SIDE THE TUNER CONSISTS OF TWO SEPARATE RECEIVERS EACH WITH ITS OWN R.F., I.F., MIXER, DETECTOR, AND NOISE LIMITER. THE OSCILLATOR, B.F.O., POWER SUPPLY & AUDIO WERE COMMON TO BOTH RECEIVERS. FRONT PANEL CONTROLS ENABLE COMPLETE CONTROL AND CHOICE OF USING RECEIVER "A," OR RECEIVER "B," OR BOTH AT THE SAME TIME FOR DIVERSITY RECEPTION. THE PRINCIPLE HERE WAS TO CONNECT A SEPARATE ANTENNA TO EACH RECEIVER SEPARATED BY AS MUCH DISTANCE AS POSSIBLE. THE INCOMING SIGNAL FADES AT DIFFERENT TIMES IN DIFFERENT LOCATIONS. IF SET PROPERLY THE PROBLEM OF FADING SIGNALS ON SHORT-WAVE CAN BE REDUCED. THE AUDIO AMPLIFIER WAS DEFINITELY HIGH FIDELITY WITH ITS PUSH-PULL 2A3s AND THE JENSEN 15 INCH SPEAKER BUT BETWEEN THE FIRST AUDIO STAGE ON THE TUNER CHASSIS AND THE POWER AMPLIFIER CHASSIS A COUPLING TRANSFORMER WITH A LIMITED FREQUENCY RESPONSE OF APPROXIMATELY 200Hz TO 6000Hz WAS USED. THE FREQUENCY COVERAGE IS .54MHz TO 46MHz IN SIX BANDS WITH A 455KHz I.F.. THERE WERE TWO METHODS PROVIDED FOR C.W. RECEPTION, THE STANDARD B.F.O., AND A "HETEROTONE" OSCILLATOR. THIS WILL PRODUCE A USER SELECTABLE TONE OF 500Hz OR 1000Hz TO MODULATE THE INCOMING C.W. SIGNAL AND WILL REMAIN AT EITHER 500 OR 1000Hz REGARDLESS OF TUNING ADJUSTMENTS. THE METERS USED WERE TWO "DIVERSITY" S-METERS SHOWING THE RELATIVE SIGNAL FOR EACH RECEIVER, A COMPOSITE S-METER SHOWING BOTH SIGNALS, AND THE "CIRCUIT BALANCE" METER USED TO BALANCE THE R.F. GAIN OF BOTH RECEIVERS. TUBES USED: EACH RECEIVER USES A 1851 FIRST R.F. AMPLIFIER, 1851 SECOND R.F. AMPLIFIER, 6L7 MIXER, 6K7 FIRST I.F. AMPLIFIER 6L7 SECOND I.F. AMPLIFIER, 6J5 S-METER AMPLIFIER, 6H6 SECOND DETECTOR, AND 6H6 AUDIO NOISE LIMITER. THE COMMON OSCILLATOR IS A 6K6, THE FIRST AUDIO IS A 6J5, A 6J5 B.F.O., 6J5 "HETROTONE" OSCILLATOR, AND A 6J7 COMPOSIT S-METER AMPLIFIER. THE POWER SUPPLY FOR THE TUNER CHASSIS USES A 5Z3 RECTIFIER. THE AUDIO POWER AMPLIFIER USES A 5Z3 RECTIFIER, 6J5 DRIVER AND TWO 2A3 IN PUSH PULL POWER OUTPUT.

Front and rear views of new old-stock cast aluminum panels for the tuner section of the DD-1, circa 1938.

SKYRIDER DIVERSITY (TABLETOP)

SKYRIDER DIVERSITY (CONSOLE)

S-18   SKY CHALLENGER II   1938   **$89.00** with crystal
SX-18   **$77.00** without crystal

A 9-TUBE 5-BAND SUPERHET COVERING .54MHz TO 38MHz, 465KHz I.F., WITH BAND SPREAD, B.F.O., AND A IMAGE REJECTION CIRCUIT WORKING ON THE 4th AND 5th BANDS TO ELIMINATE IMAGES OF STRONG COMMERCIAL STATIONS. THERE IS NO S-METER OR SPEAKER. THE POWER SOURCE IS 120 VOLTS AC. THE FRONT PANEL IS STAMPED STEEL PAINTED BLACK WITH SILK- SCREENED LETTERING. TUBES USED: 80 RECTIFIER, 6F6 AUDIO POWER OUTPUT, 6J7 B.F.O., 6Q7 SECOND DETECTOR, A.V.C., AND FIRST AUDIO, 6K7 FIRST I.F. AMPLIFIER, 6K7 SECOND I.F. AMPLIFIER, 6J5 OSCILLATOR, 6L7 FIRST DETECTOR AND MIXER, 6K7 R.F. AMPLIFIER.

S-18, SX-18 SKY CHALLENGER II

S-19   SKY BUDDY   1938   **$29.50**

THE SECOND IN THE SKY BUDDY SERIES, FIVE TUBES AND THREE BANDS COVERING .54MHz TO 18NHz WITH A 465KHz I.F. WITH BUILT-IN SPEAKER, AND B.F.O., NO BAND SPREAD. THE CENTER DIAL IS A LOGGING SCALE ONLY. THE S-19 HAD A SHORT PRODUCTION RUN AND IS QUITE RARE THESE DAYS. THE FRONT PANEL IS PART OF THE CASE, WITH SILK-SCREENED LETTERING. TUBES USED: 80 RECTIFIER, 6K6 AUDIO POWER OUTPUT, 6K8 OSCILLATOR AND MIXER, 6P7 I.F. AMPLIFIER & B.F.O., 6Q7 DETECTOR & FIRST AUDIO. POWER SOURCE IS 120 VOLTS AC.

S-19R   SKY BUDDY   1939   **$29.50**

THE THIRD AND LAST OF THE SKY BUDDY SERIES AND THE MOST COMMON. SIX TUBES AND FOUR BANDS COVERING .54MHz TO 46MHz WITH A 455KHz I.F., BUILT-IN SPEAKER, BAND SPREAD, AND B.F.O. HERE THE CENTER DIAL IS THE BAND SPREAD DIAL. THE FRONT PANEL AND CHASSIS ARE BLACK AND BOTH ARE PART OF THE CASE. TUBES USED: 80 RECTIFIER, 41 AUDIO POWER OUTPUT, 76 B.F.O., 6Q7 SECOND DETECTOR AND FIRST AUDIO, 6K7 I.F. AMPLIFIER, 6K8 FIRST DETECTOR, OSCILLATOR AND MIXER. THERE WERE TWO VERSIONS OF THE S-19R, WHAT I CALL THE EARLY AND THE LATE. IN THE LATE VERSION A 6SK7 WAS USED IN PLACE OF THE 6K7, AND A 6SQ7 WAS USED IN PLACE OF THE 6Q7. ALSO, THERE WERE VARIOUS COMBINATIONS OF SLIDE AND TOGGLE SWITCHES USED IN THE TWO RUNS. THE EXTERNAL "SILVER" MAIN TUNING DIAL HAD SILK-SCREENED RATHER THAN ENGRAVED LETTERING.

S-19 SKY BUDDY

The S-19-R

The S-19-R was the most popular and last version of the Sky Buddy. There were two production runs, late and early. The early had three slide switches on the panel, and used a 6K7 and 6Q7. The late had two slide switches and one toggle switch (the send/receive switch), and used a 6SK7 and 6SQ7.

S-19R SKY BUDDY (EARLY)

S-19R SKY BUDDY (LATE)

S-20 **SKY CHAMPION** **1938-39** **$49.50**

EIGHT TUBES, FOUR BANDS, COVERING .54KHz TO 44MHz WITH A 455KHz I.F., BUILT-IN
SPEAKER, B.F.O., NO BAND SPREAD. THE CENTER DIAL IS A LOGGING SCALE ONLY AND
THE EXTERNAL MAIN TUNING DIAL HAS SILK-SCREENED LETTERING. THE FRONT PANEL
IS STEEL PAINTED GRAY AND IS PART OF THE CASE. LIKE THE S-19 THE S-20 IS NOT VERY
COMMON. OPTIONS INCLUDE AN EXTERNAL S-METER (MODEL SM-18) WHICH PLUGS INTO
ACCESSORY OUTLET ON THE REAR APRON OF THE CHASSIS. POWER SOURCE IS 120 VOLTS
AC. TUBES USED: 80 RECTIFIER, 6F6 AUDIO POWER OUTPUT, 6J5 B.F.O., 6Q7 SECOND DE-
TECTOR, A.V.C. AND FIRST AUDIO, 6K7 I.F. AMPLIFIER, 6J5 OSCILLATOR, 6L7 FIRST DETEC-
TOR AND MIXER, 6K7 R.F. AMPLIFIER.

S-20 SKY CHAMPION

S-20R   SKY CHAMPION   1939-45 $49.50

NINE TUBES, FOUR BANDS, COVERING .54MHz TO 44MHz WITH A 455KHz I.F., BUILT-IN SPEAKER, B.F.O., BAND SPREAD, AND A.N.L. OPTIONS INCLUDE AN EXTERNAL S-METER IN A SMALL SLOPE FRONT STEEL CASE (MODEL SM-20). THE FRONT PANEL IS STEEL PAINTED GRAY AND IS PART OF THE CASE. THE MAIN TUNING DIAL IS "PLASTIC" AND BEHIND AN ESCUTCHEON. IT IS INTERESTING TO NOTE THAT WHEN NEW THE DIALS WERE WHITE WITH BLACK LETTERING. THEY WERE MADE OF A "PHOTO SENSITIVE" MATERIAL THAT YELLOWED WITH EXPOSURE TO LIGHT. THAT IS WHY MOST OF THESE DIALS APPEAR AMBER NOW. THE S-20R WAS ALSO THE FIRST RADIO THAT WOULD BE "REPACKAGED" AND GIVEN SEVERAL DIFFERENT MODEL NUMBERS. THE S-40, S-85, AND THE S-108 WERE BASICALLY THE SAME RADIO WITH COSMETIC AND MINOR ELECTRICAL DIFFERENCES. TUBES USED: 80 RECTIFIER, 6F6 AUDIO POWER OUTPUT, 6J5 B.F.O., 6H6 A.N.L., 6SQ7 SECOND DETECTOR, A.V.C., AND FIRST AUDIO, 6SK7 FIRST I.F. AMPLIFIER, 6SK7 SECOND I.F. AMPLIFIER, 6K8 MIXER & OSCILLATOR, 6SK7 R.F. AMPLIFIER. POWER SOURCE IS 120 VOLTS AC.

S-20R SKY CHAMPION

S-21   SKYRIDER 5-10   1938 $69.50

EIGHT TUBES, TWO BANDS COVERING 27MHz TO 68MHz WITH A 1600KHz I.F., BUILT-IN SPEAKER, B.F.O., A.N.L., VARIABLE SELECTIVITY I.F. (BROAD AND SHARP), OPTIONS INCLUDE THE MODEL XP4 SIX VOLT DC VIBRAPACK FOR MOBILE OPERATION AND EXTERNAL S-METER MODEL SM-21 BOTH CONNECTED THROUGH SOCKETS ON THE REAR APRON OF THE CHASSIS. POWER SOURCE IS 120 VOLTS AC OR 6 VOLTS DC WITH XP4. NO BAND SPREAD. TUBES USED: 80 RECTIFIER, 6F6 AUDIO POWER OUTPUT, 6Q7 SECOND DETECTOR, A.V.C, AND FIRST AUDIO, 6P7 SECOND I.F. AMPLIFIER AND B.F.O., 6K7 FIRST I.F. AMPLIFIER, 6J5 OSCILLATOR, 6L7 FIRST DETECTOR AND MIXER, AND 1852 (6AC7) AS R.F. AMPLIFIER. THE FRONT PANEL IS STEEL PAINTED GRAYISH TAN AND IS PART OF THE CASE. THE LETTERING IS SILK-SCREENED.

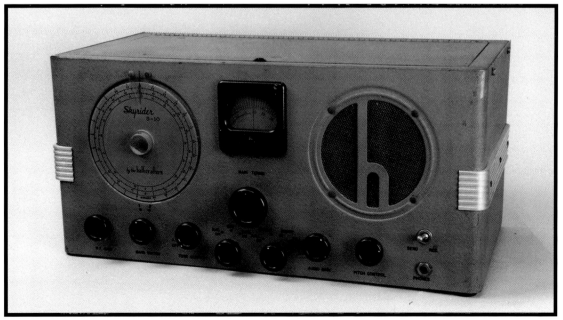

S-21 SKYRIDER 5-10

S-22   SKYRIDER MARINE   1938 $64.50

EIGHT TUBES, FOUR BANDS, COVERING 140KHz TO 18.5MHz WITH A 1600KHz I.F., BUILT-IN SPEAKER, B.F.O., NO BAND SPREAD. THE FRONT PANEL IS STEEL PAINTED SMOOTH BLACK AND IS PART OF THE CASE, THE LETTERING IS SILK-SCREENED. THE POWER SOURCE IS 120 VOLTS AC OR DC, OR 240 VOLTS AC OR DC DEPENDING ON THE BK29B RESISTOR BAL-

LAST TUBE. TUBES USED: 25Z5 RECTIFIER, 25L6 AUDIO POWER OUTPUT, 6J5 B.F.O., 6Q7 SECOND DETECTOR, A.V.C., AND FIRST AUDIO, 6K7 I.F. AMPLIFIER, 6J5 OSCILLATOR, 6L7 FIRST DETECTOR AND MIXER, AND 6K7 R.F. AMPLIFIER. THE UNIT PICTURED HERE HAD AN EXTRA HOLE IN THE UPPER RIGHT HAND CORNER OF THE PANEL WHICH HAS BEEN TEMPORAIRILY PLUGGED AND IS AWAITING PERMANENT REPAIR.

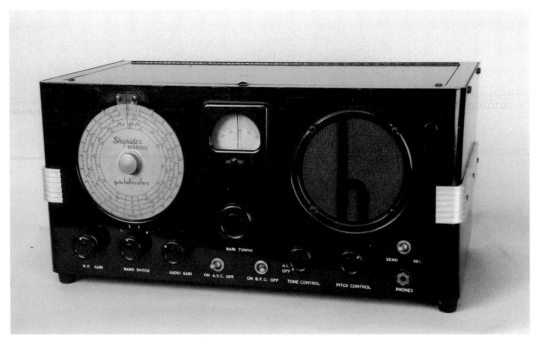

S-22 SKYRIDER MARINE

S-22R   SKYRIDER MARINE   1940 $74.50

EIGHT TUBES, FOUR BANDS, COVERING 110KHz TO 18MHz WITH A 1600KHz I.F., B.F.O. AND BUILT-IN SPEAKER. THE DIAL IS PLASTIC AND BEHIND AN ESCUTCHEON. THE PANEL IS BLACK WRINKLE FINISH AND IS PART OF THE CASE. POWER SOURCE IS 120 OR 240

VOLTS AC OR DC DEPENDING ON THE VALUE OF THE BK29D BALLAST TUBE. TUBES USED: 25Z5 RECTIFIER, 25L6 AUDIO POWER OUTPUT, 6J5 B.F.O., 6SQ7 SECOND DETECTOR, A.V.C. AND FIRST AUDIO, 6SK7 FIRST I.F. AMPLIFIER, 6SK7 SECOND I.F. AMPLIFIER, 6K8 OSCILLATOR AND MIXER, 6SK7 R.F. AMPLIFIER. NO BAND SPREAD.

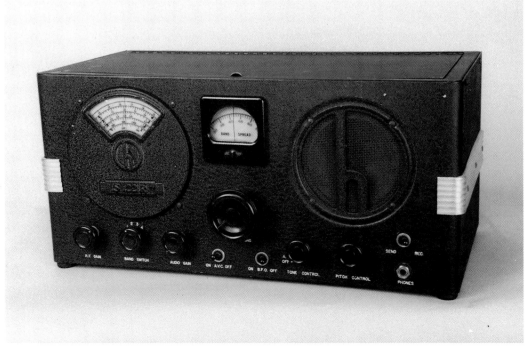

S-22R SKYRIDER MARINE

SX-23   SKYRIDER 23   1939 $115.50

THIS IS ANOTHER VERY UNUSUAL RADIO, WITH ITS DECO LOOK, POT-
TED OR COVERED TRANSFORMERS WITH EMBOSSED LOGOS AND THE
ENTIRE CHASSIS AND ALL COVERS PAINTED DARK GRAY. THE FRONT
PANEL AND CHASSIS ARE PART OF THE CASE. THE R.F. SECTION USED
CERAMIC CAPACITORS THAT WERE INDIVIDUALLY "TUNED" FOR EACH
RADIO, A VERY EXPENSIVE AND SLOW PROCESS. A FULL FEATURED SET
WITH ELEVEN TUBES AND FOUR BANDS COVERING .54MHz TO 34MHz
AND FOUR CALIBRATED SPREAD BANDS FOR 10, 20, 40, AND 80 METERS.
THIS IS THE FIRST RECEIVER THE COMPANY PRODUCED WITH CALI-
BRATED BAND SPREAD. THE I.F. IS 455KHz. WITH B.F.O., A.N.L., S-METER
AND CRYSTAL FILTER. OPTIONAL EXTERNAL SPEAKER (PM-23). POWER
SOURCE IS 120 VOLTS AC OR 25 TO 60 CYCLE 120 OR 240 VOLT AC
WITH OPTIONAL "UNIVERSAL" POWER TRANSFORMER. THERE MAY
ALSO BE A RACK MOUNT VERSION BUT I HAVE NEVER SEEN ONE. TUBES
USED: 80 RECTIFIER, 6F6 AUDIO POWER OUTPUT, 6B8 A.V.C. AMPLIFIER,
6H6 A.N.L., 6SJ7 B.F.O., 6SQ7 SECOND DETECTOR AND FIRST AUDIO,
6SK7 FIRST I.F. AMPLIFIER, 6SK7 SECOND I.F. AMPLIFIER, 6SJ7 OSCILLA-
TOR, 6SA7 FIRST DETECTOR AND MIXER, AND 6SK7 R.F. AMPLIFIER.

SX-23 SKYRIDER 23 (FRONT VIEW)

SX-23 SKYRIDER 23 (INSIDE VIEW)

SX-24 SKYRIDER DEFIANT

SX-24   SKYRIDER DEFIANT   1939 $69.50

A 9-TUBE 4-BAND SET COVERING .54MHz TO 43.5MHz WITH A 455KHz
I.F., S-METER, B.F.O., CALIBRATED BAND SPREAD FOR 10, 20, 40, AND 80
METERS, A.N.L., CRYSTAL FILTER, AND VARIABLE SELECTIVITY. OPTIONAL
EXTERNAL SPEAKER (PM-23). POWER SOURCE IS 120 VOLTS AC, OR MAY
BE RUN MOBILE WITH OPTIONAL VIBRAPACK CONNECTED THROUGH
A SOCKET ON THE REAR APRON OF THE CHASSIS. TUBES USED. 80 REC-
TIFIER, 6F6 AUDIO OUTPUT, 76 B.F.O., 6H6 A.N.L., 6SQ7 SECOND DETEC-
TOR, A.V.C., AND FIRST AUDIO, 6SK7 FIRST I.F. AMPLIFIER, 6SK7 SECOND
I.F. AMPLIFIER, 6K8 FIRST DETECTOR, MIXER, AND OSCILLATOR, 6SK7 R.F.
AMPLIFIER.

SX-25   SUPER DEFIANT   1940-45 $94.50

TWELVE TUBES, FOUR BANDS COVERING .54MHz TO 42MHz WITH A 455KHz I.F., TWO STAGES OF R.F. AMPLIFICATION, A.N.L., B.F.O., VARIABLE SELECTIVITY, CRYSTAL FILTER, CALIBRATED BAND SPREAD FOR 10, 20, 40, AND 80 METERS, AND S-METER. OPTIONAL EXTERNAL SPEAKER PM-23. SILK-SCREENED LETTERING ON THE STEEL PANEL WHICH IS PART OF THE CASE. POWER SOURCE IS 120 VOLTS AC OR 120-240 VOLTS AC 25 TO 60 CYCLES WITH UNIVERSAL POWER TRANSFORMER. TUBES USED: 80 RECTIFIER, TWO 6F6 IN PUSH-PULL AUDIO POWER OUTPUT, 6J5 B.F.O., 6H6 A.N.L., 6SQ7 PHASE INVERTER, 6SQ7 2nd DETECTOR, A.V.C., 1st AUDIO, 6SK7 1st I.F. AMP., 6SK7 2nd I.F. AMP., 6K8 1st DETECTOR, MIXER, AND OSCILLATOR, 6SK7 1st R.F. AMP., 6SK7 2nd R.F. AMP.

SX-25 SUPER DEFIANT

S-26F   NONE   1938   unknown

THIS 8-TUBE SET WAS CUSTOM BUILT FOR THE FEDERAL COMMUNICATIONS COMMISSION AND WAS NOT OFFERED FOR SALE TO THE GENERAL PUBLIC. THE CHASSIS LAYOUT AND DESIGN IS ALMOST IDENTICAL TO THE S-21 BUT THE CABINET AND PANEL ARE RADICALLY DIFFERENT. THE FREQUENCY COVERAGE IS 27MHz TO 82MHz IN TWO BANDS WITH A 1600KHz I.F., B.F.O., S-METER, A.N.L., AND VARIABLE SELECTIVITY I.F. THE S-METER ZERO ADJUSTMENT IS ON THE FRONT PANEL. POWER SOURCE IS 120 VOLTS AC, OR 6 VOLT MOBILE OPERATION WITH OPTIONAL XP4 VIBRAPACK. OPTIONAL EXTERNAL SPEAKER. TUBES USED: 80 RECTIFIER, 6F6 AUDIO OUTPUT, 6P7 2nd I.F. & B.F.O., 6K7 1st I.F., 6Q7 2nd DETECTOR, A.V.C., & 1st AUDIO, 6J5 OSCILLATOR 6L7 1st DETECTOR & MIXER, AND 1852 (6AC7) R.F. AMP.

S-26F

S-27	NONE	1940	$175.00
S-27B			
S-27D			
S-27-FCC			

THIS ULTRA HIGH FREQUENCY SET HAS FIFTEEN TUBES AND THREE BANDS, AND COVERS 27MHz TO 143MHz WITH A CHOICE OF RECEPTION MODE OF AM, FM, OR CW ON ALL FREQUENCIES. THE I.F. FREQUENCY IS 5.25MHz. WITH S-METER, B.F.O., A.N.L., AND VARIABLE I.F. SELECTIVITY (BROAD & SHARP). THE PANEL IS HEAVY STEEL, RACK MOUNTABLE, AND HAS ENGRAVED LETTERING. MOST ARE PAINTED BLACK, SOME ARE LIGHT GRAY. POWER SOURCE IS 120 VOLTS AC, OR DC MOBILE OPERATION WITH OPTIONAL VIBRAPACK. OPTIONAL EXTERNAL SPEAKER. THESE RADIOS WERE SOLD TO THE MILITARY AS THE RBK SERIES AND WERE INTERCHANGEABLE WITH THE S-36A FOR MILITARY PURPOSES. THE OSCILLATOR, MIXER, AND R.F. AMP. TUBES WERE ACORN TYPE. TUBES USED: 5Z3 RECTIFIER, 956 R.F. AMP., 954 1st DETECTOR, & MIXER, 955 OSCILLATOR, 6AC7 1st I.F., 6AB7 2nd I.F., 6SK7 3rd I.F., 6H6 AM DETECTOR & A.N.L., 6AC7 LIMITER, 6H6 FM DETECTOR, 6C8 1st AUDIO, VR-150 (OD3) VOLTAGE REGULATOR, TWO 6V6 IN PUSH-PULL AUDIO OUTPUT, AND 6J5 B.F.O. THE S-27B IS THE SAME RADIO WITH SLIGHTLY DIFFERENT FREQUENCY COVERAGE (36Mhz TO 165Mhz). I SEE NO NOTICEABLE DIFFERENCE BETWEEN THE "D" MODEL AND THE S-27. I DON'T HAVE THE FCC MODEL FOR COMPARISON BUT SUSPECT IT IS VERY SIMILAR TO THE S-27. THE SET PICTURED HERE IS THE S-27.

S-27

SX-28 SUPER SKYRIDER WITH R-12 CONSOLE SPEAKER

SX-28 SUPER SKYRIDER

SX-28	SUPER SKYRIDER	1940	$159.50

THE EPITOME OF A COMMUNICATIONS RECEIVER, THIS 15-TUBE 6-BAND RADIO COVERS .54MHz TO 43MHz WITH A 455KHz I.F.. FEATURES INCLUDE A B.F.O., VARIABLE STRENGTH A.N.L., S-METER, MAIN TUNING DIAL LOCK, VARIABLE I.F. SELECTIVITY (BROAD, MEDIUM, SHARP), CRYSTAL FILTER, TWO STAGES OF R.F. AMPLIFICATION, AND CALIBRATED BAND SPREAD. THE FRONT PANEL IS HEAVY STEEL PAINTED BLACK WITH ENGRAVED LETTERING AND IMITATION "LEATHER GRAINING." POWER SOURCE IS 120 VOLTS AC, OR 120-240 VOLTS AC 25-60 CYCLES WITH UNIVERSAL POWER TRANSFORMER. PROVISION IS ALSO MADE FOR 6 VOLT DC OPERATION WITH OPTIONAL VIBRAPACK. OPTIONAL EXTERNAL SPEAKER PM-23 OR R-12 CONSOLE. TUBES USED: 5Z3 RECTIFIER, TWO 6V6 IN PUSH-PULL AUDIO OUTPUT, 6SC7 1st AUDIO, 6J5 B.F.O., 6H6 A.N.L., 6AB7 A.N.L. AMP., 6B8 A.V.C. AMP., 6B8 2nd DETECTOR & S-METER AMP., 6SK7 2nd I.F. 6L7 1st I.F. & A.N.L AMP., 6SA7 OSCILLATOR, 6SA7 MIXER, 6SK7 2nd R.F. AMP., AND 6AB7 1st R.F. AMP.

SX-28A   SUPER SKYRIDER   1944 $223.00
SXC-28-FCC
AN/GRR-2

THIS IS THE LATE-WAR VERSION USING THE SAME TUBES AND HAVING THE SAME FEA-
TURES AND SPECIFICATIONS AS THE SX-28. IN MOST CASES THERE WAS NO "A" DESIGNA-
TION ON THE RADIO, MAKING IDENTIFICATION AS THE "A" MODEL DIFFICULT AS THE
OUTWARD APPEARANCE WAS NEARLY IDENTICAL TO THE SX-28. SOME WERE PRODUCED
WITH THE "A" DESIGNATION ON THE PANEL. THE MAJOR DIFFERENCES BETWEEN THE

TWO RADIOS IS THE LAYOUT AND TYPE OF COMPONENTS USED IN THE R.F. SECTION. A
MINOR VISIBLE DIFFERENCE IS THE ADDITION OF AN AC LINE FUSE ON THE REAR APRON
OF THE CHASSIS OF THE "A" MODEL. ALTHOUGH I HAVE NO HARD EVIDENCE I BELIEVE IN
TOTAL ABOUT 50 THOUSAND SX-28 AND 28A WERE BUILT, MAKING THIS UNIT FAIRLY
COMMON. THE MILITARY NUMBER FOR THE SX-28A IS AN/GRR-2. OUTWARDLY THE ONLY
NOTICEABLE DIFFERENCE IS A POTTED POWER TRANSFORMER. I SEE NO NOTICEABLE
DIFFERENCE IN THE FCC MODEL. SHOWN HERE IS THE SX-28A.

SX-28A SUPER SKYRIDER

S-29   SKY TRAVELER   1940 $59.50

A 9-TUBE 4-BAND TOTALLY PORTABLE RADIO COVERING .54MHz TO 30.5MHz. 455KHz I.F.,
POWER SOURCE IS 120 VOLTS AC OR DC, AND INTERNAL BATTERIES FOR PORTABLE USE.
WITH BAND SPREAD, A.N.L., B.F.O., AND BUILT-IN SPEAKER. FOR 120 VOLT AC OR DC OP-

ERATION THE LINE CORD HAS A VOLTAGE DROPPING RESISTOR. TUBES USED: 50Y6 RECTI-
FIER, 1G4 A.N.L., 1G4 B.F.O., 3Q5 AUDIO OUTPUT, 1H5 2nd DETECTOR, A.V.C., & 1st AUDIO,
1P5 1st I.F., 1P5 2nd I.F., 1R5 1st DETECTOR & OSCILLATOR, AND 1T4 R.F. AMP. HAS BUILT-IN
TELESCOPING ANTENNA

S-29 SKY TRAVELLER

S-30   RADIO COMPASS   1940 $99.50

THIS IS A 6-TUBE 3-BAND RADIO DIRECTION-FINDER COVERING 220KHz TO 3MHz. I.F. FREQUENCY IS 175KHz. WITH BUILT-IN ROTATABLE LOOP ANTENNA CALIBRATED SUCH THAT THE DIRECTION AND COURSE OF THE VEHICLE THE UNIT IS INSTALLED IN (USUALLY A SHIP) CAN BE DETERMINED. SIGNALS FROM BROADCAST STATIONS OR MARINE BEACONS ARE HEARD THROUGH THE SUPPLIED HEADPHONES, OR THE OPTIONAL EXTERNAL SPEAKER. THE POWER SOURCE IS 6 VOLTS DC WITH SUPPLIED VIBRAPACK POWER SUPPLY. TUBES USED: 6U5 EYE TUBE FOR NULL INDICATOR, 6SK7 R.F. AMP., 6K8 1st DETECTOR, MIXER, & OSCILLATOR, 6SK7 I.F. AMP., 6SQ7 2nd DETECTOR & 1st AUDIO, 6G6 AUDIO OUTPUT. THESE UNITS ARE RARE AND DIFFICULT TO FIND. IN OVER 20 YEARS OF COLLECTING HALLICRAFTERS EQUIPMENT, I HAVE BEEN AWARE OF ONLY TWO UNITS. I DO NOT HAVE THE VIBRAPACK. IT IS INTERESTING TO NOTE THAT THIS ENTIRE UNIT IS MADE OF ALUMINUM (INCLUDING ALL PANELS, CABINET, CHASSIS, LOOP HOUSING, AND TRANSFORMER CANS) RATHER THAN STEEL.

S-30 RADIO COMPASS

S-30 RADIO COMPASS

S-31   NONE   1940 $74.50

A 9-TUBE 2-BAND AM/FM BROADCAST TUNER COVERING .54Mhz TO 1.65Mhz, AND THE OLD COMMERCIAL FM BAND OF 40MHz TO 51MHz. THE AM I.F. IS 455KHz, THE FM I.F. IS 4.3Mhz. WITH S-METER, AUDIO PRE-AMP, AND RACK MOUNT PANEL. OPTIONAL AUDIO POWER AMPLIFIER (S-31A) AND EXTERNAL SPEAKER (PM-23). POWER SOURCE IS 120 VOLTS AC. TUBES USED: 80 RECTIFIER, 6SK7 R.F. AMP., 6SA7 OSCILLATOR & MIXER, 1852 (6AC7) 1st FM I.F. AMP., 1853 (6AB7) 2nd FM I.F. AMP., 6SJ7 LIMITER, 6H6 DISCRIMINATOR, 6SK7 AM I.F. AMP., 6SR7 AM DETECTOR, A.V.C., & 1st AUDIO. THE UNIT SHOWN HERE HAS A HOMEMADE DIAL ESCUTCHEON. IT IS CLOSE TO ORIGINAL APPEARANCE BUT NOT EXACT.

S-31

S-31A   **NONE**   1940 $54.00

THIS IS THE COMPANION AUDIO POWER AMPLIFIER FOR THE S-31 TUNER, HAVING SIX TUBES, A POWER OUTPUT OF 25 WATTS, AND A FREQUENCY RESPONSE OF 30hz TO 20Khz. SEPARATE BASS AND TREBLE TONE CONTROLS, OUTPUTS FOR 4, 8, AND 500 OHM SPEAKERS. THIS UNIT IS ALSO RACK MOUNTABLE. TUBES USED: 5Z3 RECTIFIER, TWO 6L6 IN PUSH-PULL AUDIO OUTPUT, 6F5 INPUT PRE-AMP., 6SQ7 FIRST AUDIO, AND 6SC7 AS DUAL DRIVER & INVERTER. POWER SOURCE IS 120 VOLTS AC.

S-31A

SX-32   **SKYRIDER 32**   1941 $149.50

THIRTEEN TUBES AND SIX BANDS COVERING .5MHz TO 42MHz WITH A 455KHz I.F., S-METER, CALIBRATED BAND SPREAD, FIXED A.N.L., CRYSTAL FILTER, VARIABLE SELECTIVITY, AND B.F.O. POWER SOURCE IS 120 VOLTS AC, OPTIONAL EXTERNAL SPEAKER PM-23. THIS RADIO LOOKS VERY SIMILAR TO THE SX-28 BUT HAS FEWER TUBES AND FEATURES. TUBES USED: 5Z3 RECTIFIER, TWO 6V6 IN PUSH-PULL AUDIO OUTPUT 6SC7 1st AUDIO, 6J5 B.F.O., 6H6 2nd DETECTOR & A.N.L., 6B8 A.V.C. AMP., 6SK7 2nd I.F. AMP., 6K7 1st I.F. AMP., 6SA7 OSCILLATOR, 6SK7 2nd R.F. AMP., AND 6AB7 1st R.F. AMP.

S-33   **SKY TRAINER**   1941 $29.50

A COMPLETELY SELF-CONTAINED, BATTERY-OPERATED PORTABLE TRANSCEIVER WITH SPEAKER AND ANTENNA. THREE TUBES AND ONE BAND COVERING 112MHz TO 118MHz. TUBES USED: 3Q5 OSCILLATOR, 1H5 AUDIO AMP., AND 3Q5 POWER AMPLIFIER. POWER SOURCE IS TWO EVERREADY #746 BATTERIES. THE TOTAL WEIGHT OF THE SET WITH BATTERIES IS 16 POUNDS. THE PHOTO SHOWN HERE WAS TAKEN FROM A 1942 HALLICRAFTERS SALES BROCHURE.

SX-32 SKYRIDER 32

S-33 SKY TRAINER

S-35   NONE   1942 $375.50

A 14-TUBE PANORAMIC ADAPTOR WITH A 5" SCREEN. IT WAS USUALLY SOLD PACKAGED
WITH AN SX-28 IN A RACK CABINET, BUT COULD BE USED WITH ANY RECEIVER HAVING
A 455KHz I.F. SYSTEM. POWER SOURCE IS 120 VOLTS AC. TUBES USED: 5AP1 C.R.T., VR-105
& VR-150 AS VOLTAGE REGULATORS, 80 LOW VOLTAGE RECTIFIER, 2X2 HIGH VOLTAGE
RECTIFIER, 6SG7 I.F. AMP., 6SK7 I.F. AMP., 6SA7 MIXER/CONVERTER, 6J5 OSCILLATOR, 6SQ7
DETECTOR AND VERTICAL AMP., 6SC7 HORIZONTAL AMP., 6SN7 HORIZONTAL OSCILLA-
TOR, 6SJ7 BLANKING OSCILLATOR, AND 6AC7 MODULATOR. THE PHOTO SHOWN HERE
IS FROM A HALLICRAFTERS ADVERTISING BROCHURE.

S-35 (FRONT VIEW)

S-36   NONE   1942 $307.50
S-36A   1944
RBK-13
RBK-15

A 15-TUBE 3-BAND U.H.F. RECEIVER COVERING 27.8MHz TO 143MHz WITH CHOICE OF AM,
FM, OR CW RECEPTION. THE I.F. IS 5.25MHz. WITH S-METER, B.F.O., A.N.L., AND VARIABLE
I.F. SELECTIVITY. ALL FUNCTIONS AND FEATURES ARE IDENTICAL TO THE S-27. THE CON-
TROL AND COMPONENT LAY-OUT IS SLIGHTLY DIFFERENT. POWER SOURCE IS 120 VOLTS
AC. TUBES USED: 5U4 RECTIFIER, OD3/VR-150 VOLTAGE REGULATOR, TWO 6V6 IN PUSH-
PULL AUDIO OUTPUT, 956 R.F. AMP., 954 MIXER, 955 OSCILLATOR, 6J5 B.F.O., 6SL7 AUDIO
PHASE INVERTER, 6H6 FM DISCRIMINATOR, 6AC7 FM LIMITER, 6H6 AM DETECTOR AND
A.N.L., 6AC7 1st I.F., 6AB7 2nd I.F., AND 6SK7 3rd I.F. THE S-36A IS ALMOST IDENTICAL WITH
EXCEPTION OF A DIFFERENT STYLE S-METER AND SOME MINOR COMPONENT DIFFER-
ENCES. OPTIONAL EXTERNAL SPEAKER. RBK-13 & RBK-15 ARE THE MILITARY NUMBERS FOR
THE S-36 & 36A RESPECTIVELY. THE RBK-15 HAS 16 TUBES WITH THE ADDITION OF A 956
USED AS A "RADIATION SUPPRESSOR" BETWEEN THE ANTENNA AND THE RF AMPLIFIER.
SHOWN HERE IS THE S-36A.

S-35 (CHASSIS, TOP VIEW)

S-36A

S-37   **NONE**   **1944**   **$591.75**

A 14-TUBE SINGLE-BAND V.H.F. RECEIVER COVERING 130MHz TO 210MHz WITH CHOICE OF AM OR FM RECEPTION. THE I.F. IS 16MHz. WITH S-METER AND A.N.L., OPTIONAL EXTERNAL SPEAKER. THE PANEL IS HEAVY STEEL WITH ENGRAVED LETTERING. REGULAR POWER SOURCE IS 120 VOLTS AC, BUT CAN BE USED FOR 6 VOLT MOBILE OPERATION WITH OPTIONAL VIBRAPACK. TUBES USED: 5U4 RECTIFIER, OD3/VR-150 VOLTAGE REGULATOR, 6V6 AUDIO OUTPUT, 954 1st R.F. AMP., 954 2nd R.F. AMP., 954 MIXER, 955 OSCILLATOR, 6SL7 1st AUDIO, 6H6 FM DISCRIMINATOR, 6AC7 FM LIMITER, 6H6 AM DETECTOR AND A.N.L., 6AC7 1st I.F., 6AB7 2nd I.F., AND 6SK7 3rd I.F.

S-37

S-38 (SMOOTH FINISH)

S-38   **NONE**   **1946**   **$47.50**

SIX TUBES AND FOUR BANDS COVERING .54MHz TO 32MHz WITH A 455KHz I.F. FEATURES INCLUDE A VARIABLE PITCH B.F.O., A.N.L., BAND SPREAD AND BUILT-IN SPEAKER. THE S-38 SERIES WAS THE POST-WAR REPLACEMENT FOR THE SKY BUDDY, USED AS AN "ENTRY LEVEL" RADIO. THE CASE FINISH ON MOST IS SMOOTH BLACK, ALTHOUGH I HAVE SEEN SOME WITH A WRINKLE FINISH. POWER SOURCE IS 120 VOLTS AC OR DC. TUBES USED: 35Z5 RECTIFIER, 35L6 AUDIO OUTPUT, 12SQ7 A.N.L., AND B.F.O., 12SQ7 DETECTOR, A.V.C., AND 1st AUDIO, 12SK7 I.F., 12SA7 MIXER AND OSCILLATOR.

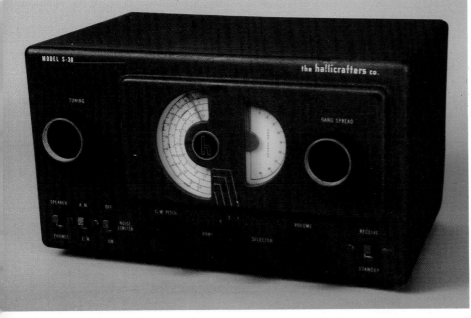

S-38 (WRINKLE FINISH)

The S-38

There were two versions of the S-38 with a major electrical change, as well as with some physical layout changes to the components on the chassis and back apron of the chassis. The Standard S-38 has six tubes, a metal bottom plate, and a smooth black finish to the cabinet. At the end of the production run and just before introduction of the "A" model there were a number of S-38 sets produced with only five tubes, a cardboard bottom cover and a black wrinkle finish on the cabinet. They still had all the other features of the S-38, including the variable pitch BFO, but used the "A" chassis.

S-38A	NONE	1946-47	$49.50
S-38B		1947-53	
S-38C		1953-55	

FIVE TUBES, FOUR BANDS, .54MHz TO 31MHz, 455KHz I.F. FIXED FREQUENCY B.F.O. (NO PITCH CONTROL), WITH BAND SPREAD AND BUILT-IN SPEAKER. NO A.N.L. THE CASE FINISH IS SMOOTH BLACK. POWER SOURCE IS 120 VOLTS AC OR DC. TUBES USED: 35Z5 RECTIFIER, 50L6 AUDIO OUTPUT, 12SQ7 DETECTOR, A.V.C., 1st AUDIO, 12SK7 I.F., B.F.O. AND 12SA7 MIXER, OSCILLATOR. THE S-38B AND THE S-38C WERE ELECTRONICALLY NEARLY IDENTICAL TO THE "A" MODEL. THE DIFFERENCES WERE IN THE COLOR AND FINISH OF THE DIALS AND CASE. THE "B" MODEL HAS A BLACK WRINKLE FINISH AND THE "C" MODEL HAS A "HAMMERTONE" GRAY FINISH. THE "C" MODEL USED A 12SG7 RATHER THAN A 12SK7 AS THE I.F. AMPLIFIER. OTHER MINOR DIFFERENCES BETWEEN THESE MODELS WERE THE BACK PANEL AND POWER CORD ATTACHMENT.

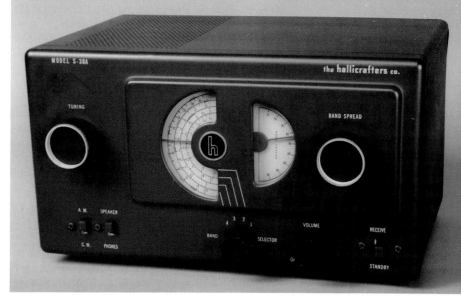

S-38A

S-38B

S-38C

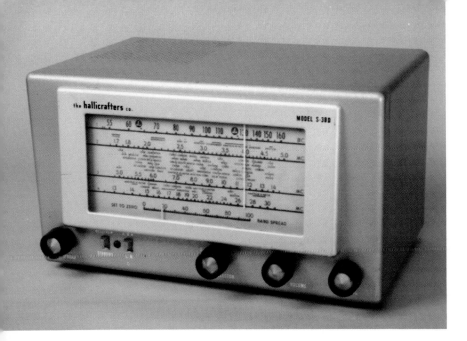

S-38D   NONE   1955-57 $59.95

FIVE TUBES, SAME FREQUENCY COVERAGE ,FEATURES AND SPECIFICA-
TIONS AS THES-38C BUT RADICALLY DIFFERENT APPEARANCE AS CAN
BE SEEN. SLIDE RULE DIAL, SMOOTH LIGHT GRAY FINISH.

S-38D

S-38E   NONE   1957-61 $59.95
S-38EM, -EB
MARK-IA
MARK-II

FIVE TUBES, FOUR BANDS COVERING .54MHz TO 31MHz. THE OTHER
FEATURES ARE THE SAME AS THE "A" THROUGH "D" MODELS WITH EX-
CEPTION OF THE TUBES USED AND ADDITION OF A B.F.O. INJECTION
CONTROL ON THE REAR APRON OF THE CHASSIS. THE LETTER DESIG-
NATION AFTER "E" IN THE MODEL NUMBER INDICATES THE COLOR OF
THE CABINET. "E" IS GRAY, "EM" IS MAHOGANY, "EB" IS BEIGE. TUBES USED:
35W4 RECTIFIER, 50C5 AUDIO OUTPUT, 12AV6 DETECTOR & 1st AU-
DIO, 12BE6 I.F. & B.F.O., 12BE6 MIXER AND OSCILLATOR.

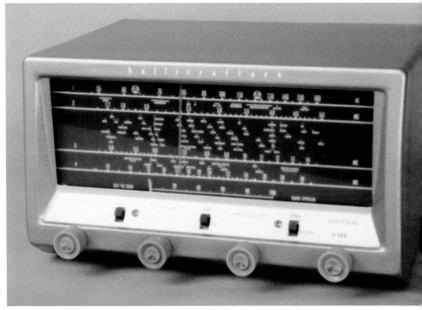

S-38E

S-38EM

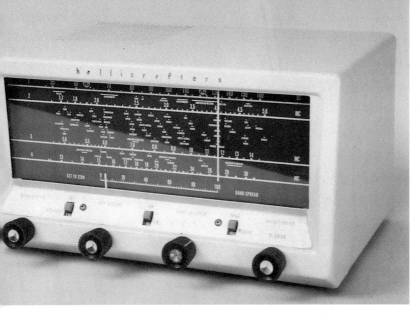

SX-38   NONE   1944 $225.00

THE LITTLE I KNOW ABOUT THIS MODEL IS RUMOR AND HEARSAY. IT IS SUPPOSED TO BE SIMILAR IN APPEARANCE AND SIZE TO THE SX-28 AND BEARS NO RESEMBLANCE TO THE STANDARD S-38 SERIES. I HAVE NEVER SEEN OR KNOWN ANYONE WHO HAS SEEN ONE OF THESE UNITS AND I HAVE NO TECHNICAL DATA OR PHOTOGRAPHS. IT MAY HAVE BEEN AN EXPERIMENTAL PROTOTYPE BASED ON THE SX-28 THAT NEVER WENT INTO PRODUCTION.

S-38EB

S-39   SKY RANGER   1942 $110.00

R-80

A 9-TUBE 4-BAND PORTABLE RADIO COVERING .550MHz TO 30MHz. I.F. IS 455KHz. WITH B.F.O., BAND SPREAD, A.N.L., TELESCOPING ANTENNA, BUILT-IN SPEAKER AND ONE STAGE OF R.F. AMPLIFICATION. POWER SOURCE IS 120 VOLTS AC OR DC OR SELF CONTAINED BATTERY POWER. THIS SET IS SIMILAR TO THE S-29 AND WAS USED BY THE MILITARY AS A TROOP ENTERTAINMENT AND MORALE BOOSTER UNIT. ITS MILITARY NUMBER IS R-80. TUBES USED: TWO 35Z5 RECTIFIER, 3Q5 AUDIO OUTPUT, 1H5 B.F.O. & A.N.L., 1H5 DETECTOR, A.V.C., & 1st AUDIO, 1P5 1st I.F., 1P5 2nd I.F., 1R5 MIXER (CONVERTER), OSCILLATOR, AND 1T4 R.F. AMP.

S-40   NONE   1946-49 $79.50

S-40U

S-40A   1949-50 $87.50

S-40AU

NINE TUBES, FOUR BANDS, COVERING .54MHz TO 43MHz. THE I.F. IS 455KHz. WITH BAND SPREAD, B.F.O., A.N.L., AND BUILT-IN SPEAKER. OPTIONS INCLUDE AN EXTERNAL S-METER MODEL SM-40 AND A UNIVERSAL POWER TRANSFORMER FOR OPERATION ON 120 OR 240 VOLTS 25-60Hz AC. THE STANDARD POWER SOURCE IS 120 VOLTS AC. THE "U" IN THE MODEL NUMBER INDICATES THE UNIVERSAL TRANSFORMER OPTION. TUBES USED: 80 RECTIFIER, 6F6 AUDIO OUTPUT, 6J5 BFO, 6H6 ANL, 6SQ7 DETECTOR & 1st AUDIO, 6SK7 1st

S-39 SKY RANGER

I.F., 6SK7 2nd I.F., 6SA7 MIXER & OSCILLATOR, AND 6SG7 R.F. AMPLIFIER. THE ONLY DIFFERENCE I HAVE FOUND BETWEEN THE S-40 AND THE S-40A IS THE COLOR OF THE DIAL. SOME OF THE S-40 DIALS WERE WHITE (AMBER WITH AGE), THE S-40A DIAL WAS GREEN. THERE MAY ALSO BE SOME VALUE CHANGES ON SOME CAPACITORS & RESISTORS. THE DIAL ESCUTCHEON & SPEAKER GRILL OF BOTH IS A SEPARATE ASSEMBLY ATTACHED TO THE FRONT PANEL. THE PRICE OF THE S-40 WAS 79.50, THE S-40A 87.50

S-40

S-40A

S-40B   NONE   1950-55 $89.95
S-40BU

EIGHT TUBES AND FOUR BANDS COVERING .54MHz TO 44MHz. ALL OTHER FEATURES AND OPTIONS ARE THE SAME AS THE S-40. ELECTRICAL DIFFERENCES INCLUDE THE USE OF MINIATURE I.F. TRANSFORMERS AND SOME DIFFERENT TUBES. COSMETIC DIFFERENCES INCLUDE A ONE-PIECE FRONT PANEL WITH DIAL ESCUTCHEON AND SPEAKER GRILL STAMPED INTO THE PANEL. TUBES USED: 5Y3 RECTIFIER, 6K6 AUDIO OUTPUT, 6H6 ANL, AVC, & DETECTOR, 6SC7 BFO & 1st AUDIO, TWO 6SK7 AS 1st & 2nd I.F. AMP., 6SA7 MIXER & OSCILLATOR, AND 6SG7 R.F. AMPLIFIER. STANDARD POWER SOURCE OF 120 VOLTS AC, OR 120-240 VOLTS 25-60Hz WITH UNIVERSAL TRANSFORMER. UNIVERSAL TRANSFORMER OPTION COST $10.00 MORE.

S-40B

-41G   SKYRIDER JR.   1945-46 $33.50

-41W

THIS IS A 6-TUBE 3-BAND ENTRY LEVEL RADIO COVERING .54MHz TO 30MHz. THE I.F. IS
55KHz. WITH BAND SPREAD, BFO, ANL, AND BUILT-IN SPEAKER. THE POWER SOURCE IS
20 VOLTS AC OR DC. IT IS INTERESTING TO NOTE THAT THE S-41G & W WERE PRODUCED
JST PRIOR TO THE INTRODUCTION AND PRODUCTION OF THE S-38 DESPITE THE HIGHER
MODEL NUMBER. IT HAD A RELATIVELY SHORT PRODUCTION RUN, BUT EVEN SO IS STILL
COMMON. TUBES USED: 35Z5 RECTIFIER 35L6 AUDIO OUTPUT, 12SQ7 BFO, & ANL, 12SQ7
VC, DETECTOR & 1st AUDIO, 12SK7 I.F., AND 12SA7 MIXER AND OSCILLATOR. "G" OR "W"
N THE MODEL NUMBER DESIGNATES GRAY OR WHITE CABINET COLOR & KNOB STYLE.

S-41G

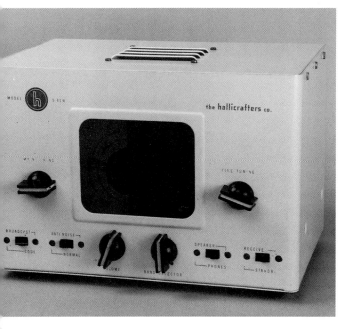

-41W

SX-42   NONE   1946-48 $275.00

SX-42 U

THE TOP OF THE LINE FOR 1946, THIS 15-TUBE SET REPLACES THE SX-28. WITH ITS CON-
TINUOUS FREQUENCY COVERAGE OF .54MHz TO 110MHz IN SIX BANDS IT HAS THE
BROADEST FREQUENCY RANGE OF ANY RADIO ON THE MARKET. CAPABLE OF AM OR
CW RECEPTION ON THE FIRST FOUR BANDS (.54MHz TO 30MHz) AND AM, CW, OR FM
RECEPTION ON BANDS 5 & 6 (27MHz TO 110MHz). THE AM I.F. IS 455KHz AND THE FM I.F. IS
10.7MHz. FEATURES INCLUDE CALIBRATED BAND SPREAD, BFO, CRYSTAL FILTER, ANL, S-
METER, VARIABLE I.F. SELECTIVITY, AND A PHONOGRAPH INPUT FOR THOSE WHO WISHED
TO TAKE ADVANTAGE OF THE HI-FI AUDIO SECTION. OPTIONS INCLUDE AN EXTERNAL
SPEAKER MODEL R-42, AND TILT BASE MODEL B-42 (A $7.00 OPTION). POWER SOURCE IS
120 VOLTS AC. TUBES USED: 5U4 RECTIFIER, OD3/VR-150 VOLTAGE REGULATOR, TWO
6V6 IN PUSH-PULL AUDIO OUTPUT, 7A4 BFO & FM TUNING METER AMPLIFIER, 6SL7 AUDIO
PHASE INVERTER, 6H6 DISCRIMINATOR, 7H7 AM DETECTOR, 6SK7 1st I.F. AMP., 6SC7 2nd I.F.
AMP., 7H7 3rd I.F. AMP., 6H6 ANL, 7F8 OSCILLATOR AND CONVERTER, AND TWO 6AG5 AS
1st AND 2nd R.F. AMPLIFIER. A UNIVERSAL POWER TRANSFORMER WAS AVAILABLE FOR
120-240 VOLT 25-60Hz OPERATION.

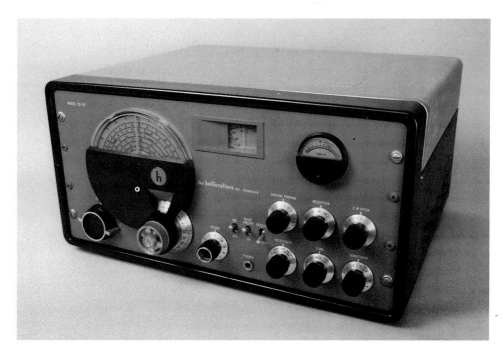

SX-42

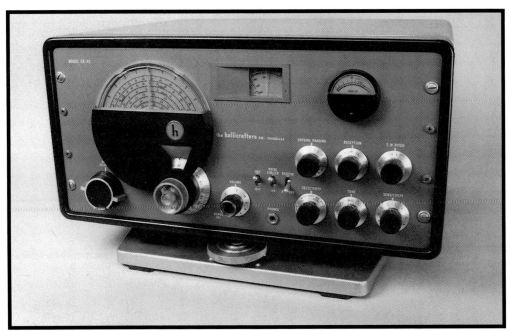

SX-42 WITH B-42 TILT BASE

SX-43   **NONE**   **1947**   **$169.50**

SX-43U

ELEVEN TUBES AND SEVEN BANDS, THE LITTLE BROTHER TO THE SX-42. BAND 3A IS A SPREAD BAND COVERING THE 20 METER AMATEUR BAND ONLY (14MHz TO 14.4MHz). COVERAGE OF BANDS 1 THROUGH 5 IS .54MHz TO 44MHz WITH AM OR CW RECEPTION ON 1 THROUGH 4, AND AM, CW, OR FM RECEPTION ON BAND 5 (44MHz TO 56MHz). BAND 6 COVERS 86MHz TO 109MHz WITH FM RECEPTION ONLY. THE AM I.F. IS 455KHz AND THE FM I.F. IS 10.7MHz. FEATURES INCLUDE CALIBRATED BAND SPREAD, BFO, VARIABLE SELECTIVITY, ANL, S-METER & CRYSTAL FILTER. POWER SOURCE IS 120 VOLTS AC OR 120-240 VOLTS AC 25-60Hz WITH OPTIONAL UNIVERSAL POWER TRANSFORMER. OPTIONAL EXTERNAL SPEAKER R-44. TUBES USED: 5Y3 RECTIFIER, 6V6 AUDIO OUTPUT, 6SQ7 1st AUDIO, 6SG7 1st I.F., 6SH7 2nd I.F. & 2nd MIXER, 6SH7 3rd I.F., 6AL5 FM RATIO DETECTOR, 6H6 AM DETECTOR, 6J5 BFO, 7F8 OSCILLATOR AND MIXER, AND 6BA6 RF AMPLIFIER.

SX-43, SX-43U

SX-46   NONE   1947 $115.00 proposed price

NINE TUBES, FIVE BANDS, .54MHz TO 43MHz, 455KHz, WITH BFO, "S"-METER, CALIBRATED BAND SPREAD, CRYSTAL FILTER, VARIABLE SELECTIVITY, AND ANL. TUBES USED: 5Y3 RECTIFIER, 6V6 AUDIO OUTPUT, 6J5 BFO, 6H6 ANL, 6SQ7 2nd DETECTOR AND 1st AUDIO, 6SK7 1st I.F., 6SK7 2nd I.F., 7F8 OSCILLATOR, AND 6BA6 R.F. AMPLIFIER. POWER SOURCE IS 120 VOLTS AC. OPTIONAL EXTERNAL SPEAKER. PHOTO SHOWN HERE IS FROM A HALLICRAFTERS ADVERTISING BROCHURE. THIS RADIO SEEMS TO BE A CROSS BETWEEN THE S-40 AND SX-43 AND NEVER WENT INTO PRODUCTION.

S-47   NONE   1947 $200.00

A 15-TUBE 5-BAND HOME ENTERTAINMENT TYPE RECEIVER COVERING THE AM & FM STANDARD BROADCAST BANDS (.54MHz TO 1.70MHz & 88MHz TO 108MHz) AND THREE SHORT-WAVE BANDS, 5.8 TO 18MHz, 9 TO 12MHz, AND 15 TO 18MHz. THE AM I.F. IS 455KHz AND THE FM I.F. IS 10.7MHz. FEATURES INCLUDE SEPARATE BASS AND TREBLE TONE CONTROLS, SEPARATE TUNING CONTROLS FOR AM AND FM, TEN PRESET MECHANICAL TUNING PUSH BUTTONS (5 FOR AM AND 5 FOR FM), FM AFC, AND A PUSH-PULL AUDIO OUTPUT. OPTIONAL EXTERNAL SPEAKER. POWER SOURCE IS 120 VOLTS AC. TUBES USED: 5U4 RECTIFIER, TWO 6V6 IN PUSH-PULL AUDIO OUTPUT, 6SQ7 PAHAS INVERTER, 6J5 1st AUDIO, 6J5 2nd AUDIO, 6SQ7 3rd AUDIO, 6AL5 FM DETECTOR, 6SG7 1st I.F., 6SG7 2nd I.F., 6SG7 3rd FM I.F. & AM DETECTOR, 6SH7 4th FM I.F., 6J6 OSCILLATOR & FM AFC, 6BE6 MIXER, AND 6BA6 R.F. AMP. THE S-47 CHASSIS WAS USED IN SEVERAL OTHER HALLICRAFTERS AND ECHOPHONE MODELS IN VARIOUS CONSOLE CABINETS AND WAS SOLD AS A CHASSIS

SX-46

ONLY (S-47C) FOR CUSTOM INSTALLATION IN THE USERS CABINET. HALLICRAFTERS BUILT RADIOS FOR A NUMBER OF OTHER MANUFACTURES INCLUDING DELCO. THE DELCO MODEL 1251 RADIO/PHONO CONSOLE USES AN S-47 CHASSIS. THE FRONT PANEL OF THE S-47 SHOWN HERE HAD TO BE REPAINTED SO THE MODEL NUMBER AND COMPANY NAME WHICH WOULD APPEAR IN THE UPPER LEFT AND RIGHT CORNER OF THE PANEL ARE MISSING.

S-47

The S-47

Over the years, Hallicrafters built many radios for other companies. In the mid- to late 1940s they were building radios for Delco, including a model 1251 which was the same as the Hallicrafters model S-47. I am certain that there were other models built for this company, as well as for others such as Wards, Sears, CBS Columbia, and Dewald.

S-48

S-48   NONE   1947   UNKNOWN

THIS UNIT IS A MAGNETIC PAPER TAPE RECORDER USING 1/4" PAPER TAPE COATED WITH A MAGNETIC MATERIAL. A FORERUNNER OF THE MYLAR REEL-TO-REEL TAPE RECORDERS. 120 VOLTS AC, BUILT-IN SPEAKER WITH PROVISION FOR EXTERNAL SPEAKER. THIS SET NEVER WENT INTO PRODUCTION, AND I HAVE NO OTHER TECHNICAL INFORMATION. THE PHOTO IS FROM A HALLICRAFTERS ADVERTISING BROCHURE.

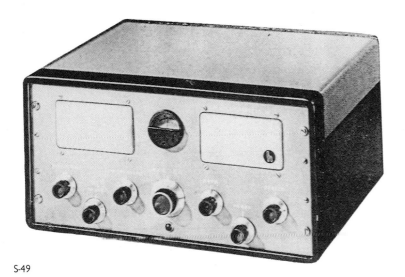

S-49   NONE   1947 $75.00 proposed price

A 7-TUBE HI-FI AUDIO AMPLIFIER WITH A FREQUENCY RESPONSE OF 50Hz TO 50KHz. TWO MICROPHONE AND TWO PHONOGRAPH IN-PUTS WITH SEPARATE VOLUME CONTROLS, SEPARATE BASS AND TREBLE TONE CONTROLS, OUTPUT METER, MASTER VOLUME CONTROL, AND A 20 WATT OUTPUT INTO 500, 2.6, 4.0, OR 8.0 OHMS. TUBES USED: 5Z3 RECTIFIER, TWO 6L6 IN PUSH-PULL AUDIO OUTPUT, TWO 12SJ7 MICRO-PHONE AMPLIFIERS, 6SJ7 VOLTAGE AMPLIFIER, REMOTE GAIN CONTROL, AND 6SL7 VOLTAGE AMP. & PHASE INVERTER. AGAIN, THIS UNIT WAS NOT PRODUCED. THE PHOTO IS FROM A HALLICRAFTERS ADVERTIS-ING BROCHURE.

S-49

S-51   NONE   1947 $129.50

TEN TUBES, FOUR BANDS, 132KHz TO 13MHz PLUS THREE FIXED FREQUENCY CRYSTAL POSITIONS, 455KHz I.f., WITH BFO, ANL, AND BUILT-IN SPEAKER. POWER SOURCE IS 105-120 VOLTS AC-DC, OR 6, 12, OR 32 VOLTS DC WITH OPTIONAL VIBRAPACK. TUBES USED: 35Z5 RECTIFIER, 35L6 AUDIO OUTPUT FOR 120 VOLT OPERATION, 6V6 AUDIO OUTPUT FOR 6, 12, & 32 VOLT DC OPERATION, 7A6 ANL, 7C6 2nd DETECTOR & 1st AUDIO, 6SS7 BFO, 6SS7 1st I.F., 6SS7 2nd I.F., 7A8 OSCILLATOR & MIXER, AND 6SS7 R.F. AMPLIFIER.

S-51

S-52   NONE   1948 $99.50

EIGHT TUBES, FOUR BANDS, .54-44MHz, 455KHz IF, WITH BAND SPREAD, BFO, ANL, AND BUILT-IN SPEAKER. POWER SOURCE IS 120 OR 240 VOLTS AC OR DC WITH CHANGEABLE BALLAST RESISTOR TUBE. THIS SET'S OUTWARD APPEARANCE IS IDENTICAL TO THE S-40. TUBES USED: 25Z5 RECTIFIER, 25L6 AUDIO OUTPUT, 6SC7 1st AUDIO & BFO, 6H6 2nd DE-TECTOR & ANL, 6SK7 1st I.F., 6SK7 2nd I.F., 6SA7 OSCILLATOR AND MIXER, AND 6SG7 R.F. AMPLIFIER.

S-52

S-53, S-53U (SMOOTH GRAY)

S-53   NONE   1948-50 $79.50

S-53U

EIGHT TUBES, FIVE BANDS, .55-32MHz AND 48-55MHz, 2075KHz IF, WITH BFO, BAND SPREAD, ANL, AND BUILT-IN SPEAKER. POWER SOURCE IS 120 VOLTS AC. OR 240 VOLTS AC WITH UNIVERSAL POWER TRANSFORMER. THERE WERE TWO DIFFERENT DIAL ESCUTCHEONS USED ON THE MODEL, ONE SMOOTH METAL PAINTED LIGHT GRAY, THE OTHER "QUILTED" AND OF BRIGHT ALUMINUM. BOTH ARE SHOWN HERE. TUBES USED: 5Y3 RECTIFIER, 6K6 AUDIO OUTPUT, 6SC7 1st AUDIO & BFO, 6H6 ANL & 2nd DETECTOR, TWO 6BA6 AS 1st & 2nd I.F., 6C4 OSCILLATOR, AND 6BA6 MIXER.

The S-53

There were two different cabinets produced with the S-53. One version had a solid top, perforated only where the speaker was mounted in the center, with a smooth metal dial escutcheon painted light silver-gray. The other had a completly perforated top, and a quilted bright metal escutcheon.

S-53, S-53U (BRIGHT QUILTED)

S-53A   NONE   1950-58 $89.50
S-53AU

EIGHT TUBES AND FIVE BANDS COVERING .54MHz TO 31MHz AND 48MHz TO 54.5MHz WITH A 455KHz I.F. FEATURES INCLUDE BAND SPREAD, ANL, BFO, AND BUILT-IN SPEAKER. POWER SOURCE IS 120 VOLTS AC OR 240 VOLTS AC WITH OPTIONAL UNIVERSAL POWER TRANS-FORMER. THE TUBES USED ARE THE SAME AS THE S-53, HOWEVER THE I.F. TRANSFORMERS ARE OF THE MINIATURE TYPE.

S-53A, S-53AU

S-55   NONE   1948 $129.50

AN 11-TUBE HOME ENTERTAINMENT TYPE AM-FM BROADCAST RECEIVER COVERING 540KHz TO 1750KHz AND 88MHz TO 108MHz. THE AM I.F IS 455KHz AND THE FM I.F. IS 21.75MHz. FEATURES INCLUDE FM AFC, PHONO INPUT, AND A HI-FI AUDIO SYSTEM. POWER SOURCE IS 120 VOLTS AC. OPTIONAL EXTERNAL SPEAKER. TUBES USED: 5Y3 RECTIFIER, TWO 6K6 IN PUSH-PULL AUDIO OUTPUT, 6SJ7 1st AUDIO, 6H6 FM DETECTOR, 6SH7 LIM-ITER & AM DETECTOR, 6BA6 1st I.F., 6SH7 2nd I.F., 6BA6 MIXER, 6J6 OSCILLATOR & FM AFC, AND 6AU6 R.F. AMPLIFIER.

S-55

S-56   NONE   1948 $110.00

THE SAME RADIO AS THE S-55 BUT SOLD AS A CHASSIS ONLY FOR CUSTOM INSTALLA-TION IN THE USER'S CABINET. WITH DIAL ESCUTCHEON & KNOBS.

S-56

S-58 NONE 1948 $59.50

A 7-TUBE AM-FM STANDARD BROADCAST BAND RECEIVER. THE AM I.F. IS 455KHz AND THE FM I.F. IS 10.7MHz. BUILT-IN SPEAKER AND PHONO INPUT. POWER SOURCE IS 120 VOLTS AC OR DC. TUBES USED: 35Z5 RECTIFIER, 35L6 AUDIO OUTPUT, 12SQ7 1st AUDIO, 12AL5 FM DETECTOR, 6BJ6 1st I.F., 6BJ6 2nd FM I.F. & AM DETECTOR, AND 12BE6 OSCILLATOR AND MIXER.

S-59 NONE 1948 $49.50

EIGHT TUBES, TWO BANDS, 540-1600KHz AND 88-108MHz, AM-FM, 455KHz AM IF, 10.7MHz FM IF. SOLD AS A CHASSIS ONLY FOR CUSTOM INSTALLATION IN USER'S CABINET. WITH DIAL ESCUTCHEON, KNOBS AND LOOP ANTENNA. TUBES USED: 5Y3 RECTIFIER, TWO 6K6 IN PUSH-PULL AUDIO OUTPUT, 6SQ7 1st AUDIO, 6AL5 FM DETECTOR, 6BA6 2nd FM I.F, AM DETECTOR & AVC, 6BA6 1st I.F., 6BE6 OSCILLATOR & MIXER. POWER SOURCE IS 120 VOLTS AC.

S-58

SX-62 NONE 1948-50 $269.50
SX-62U

SIXTEEN TUBES, SIX BANDS, .55-109MHz CONTINUOUS, AM-CW RECEPTION ON BANDS 1 THROUGH 4 (.55MHz-32MHz), AND AM, CW, OR FM RECEPTION ON BANDS 5 & 6 (27MHz -109MHz). AM I.F. IS 455KHz & FM I.F. IS 10.7MHz. WITH BFO, ANL, CRYSTAL FILTER, AND 500KHz CRYSTAL CALIBRATOR. OPTIONAL EXTERNAL SPEAKER (R-46). POWER SOURCE IS 120 VOLTS AC, OR 120-240 VOLTS AC WITH UNIVERSAL POWER TRANSFORMER. SPEAKER OUTPUT IMPEDANCE IS 500 OR 5000 OHMS. EACH FREQUENCY BAND SEGMENT ON THE DIAL IS INDIVIDUALLY LIGHTED WHEN IN USE. TUBES USED: 5U4 RECTIFIER, OD3/VR-150 VOLTAGE REGULATOR, TWO 6V6 IN PUSH-PULL AUDIO OUTPUT, 6C4 CRYSTAL CALIBRATOR OSCILLATOR, 6SL7 AUDIO PHASE INVERTER, 6J5 BFO, 6SK7 1st I.F., 6SG7 2nd I.F., 6SG7 3rd I.F. & AM DETECTOR, 6H6 ANL & FM DISCRIMINATOR, 7F8 OSCILLATOR & MIXER, AND TWO 6AG5 AS 1st & 2nd R.F. AMPLIFIERS. ELECTRICALLY THIS RADIO IS VERY SIMILAR TO THE SX-42, BUT WITHOUT BAND SPREAD IS MORE OF A SWL UNIT THAN A HAM RECEIVER

S-59

SX-62, SX-62U

SX-62A   NONE   1950-55 $349.50
SX-62AU

THE ONLY DIFFERENCE BETWEEN THE SX-62A AND THE SX-62 IS IN THE SPEAKER OUTPUT IMPEDANCE, WHICH IS 3.2, 8, OR 500 OHMS. ALL OTHER SPECIFICATIONS ARE IDENTICAL TO THE SX-62.

SX-62B   NONE   1955 $349.50
SX-62BU

AGAIN, THE SX-62B IS THE SAME AS THE SX-62A; I SEE NO ELECTRICAL DIFFERENCES. SOME PRODUCTION RUNS OF THE "B" AND "A" MODEL USED A SLIGHTLY DIFFERENT STYLE OF KNOBS.

SX-62A, SX-62AU

SX-71   NONE   1950-55 $199.50
SX-71U

THIRTEEN TUBES AND FIVE BANDS COVERING 560KHz TO 34MHz AND 46MHz TO 56MHz. RECEPTION MODES OF AM, CW, AND NBFM ON ALL BANDS. THE I.F. SYSTEM IS DUAL CONVERSION WITH I.F. FREQUENCIES OF 455KHz & 2.075MHz. OTHER FEATURES INCLUDE BFO, ANL, CRYSTAL FILTER, S-METER, AND CALIBRATED BAND SPREAD. OPTIONAL EXTER-

NAL SPEAKER (R-46 OR 46A). POWER SOURCE IS 120 VOLTS AC. OR 120-240 VOLTS AC WITH OPTIONAL UNIVERSAL POWER TRANSFORMER. TUBES USED: 5Y3 RECTIFIER, OD3/VR-150 VOLTAGE REGULATOR, 6K6 AUDIO OUTPUT, 6SC7 1st AUDIO AND BFO, 6H6 ANL & AVC, TWO 6SK7 AS 1st & 2nd I.F., 6SH7 3rd I.F., 6C4 OSCILLATOR, 6AU6 1st MIXER, 6BE6 2nd MIXER, AND 6BA6 R.F. AMPLIFIER. MOST SX-71s HAD A BLACK FACE DIAL WITH WHITE NUMBERING. SOME WERE PRODUCED WITH A WHITE DIAL AND BLACK NUMBERING.

SX-71, SX-71U (BLACK FACE DIAL)

S-72   NONE   1950-55 $79.95
S-72R
S-72L

THE S-72 & S-72R ARE 8-TUBE 4-BAND PORTABLE RADIOS COVERING 550KHz TO 30MHz. THE I.F. IS 455KHz. THE FIRST PRODUCTION RUN HAD A NOISE LIMITER CONTROLLED BY A TOGGLE SWITCH IN THE UPPER RIGHT HAND CORNER OF THE PANEL. LATER PRODUCTION RUNS OMITTED THE ANL AND SWITCH. OTHER FEATURES INCLUDE A BFO, BAND SPREAD, BUILT-IN SPEAKER, THREE-WAY POWER SOURCE OF 120 VOLTS AC OR DC AND

BATTERY POWER, A BUILT-IN LOOP ANTENNA FOR THE STANDARD BROADCAST BAND AND A TELESCOPING ANTENNA FOR THE SHORT-WAVE BANDS. TUBES USED: 3V4 AUDIO OUTPUT, 1U5 DETECTOR & 1st AUDIO, 1U5 BFO, TWO 1U4 AS 1st & 2nd I.F., 1U4 MIXER, AND 1T4 R.F. AMPLIFIER. THE RECTIFIER IS A SELENIUM TYPE. THERE IS NO DIFFERENCE I CAN SEE BETWEEN THE S-72 AND THE "R" MODEL. THE S-72L IS DIFFERENT ONLY IN FREQUENCY COVERAGE WHICH IS 175KHz TO 11.5MHz. THE RADIO SHOWN HERE IS THE S-72.

S-72 (FRONT VIEW)

S-72 (TOP VIEW WITH LID)

SX-73   NONE   1952 $975.00

R-274/FRR

R-274D/FRR

ONE OF THE BEST, MOST SOPHISTICATED, AND MOST EXPENSIVE GENERAL COVERAGE RECEIVERS PRODUCED BY THE COMPANY. THIS 19-TUBE PLUS ONE CURRENT REGULATOR BALLAST TUBE SET COVERS 540KHz TO 54MHz IN SIX BANDS. IT ALSO HAS PROVISION FOR SIX FIXED FREQUENCY CRYSTALS TO BE INSTALLED FOR USE BETWEEN 1.5MHz AND 29.7MHz. THE I.F. IS A 455KHz SINGLE CONVERSION SYSTEM UP TO 7MHz AND THEN IS DOUBLE CONVERSION THROUGH 54MHz WITH THE SECOND I.F. FREQUENCY BEING 6MHz. RECEPTION MODES ARE AM, CW, AND MCW. OTHER FEATURES INCLUDE A TURRET TUNER, S-METER, BFO, ANL, ANTENNA TRIMMER, AND CRYSTAL FILTER. THERE IS NO DIFFERENCE BETWEEN THE MILITARY AND CIVILIAN VERSIONS EXCEPT FOR THE MODEL NUMBER TAG ON THE FRONT PANEL. THE MILITARY NUMBERS ARE R-274/FRR AND R-274D/FRR, THE SAME NUMBERS GIVEN TO THE HAMARLUND SP-600 SERIES BY THE GOVERNMENT. THE TWO RADIOS WERE CONSIDERED THE SAME BY THE GOVERNMENT EVEN THOUGH COSMETICALLY THEY WERE RADICALLY DIFFERENT. THE TUNING MECHANISM IS GEARED DOWN TO SUCH A POINT THAT A SEPARATE BAND SPREAD SYSTEM IS NOT NECESSARY. TUBES USED: 6AG5 1st R.F., 6AG5 CRYSTAL OSCILLATOR, 6BA6 2nd R.F., 6BA6 6MHz I.F., 6BA6 6.455MHz OSCILLATOR, THREE 6BA6 AS 1st, 2nd, AND 3rd 455KHz I.F., 6BA6 BFO, TWO 6BE6 AS 1st & 2nd MIXER, 6C4 OSCILLATOR, 6AL5 DETECTOR & ANL, 6AL5 AVC, 6AT6 1st AUDIO, 6Y6 AUDIO OUTPUT, OC3W/VR-105 VOLTAGE REGULATOR, 5U4 RECTIFIER, AND 6BA6 I.F. OUTPUT. THE POWER SOURCE IS 95 TO 240 VOLTS AC 50-60Hz. OPTIONAL EXTERNAL SPEAKER.

R-27D/FRR

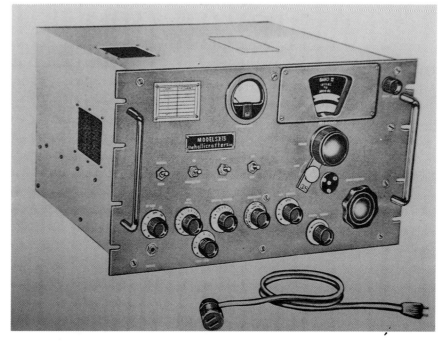

SX-73

S-76	NONE	1950-55	$169.50

S-76U

ELEVEN TUBES, FOUR BANDS, COVERING 538KHz TO 34MHz., DUAL CONVERSION I.F. SYSTEM, 1.650MHz 1st I.F., AND 50KHz 2nd I.F. FREQUENCY. FEATURES INCLUDE A BFO, CALIBRATED BAND SPREAD, ANL, VARIABLE SELECTIVITY, AND VERY LARGE 4" S-METER (SO THOSE OF US OVER 40 CAN SEE IT!). POWER SOURCE IS 120 VOLTS AC, OR 120-240 VOLTS AC WITH OPTIONAL UNIVERSAL POWER TRANSFORMER. OPTIONAL EXTERNAL SPEAKER (R-46 OR 46A). TUBES USED: 5Y3 RECTIFIER, VR-150 VOLTAGE REGULATOR, 6K6 AUDIO OUTPUT, 6SC7 1st AUDIO & BFO, 6AL5 DETECTOR, AVC, & ANL, 6BE6 OSCILLATOR & 2nd MIXER, 6BA6 1.650MHz I.F., 6BA6 50Khz I.F., 6C4 OSCILLATOR, 6AU6 1st MIXER, AND 6CB6 R.F. AMPLIFIER.

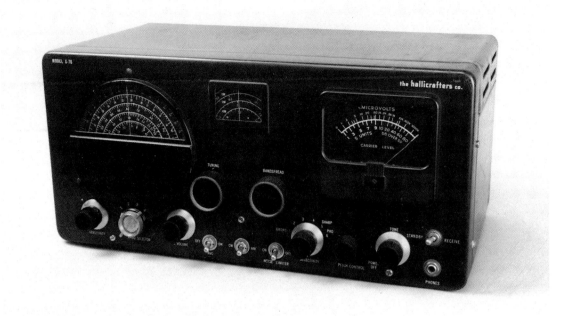

S-76, S-76U

S-77	NONE	1950-51	$89.95

EIGHT TUBES, FOUR BANDS, .54-44MHz, 455KHz I.F., WITH BFO, ANL, BUILT-IN SPEAKER, AND BAND SPREAD. POWER SOURCE IS 120 OR 240 VOLTS AC OR DC DEPENDING ON RESISTOR BALLAST TUBE R-39. THIS RADIO IS IDENTICAL IN APPEARANCE AND FUNCTION TO THE S-40B EXCEPT FOR THE AC-DC POWER SUPPLY. TUBES USED: 25Z6 RECTIFIER, 25L6 AUDIO OUTPUT, 6SC7 1st AUDIO & BFO, 6H6 DETECTOR & ANL, 6SK7 1st I.F., 6SK7 2nd I.F., 6SA7 OSCILLATOR & MIXER, AND 6SG7 R.F. AMPLIFIER.

S-77

S-77A   NONE   1952-55 $89.95

THE SPECIFICATIONS, FUNCTIONS AND APPEARANCE OF THE S-77A ARE THE SAME AS
THE S-77. I SEE NO DIFFERENCES WITH POSSIBLE EXCEPTION OF MINOR VALUE CHANGES
IN SOME COMPONENTS.

S-77A

S-78   NONE   1950 $79.50

AN 11-TUBE 2-BAND HOME ENTERTAINMENT TYPE UNIT COVERING THE STANDARD AM
& FM BROADCAST BANDS. THE AM & FM I.F. FREQUENCIES ARE 455KHz & 10.7MHz RESPEC-
TIVELY. SPEAKER OUTPUT IMPEDANCE IS 3.2 & 500 OHMS. THE POWER SOURCE IS 120
VOLTS AC. THIS UNIT WAS SOLD AS A CHASSIS ONLY WITH KNOBS & DIAL ESCUTCHEON
FOR CUSTOM INSTALLATION IN THE USER'S CABINET. TUBES USED: 5Y3 RECTIFIER. TWO
6K6 IN PUSH-PULL AUDIO OUTPUT, 6SJ7 1st AUDIO, 6J6 OSCILLATOR & FM AFC, 6H6 FM
DISCRIMINATOR, 6SH7 LIMITER, 6SH7 2nd I.F., 6BA6 1st I.F., 6BA6 MIXER, AND 6AU6 R.F.
AMPLIFIER. AUDIO POWER OUTPUT IS 8 WATTS.

S-78A   NONE   1951-54 $89.50

THE S-78A IS VERY SIMILAR TO THE S-78. THE MAJOR DIFFERENCES ARE THE WAY THE
COMPONENTS IN THE R.F. SECTION ARE LAID OUT, AND THE USE OF A 6CB6 AS THE R.F.
AMPLIFIER RATHER THAN A 6AU6. ALL OTHER SPECIFICATIONS ARE THE SAME AS THE S-
78.

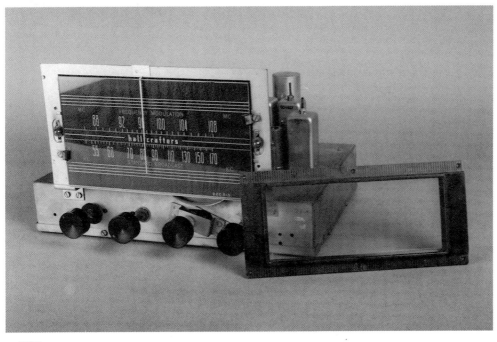

S-78A

S-80   DEFENDER   1951-52 $44.50

FOUR TUBES, TWO BANDS, 540KHz TO 1620KHz AND 6MHz TO 18MHz. THE I.F. FREQUENCY IS 455KHz. THE POWER SOURCE IS BATTERIES ONLY USING A 90 VOLT "B" AND A 1.5 VOLT "A" BATTERY. THE UNIT IS IN A LARGE ALL-BAKELITE TABLETOP CABINET, AND WAS FOR USE IN AREAS OF THE COUNTRY THAT WERE NOT ELECTRIFIED (SUCH AS SOME OUTLYING FARMS). TUBES USED: 3V4 AUDIO OUTPUT, 1U5 DETECTOR, AVC, & 1st AUDIO, 1U4 I.F., AND 1R5 MIXER & OSCILLATOR.

S-80 DEFENDER

S-81   CIVIC PATROL   1951-53 $49.50

S-82   CIVIC PATROL   1951-53

THE S-81 AND S-82 ARE IDENTICAL EXCEPT FOR FREQUENCY COVERAGE. SIX TUBES AND ONE BAND. THE RECEPTION MODE IS FM AND THE I.F. FREQUENCY IS 10.7MHz. THEY WERE THE FORERUNNERS OF THE SPECIAL SERVICES AND POLICE MONITORS OF THE PRESENT. THE S-81 COVERED THE 152MHz TO 173MHz BAND AND THE S-82 30MHz TO 50MHz. WITH BUILT-IN SPEAKER. THE POWER SOURCE IS 120 VOLTS AC OR DC. TUBES USED: 50L6 AUDIO OUTPUT, 12SQ7 1st AUDIO, 12AL5 RATIO DETECTOR, TWO 12BA6 AS 1st & 2nd I.F., AND 12AT7 MIXER AND OSCILLATOR. THE RECTIFIER IS OF THE SELENIUM TYPE.

S-81 CIVIC PATROL

S-82 CIVIC PATROL

S-85	NONE	1955-59	$119.95

S-85U

EIGHT TUBES, FOUR BANDS, COVERING 538KHz TO 34MHz, THE I.F. FREQUENCY IS 455KHz. WITH BFO, CALIBRATED BAND SPREAD, ANL, AND BUILT-IN SPEAKER. THE POWER SOURCE IS 120 VOLTS AC, OR 120-240 VOLTS AC WITH UNIVERSAL POWER TRANSFORMER. TUBES USED: 5Y3 RECTIFIER, 6K6 AUDIO OUTPUT, 6H6 DETECTOR, ANL, & AVC, 6SC7 BFO & 1st AUDIO, TWO 6SK7 AS 1st & 2nd I.F., 6SA7 MIXER & OSCILLATOR, AND 6SG7 R.F. AMPLIFIER.

S-85, S-85U

-86	NONE	1955-59	$119.95

THE S-86 HAS THE SAME APPEARANCE AND FUNCTIONS AS THE S-85 BUT ITS POWER SOURCE IS 120 VOLTS AC OR DC, OR 240 VOLTS AC OR DC DEPENDING ON THE RESISTIVE BALLAST TUBE USED. EXCEPT FOR THE 25Z6 RECTIFIER AND THE 25L6 AUDIO OUTPUT ALL OTHER TUBES ARE THE SAME AS THE S-85. SOME S-86 HAD PLASTIC DIALS, AND SOME HAD ALUMINUM DIALS.

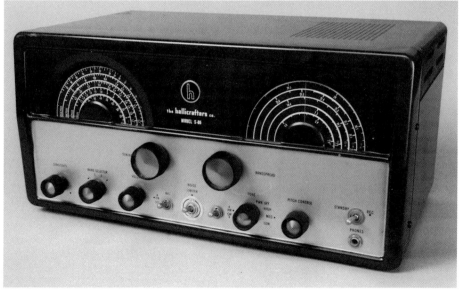

S-86

X-88	NONE	1954-55	$595.00

THIS 20-TUBE 6-BAND TOP-OF-THE-LINE RECEIVER COVERS 535KHz TO 33MHz. DUAL CONVERSION I.F. ON ALL BANDS WITH 3 DIFFERENT I.F. FREQUENCIES. FOR BANDS 1, & 3 TO 6 THE I.F. IS 50KHz & 2075KHz, FOR BAND 2 THE I.F. FREQUENCIES ARE 50KHz & 1550KHz. OTHER FEATURES INCLUDE A GEAR-DRIVEN TUNING SYSTEM FOR MAIN TUNING & BAND SPREAD, VARIABLE SELECTIVITY FROM 250Hz TO 10KHz IN SIX STEPS, A 10 WATT AUDIO AMPLIFIER, EXALTED BFO, ANTENNA TRIMMER, DELAYED AVC ACTION, 100KHz CRYSTAL CALIBRATOR, CRYSTAL CONTROLLED SECOND CONVERSION OSCILLATOR, FLY WHEEL TUNING FOR MAIN AND BAND SPREAD TUNING, CALIBRATED BAND SPREAD FOR 160, 80, 40, 20, 15, 11, AND 10 METERS, TUNING DIAL LOCKS, S-METER, 50KHz I.F. OUTPUT JACK, 2 MICROVOLT SENSITIVITY ON BANDS 2 THROUGH 6 FOR 1/2 WATT AUDIO OUTPUT, AND 10 MICROVOLTS ON BAND 1, IMAGE REJECTION IS 80 db OR BETTER UP TO 20MHz, AND 60 db OR BETTER FROM 20MHz TO 33MHz. POWER SOURCE IS 120 VOLTS AC, OR 120-240 VOLTS AC WITH UNIVERSAL POWER TRANSFORMER. OPTIONAL EXTERNAL SPEAKER (MODEL R-46A). TUBES USED: 5U4 RECTIFIER, 4H4 1st OSCILLATOR FILAMENT CURRENT REGULATOR, OD3 VOLTAGE REGULATOR, TWO 6V6 IN PUSH-PULL AUDIO OUTPUT, 12AX7 1st AUDIO & PHASE INVERTER, 12AU7 AVC RECTIFIER & I.F. OUTPUT, 6BA6 BFO AMPLIFIER, 6C4 BFO, 6AL5 DETECTOR & ANL, THREE 6BA6 AS 1st, 2nd, & 3rd 50KHz I.F., 12AT7 2nd OSCILLATOR, 6BA6 2nd CONVERTER, 6U8 1st CONVERTER & OSCILLATOR, 6BA6 2nd R.F., AND 6CB6 1st R.F. AMPLIFIER. THERE WERE THREE PRODUCTION RUNS, RUN 3 MAY HAVE USED A T-NOTCH FILTER SIMILAR TO THAT USED IN THE SX-100 & SX-101. TODAY THE SX-88 IS THE MOST SOUGHT-AFTER HALLICRAFTERS MODEL.

SX-88, SX-88U

S-93 WORLDWIDE 1954 $99.95

A 5-TUBE 4-BAND PORTABLE RADIO COVERING 170KHz TO 415KHz AND 530KHz TO 18MHz.
THE I.F. IS 455KHz, AND THE POWER SOURCE IS 120 VOLTS AC-DC, OR SELF-CONTAINED
BATTERIES. FEATURES INCLUDE BUILT-IN SPEAKER, LOOP & TELESCOPING ANTENNAS AND
A WORLD TIME MAP. THE CASE IS COVERED IN GRAY "LEATHERETTE." THE MODEL TW-500
AND TW-600 ARE THE SAME RADIO WITH A DIFFERENT COLOR CASE. TUBES USED: 3V4
AUDIO OUTPUT, 1U5 DETECTOR, AVC, & 1st AUDIO, 1U4 I.F., 1L6 CONVERTER (MIXER) &
OSCILLATOR, AND 1U4 R.F. AMPLIFIER.

S-93 WORLD-WIDE (LID CLOSED)

S-94　　CIVIC PATROL　　1955-62　　$59.95
S-95

EIGHT TUBES, ONE BAND, 30-50MHz, FM RECEPTION, WITH BUILT-IN SPEAKER AND SQUELCH CONTROL. I.F. IS 10.7MHz, AND THE POWER SOURCE IS 120 VOLTS AC OR DC. TUBES USED: 50L6 AUDIO OUTPUT, 6BH6 1st AUDIO, 12AU7 SQUELCH, 12AL5 RATIO DETECTOR, TWO 12BA6 AS 1st & 2nd I.F., 12AT7 OSCILLATOR & MIXER, 6BH6 R.F. AMPLIFIER, AND A SELENIUM RECTIFIER. THE S-95 IS IDENTICAL IN APPEARANCE AND FUNCTIONS EXCEPT FOR THE FREQUENCY COVERAGE OF 152MHz TO 173MHz AND A 6AB4 R.F. AMPLIFIER. BOTH RADIOS ARE UPDATED VERSIONS OF THE S-81 & S-82.

S-94 CIVIC PATROL

S-95　CIVIC PATROL

SX-96　　NONE　　　　1955-56　　$249.50
MARK 1 & 1A

THIS 12-TUBE 4-BAND DUAL CONVERSION SET COVERS 538KHz TO 1580KHz AND 1.72MHz TO 34MHz. THE I.F. FREQUENCIES ARE 50.5KHz AND 1650KHz. FEATURES INCLUDE CALIBRATED BAND SPREAD ON 80, 40, 20, 15, 11, AND 10 METERS, SELECTABLE SIDEBAND, BFO, ANL, CRYSTAL FILTER, VARIABLE SELECTIVITY, S-METER, DELAYED AVC THAT FUNCTIONS ON AM AND CW OR SSB SIGNALS, GEAR-DRIVEN FLY WHEEL TUNING MECHANISM WITH

ALUMINUM DIALS, AND PHONO INPUT JACK. POWER SOURCE IS 120 VOLTS AC. OPTIONAL EXTERNAL SPEAKER (MODEL R-46 OR R-46A). TUBES USED: 5Y3 RECTIFIER, VR-150/OD3 VOLTAGE REGULATOR, 6K6 AUDIO OUTPUT, 6SC7 BFO & 1st AUDIO, 6BJ7 DETECTOR, AVC, & ANL, THREE 6BA6 AS 1650KHz I.F., 2nd MIXER, AND 50.5KHz I.F., 12AT7 2nd CONVERSION OSCILLATOR, 6C4 1st CONVERSION OSCILLATOR, 6AU6 1st MIXER, AND 6CB6 R.F. AMPLIFIER.

SX-96, MARK 1, AND MARK 1A

SX-99 NONE 1955-59 $159.95

SX-99U

MARK 1

EIGHT TUBES AND FOUR BANDS COVERING 538KHz TO 34MHz. THE I.F. IS 455KHz. FEATURES INCLUDE CALIBRATED BAND SPREAD FOR 80 THROUGH 10 METERS INCLUDING 11 METERS, BFO, ANL, CRYSTAL FILTER, ANTENNA TRIMMER, VARIABLE SELECTIVITY (BROAD & SHARP), AND S-METER. POWER SOURCE IS 120 VOLTS AC, OR 120-240 VOLTS AC WITH OPTIONAL UNIVERSAL POWER TRANSFORMER. OPTIONAL EXTERNAL SPEAKER (MODEL R-46 OR 46A). TUBES USED: 5Y3 RECTIFIER, 6K6 AUDIO OUTPUT, 6SC7 BFO & 1st AUDIO, 6H6 DETECTOR, AVC, & ANL, 6SG7 1st I.F., 6SK7 2nd I.F., 6SA7 MIXER & OSCILLATOR, AND 6SG7 R.F. AMPLIFIER. AS WITH THE S-86 SOME SX-99 WERE PRODUCED WITH ALUMINUM AND SOME WITH PLASTIC DIALS.

The SX-99 Mark I

The SX-99 Mark I came with either aluminum dials lighted from the top, or plastic dials backlighted. The plastic dials are the most common. The designation on the metal dial unit is MARK I "D".

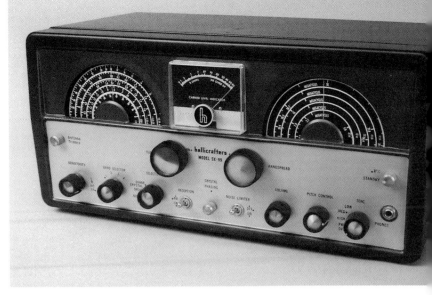

SX-99, SX-99U, AND MARK ONE

SX-100 NONE 1956-61 $295.00

MARK 1, 1A

MARK 2

FOURTEEN TUBES AND FOUR BANDS THIS DUAL CONVERSION RECEIVER COVERS 538KHz TO 1580KHz AND 1.72MHz TO 34MHz. THE I.F. FREQUENCIES ARE 50.5KHz & 1650KHz. FEATURES INCLUDE CALIBRATED BAND SPREAD FOR 80 THROUGH 10 METERS, SELECTABLE SIDE- BAND, BFO, ANL, ANTENNA TRIMMER, CRYSTAL FILTER, DELAYED AVC, VARIABLE SELECTIVITY FROM 500Hz TO 5KHz, S-METER, NOTCH FILTER, 100KHz CRYSTAL CALIBRATOR, AND GEAR DRIVEN FLY WHEEL TUNING WITH ALUMINUM DIALS. THE POWER SOURCE IS 120 VOLTS AC OR 120-240 VOLTS AC WITH OPTIONAL UNIVERSAL POWER TRANSFORMER. OPTIONAL EXTERNAL SPEAKER (MODEL R-46 0R 46A). TUBES USED: 5Y3 RECTIFIER, OA2 VOLTAGE REGULATOR, 6K6 AUDIO OUTPUT, 6SC7 1st AUDIO & BFO, 6BJ7 DETECTOR, AVC, & ANL, THREE 6BA6 AS 1650KHz I.F., 2nd MIXER, AND 50.5KHz I.F., TWO 6C4 AS 1st CONVERSION OSCILLATOR, AND 50.5KHz I.F., TWO 6AU6 AS 1st MIXER, AND CRYSTAL CALIBRATOR, 6CB6 R.F. AMPLIFIER, AND 12AT7 2nd CONVERSION OSCILLATOR. THERE WERE SOME MINOR ELECTRICAL AND COSMETIC DIFFERENCES BETWEEN THE MARK 1, 1A, & 2 SUCH AS SLIGHTLY DIFFERENT STYLE OF KNOBS.

SX-100, MARK 1, MARK 1A, MARK 2

SX-101, MARK 1, MARK 2, MARK 3, MARK 3A

SX-101 NONE 1957-58 $395.00

MARK 1

MARK 2

MARK 3 & 3A

THE SX-101 IS THE FIRST RECEIVER PRODUCED BY THE COMPANY TO EXCLUSIVELY COVER THE HAM BANDS. FIFTEEN TUBES AND SIX BANDS COVERING 160 THROUGH 10 METERS AND 10MHz WWV. DUAL CONVERSION WITH I.F. FREQUENCIES OF 50.5KHz & 1650KHz. FEATURES INCLUDE A 100KHz CRYSTAL CALIBRATOR, S-METER, SELECTABLE SIDEBAND, ANL, BFO, VARIABLE SELECTIVITY FROM 500Hz TO 5KHz, ANTENNA TRIMMER, NOTCH FILTER, A BUILT-IN HEATING ELEMENT AND SEPARATE FILAMENT TRANSFORMER FOR THE OSCILLATOR TUBES THAT IS ALWAYS ON AS LONG AS THE SET IS PLUGGED IN. THIS KEEPS THE STABILITY OF THE SET CONSTANT. THE POWER SOURCE IS 120 VOLTS AC. OPTIONAL EXTERNAL SPEAKER (MODEL R46B OR R-47). TUBES USED:

CB6 R.F. AMPLIFIER, 6BY6 MIXER, 12BY7 1st CONVERSION OSCILLATOR, OUR 6BA6 AS 1650KHz I.F., 2nd MIXER, 50.5KHz I.F., S-METER AMPLIFIER, 3J7 DETECTOR, AVC, & ANL, 6SC7 1st AUDIO & BFO, 6K6 AUDIO OUT- UT, 12AT7 2nd CONVERSION OSCILLATOR, 6C4 1st CONVERSION OS- ILLATOR & 50.5KHz I.F., 6AU6 R.F. AMPLIFIER, OA2 VOLTAGE REGULA- OR, AND 5Y3 RECTIFIER. THERE ARE MINOR ELECTRICAL AND COS- ETIC CHANGES BETWEEN THE MARK 1, 2, 3, & 3A.

X-101A   NONE   1959-62 $399.50

VHILE SIMILAR TO THE SX-101 THERE ARE A NUMBER OF SIGNIFICANT DIFFERENCES IN THE "A" MODEL. IT IS A 15-TUBE 5-BAND SET COVERING 0 THROUGH 10 METERS AND 10MHz WWV. 160 & 11 METERS HAVE EEN DROPPED. PROVISION IS MADE FOR OPERATION ON THE 6 & 2 METER BANDS WITH AN OUTBOARD CONVERTER. ALL OTHER FEA- TURES ARE THE SAME AS THE SX-101. THE I.F. FREQUENCIES ARE 50.75KHz AND 1650KHz. TUBES USED: 6DC6 R.F. AMPLIFIER, 6DC6 50.75KHz I.F., BY6 MIXER, 6BY6 CW-SSB DETECTOR, 12BY7 1st CONVERSION OSCIL- ATOR, THREE 6BA6 AS 1650KHz I.F., 2nd MIXER, S-METER AMPLIFIER, 6BJ7 M DETECTOR, AVC, & ANL, 6SC7 1st AUDIO & BFO, 6K6 AUDIO OUT- UT, 5Y3 RECTIFIER, OA2 VOLTAGE REGULATOR, 12AT7 2nd CONVER- ION OSCILLATOR, AND 6AU6 CRYSTAL CALIBRATOR.

SX-101A

S-102   NONE   1956-57 $59.95

SEVEN TUBES AND ONE BAND COVERING 143MHz TO 149MHz. AM RE- CEPTION, THE I.F. IS 10.7MHz. FEATURES INCLUDE BUILT-IN SPEAKER, AND ANL. POWER SOURCE IS 120 VOLTS AC OR DC. TUBES USED: 50L6 AU- DIO OUTPUT, 6BH6 1st AUDIO, 12AT7 OSCILLATOR & MIXER, TWO 6BA6 AS 1st & 2nd I.F., 12AL5 RATIO DETECTOR, 6AB4 R.F. AMPLIFIER, AND A SELENIUM RECTIFIER.

S-103 CONTINENTAL

-102

103   CONTINENTAL   1956-57 $44.95

4-TUBE 2-BAND PORTABLE COVERING 535KHz TO 1620KHz AND .8MHz TO 18.3MHz. THE I.F. IS 455KHz. POWER SOURCE IS 120 VOLTS C-DC OR SELF CONTAINED BATTERIES. TUBES USED: 3V4 AUDIO OUT- UT, 1U5 DETECTOR, AVC, & 1st AUDIO, 1U4 I.F., 1R5 MIXER & OSCILLA- OR, AND A SELENIUM RECTIFIER FOR AC USE. THE S-103 IS THE SAME S THE 5R40, 41, & 42 EXCEPT FOR CASE COLOR.

SX-104   NONE   1957-58 $89.95

EIGHT TUBES, ONE BAND, COVERING 30MHz TO 50MHz. THE I.F. IS 10.7MHz AND THE RECEPTION MODE IS AM. FEATURES INCLUDE A SWITCH SELECTABLE USER SUPPLIED CRYSTAL FOR FIXED FREQUENCY OPERATION, SQUELCH CONTROL, AND BUILT-IN SPEAKER. THE POWER SOURCE IS 120 VOLTS AC. TUBES USED: 12BD6 R.F. AMPLIFIER, 6U8 OSCILLATOR & MIXER, TWO 12BA6 AS 1st & 2nd I.F., 12AL5 RATIO DETECTOR, 12AU7 SQUELCH, 6BH6 1st AUDIO, 50L6 AUDIO OUTPUT, AND A SELENIUM RECTIFIER.

SX-104

SX-105   NONE   1957-58 $89.95

THE SX-105 HAS THE SAME FUNCTIONS AND SPECIFICATIONS AS THE SX-104 WITH EXCEPTION OF THE FREQUENCY COVERAGE WHICH IS 152MHz TO 173MHz, AND USE OF A 12AT7 OSCILLATOR & MIXER, AND A 6AB4 R.F. AMPLIFIER RATHER THAN THE 6U8 AND 12BD6 OF THE SX-104.

SX-105

S-106

S-106   NONE   1956-57 $59.95

SEVEN TUBES AND ONE BAND COVERING 50MHz TO 54MHz. THE I.F. IS 10.7MHz AND THE RECEPTION MODE IS AM. FEATURES INCLUDE A BUILT-IN SPEAKER, AND ANL. POWER SOURCE IS 120 VOLTS AC OR DC. TUBES USED: 6BH6 R.F AMPLIFIER, 12AT7 OSCILLATOR & MIXER, TW0 12BA6 AS 1st & 2nd I.F., 12AL5 RATIO DETECTOR, 6BH6 1st AUDIO, 50L6 AUDIO OUTPUT, AND A SELENIUM RECTIFIER.

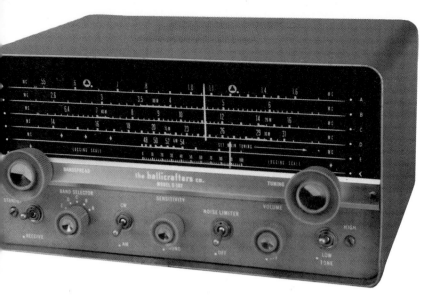

S-107　　　NONE　　　　　1958-62　　$59.95

EIGHT TUBES, FIVE BANDS, COVERING 540KHz TO 1630KHz, 2.5MHz TO 31MHz, AND 48MHz TO 54.5MHz. THE I.F. IS 455KHz. FEATURES INCLUDE BAND SPREAD, BUILT-IN SPEAKER, BFO, AND ANL. POWER SOURCE IS 120 VOLTS AC. TUBES USED: 5Y3 RECTIFIER, 6AQ5 AUDIO OUTPUT, 12AX7 1st AUDIO & BFO, 6C4 OSCILLATOR, 6AL5 DETECTOR & ANL, THREE 6BA6 AS 1st & 2nd I.F., AND MIXER.

S-107

S-108　　　NONE　　　　　1959-61　　$129.95

EIGHT TUBES, FOUR BANDS, COVERING 540KHz TO 34MHz WITH AN I.F. OF 455KHz. FEATURES INCLUDE CALIBRATED BAND SPREAD, BFO, ANL, AND BUILT-IN SPEAKER. POWER SOURCE IS 120 VOLTS AC. THE LARGE SLIDE-RULE DIAL IS BAND SPREAD, THE MAIN TUNING IS THE SMALLER CIRCULAR DIAL. TUBES USED: 5Y3 RECTIFIER, 6K6 AUDIO OUTPUT, 6SC7 1st AUDIO & BFO, 6H6 ANL, AVC, AND DETECTOR, TWO 6SK7 AS 1st & 2nd I.F., 6SA7 MIXER & OSCILLATOR, AND 6SG7 R.F. AMPLIFIER.

S-109　　　NONE　　　　　1959　　$129.95

THE S-109 HAS THE SAME APPEARANCE, FUNCTIONS AND FEATURES AS THE S-108 EXCEPT THAT IT HAS A 120 VOLT AC OR DC POWER SUPPLY. I HAVE NO OTHER TECHNICAL INFORMATION ON THIS SET.

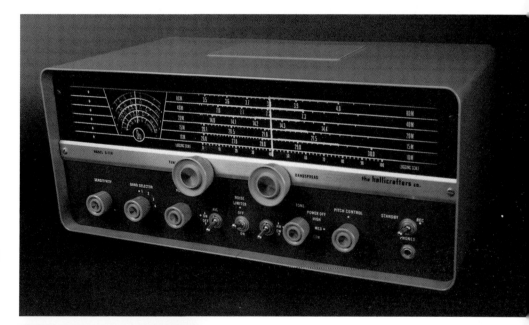

S-108

SX-110

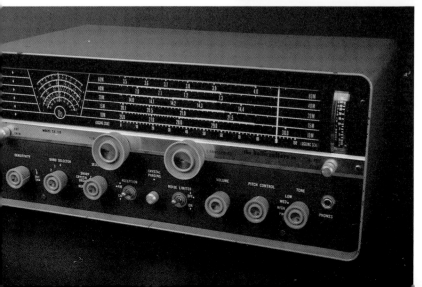

SX-110　　　NONE　　　　　1959-61　　$159.95

EIGHT TUBES AND FOUR BANDS COVERING 538KHz TO 34MHz WITH A 455KHz I.F. FEATURES INCLUDE CALIBRATED BAND SPREAD, BFO, ANL, ANTENNA TRIMMER, CRYSTAL FILTER, VARIABLE SELECTIVITY (BROAD & SHARP), AND S-METER. A FULLER FEATURED VERSION OF THE S-108. POWER SOURCE IS 120 VOLTS AC. OPTIONAL EXTERNAL SPEAKER (MODEL R-46B OR R-47). TUBES USED: 5Y3 RECTIFIER, 6K6 AUDIO OUTPUT, 6SC7 1st AUDIO & BFO, 6H6 DETECTOR, ANL, & AVC, 6SG7 1st I.F., 6SK7 2nd I.F., 6SA7 MIXER & OSCILLATOR, AND 6SG7 R.F. AMPLIFIER.

SX-111 NONE 1959-62 $249.50

FOURTEEN TUBES, HAM BANDS ONLY, COVERING 80, 40, 20, 15, AND 10 METERS PLUS 10MHz WWV. FEATURES INCLUDE DUAL CONVERSION WITH I.F. FREQUENCIES OF 50.75KHz & 1650KHz, SELECTABLE SIDEBAND, CRYSTAL FILTER, VARIABLE SELECTIVITY FROM 500Hz TO 5KHz IN FIVE STEPS, NOTCH FILTER, ANL, BFO WITH PRODUCT DETECTOR, 100KHz CALIBRATOR, ANTENNA TRIMMER, AND S-METER. POWER SOURCE IS 120 VOLTS AC. OPTIONAL EXTERNAL SPEAKER (MODEL R-46B, R-47, OR R-48). TUBES USED: 5Y3 RECTIFIER, 0A2 VOLTAGE REGULATOR, 6AQ5 AUDIO OUTPUT, 12AX7 1st AUDIO & BFO, 6AU6 CRYSTAL CALIBRATOR, 12AT7 2nd CONVERSION OSCILLATOR, 6BA6 2nd MIXER, 6C4 1st CONVERSION OSCILLATOR, 6BJ7 AVC, DETECTOR & ANL, 6BY6 MIXER, 6BY6 PRODUCT DETECTOR, THREE 6DC6 AS 50.75KHz I.F., 1650KHz I.F., AND R.F. AMPLIFIER.

SX-112 NONE 1960 $599.50 proposed price

THE SX-112 NEVER WENT INTO PRODUCTION. THERE WERE THREE WORKING ACCEPTANCE PROTOTYPE MODELS BUILT. THE PHOTOGRAPH HERE IS OF SERIAL NUMBER ONE, AND IS COURTESY OF FRANK DRONG, WHO BUILT ALL THREE PROTOTYPE UNITS WHILE WORKING FOR HALLICRAFTERS. THE SX-112 HAS 14 TUBES, 6 BANDS COVERING .54 TO 34 MHz, A SEPARATE INDIVIDUALLY-LIGHTED SCALE FOR EACH OF THE AMATEUR AND GENERAL COVERAGE BANDS, MAKING A TOTAL OF 11 SEGMENTS. IT ALSO HAS A DUAL CRYSTAL CALIBRATOR WITH 100KHz AND 1MHz MARKERS. A "DAMP CHASER" RESISTOR AND DC FILAMENT SUPPLY TO THE OSCILLATOR TUBE THAT ARE ON AS LONG AS THE POWER CORD IS CONNECTED TO THE 120 VOLT AC SOURCE. OTHER FEATURES INCLUDE NOTCH FILTER, PRODUCT DETECTOR, CRYSTAL FILTER, VARIABLE SELECTIVITY, S-METER, GEAR-DRIVEN DIALS, AND PROVISION FOR EXTERNAL SPEAKER.

SX-112

SX-111

TER, BFO, PRODUCT DETECTOR, SELECTABLE SIDEBAND, NOTCH FILTER, DUAL ANL, GEAR-DRIVEN ALUMINUM DIALS, AND S-METER. THE POWER SOURCE IS 120 VOLTS AC. TUBES USED: 6DC6 R.F AMPLIFIER, 6BA7 1st MIXER, 12AT7 CRYSTAL OSCILLATOR, 6DC6 1st I.F (6-6.5MHz), 6BA7 2nd MIXER, 6CB6 LINEAR VARIABLE FREQUENCY OSCILLATOR (VFO), 6DC6 2nd I.F. (1005KHz), 6BA6 3rd MIXER, 12AT7 SSB SWITCHING OSCILLATOR, 6DC6 3rd I.F. (50.75KHz), 6BY6 PRODUCT DETECTOR, 6BJ7 AM DETECTOR, 2nd AVC RECTIFIER, & AM ANL, 12AX7 1st AUDIO & BFO, 6AQ5 AUDIO OUTPUT, 6AU6 100KHz CRYSTAL CALIBRATOR, 6AU6 S-

SX-115 PRODUCTION MODEL

SX-115 PROTOTYPE

SX-115 NONE 1961-64 $599.50

THIS TOP-OF-THE-LINE 18-TUBE, TRIPLE-CONVERSION, HAM-BAND-ONLY SET COVERS 80, 40, 20, 15, AND 10 METERS PLUS 10MHz WWV. THE 10 METER COVERAGE IS DIVIDED INTO 4 SEPARATE SPREAD BANDS EACH COVERING 500KHz FROM 28.0MHz TO 30.0MHz. THE I.F. FREQUENCIES ARE 1005KHz, 50.75KHz, AND A VARIABLE I.F. OF 6.005MHz TO 6.505MHz. AM SENSITIVITY OF 1 MICROVOLT AND SSB OF 1/2 MICROVOLT FOR 10 db SIGNAL TO NOISE RATIO. OTHER FEATURES INCLUDE VARIABLE SELECTIVITY FROM 500Hz TO 5KHz, CRYSTAL CALIBRATOR, CRYSTAL FIL-

METER AMPLIFIER, 6AU6 1st LOOP AVC AMPLIFIER, AND OA2 VOLTAGE REGULATOR. THE POWER RECTIFIER IS TWO SILICON DIODES. OPTIONAL EXTERNAL SPEAKER (MODEL R-46B, R-47, OR R-48). THE UNITS SHOWN HERE ARE THE STANDARD PRODUCTION MODEL, AND THE WORKING HAND-BUILT ENGINEERING MODEL SHOP PRE-PRODUCTION PROTOTYPE.

SX-116	NONE	1961	UNKNOWN
(SWE)			

A SINGLE SIDE BAND "STRIP" RECEIVER, WITH INDUCTIVE TUNING, FOUR BANDS COVERING 2-30MHz, CRYSTAL-CONTROLLED OSCILLATORS FOR EACH BAND, BUILT-IN CRYSTAL OVEN FOR DRIFT-FREE OPERATION, CRYSTAL LATTICE FILTER, & S-METER. THERE ARE 20 TUBES IN ALL, AND SOLID-STATE DIODE RECTIFIERS. MOST CONTROLS ARE ACCESSIBLE ONLY WITH A SCREWDRIVER THROUGH HOLES IN THE RACK MOUNT PANEL. POWER SOURCE IS 120 VOLTS AC. THIS UNIT WAS BUILT PRIMARILY FOR THE AIR FORCE. THE USAF MODEL NUMBER IS "SWE."

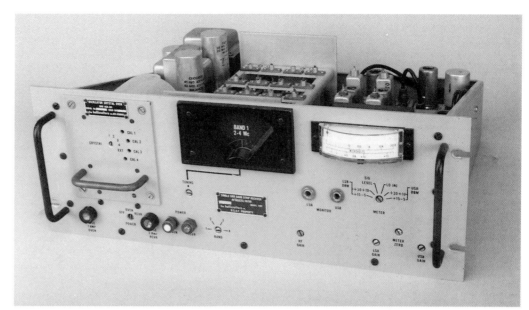

SX-116 (SWE)

SX-117

SX-117	NONE	1962-64	$379.95

THIRTEEN TUBES, HAM BANDS ONLY, 80-10 METERS, PLUS 10MHz WWV, XTAL CALIBRATOR TRIPLE CONVERSION, CRYSTAL CONTROLLED 1st & 3rd CONVERSION OSCILLATORS, SELECTABLE SIDEBAND, VARIABLE SELECTIVITY FROM 500Hz TO 5KHz IN 3 STEPS, NOTCH FILTER, PRODUCT DETECTOR, BFO, S-METER, AND ANL. THIS RECEIVER CAN OPERATE ON MOST FREQUENCIES FROM 3MHz TO 30MHz WITH USE OF PROPER CRYSTALS, AND WITH THE OPTIONAL LOW FREQUENCY CONVERTER MODEL HA-10 CAN RECEIVE SIGNALS FROM 85KHz TO 3MHz. OPTIONAL AUXILIARY CRYSTAL OSCILLATOR & EXTERNAL SPEAKER (MODEL R-47 OR R-48A) THE I.F. FREQUENCIES ARE 50.75KHz, VARIABLE 6MHz TO 6.5MHz, AND 1650KHz. TUBES USED: 6DC6 R.F. AMPLIFIER 12AT7 HAM BAND CRYSTAL OSCILLATOR, 6EA8 OPTIONAL CRYSTAL OSCILLATOR (NOT SUPPLIED), 6BA6 6MHz TO 6.5MHz I.F., 6BA6 50.75KHz I.F., 6DC6 1650KHz I.F., 6BE6 2nd MIXER, 6EA8 VFO & CATHODE FOLLOWER, 6EA8 3rd MIXER & SSB SWITCHING OSCILLATOR, 6BE6 PRODUCT DETECTOR & BFO, 6BN8 AM DETECTOR, AVC AMPLIFIER & AVC RECTIFIER, 6GW8 1st AUDIO & AUDIO OUTPUT, 6AU6 CRYSTAL CALIBRATOR, 6EA8 1st MIXER & CATHODE FOLLOWER, SILICON DIODE ANL, AND TWO SILICON DIODE POWER RECTIFIERS. THE POWER SOURCE IS 120 VOLTS AC.

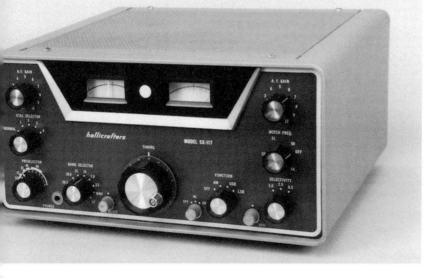

S-118	NONE	1962	$99.95
S-118 MARK II			

FIVE TUBES AND FIVE BANDS COVERING 190KHz TO 30MHz. THE I.F. FREQUENCY IS 455KHz. FEATURES INCLUDE BAND SPREAD, BFO, ANL, BUILT-IN SPEAKER, AND BUILT-IN FERRITE LOOP ANTENNA FOR BANDS 1 & 2 (190KHz TO 1600KHz). TUBES USED: 6BL8 MIXER & OSCILLATOR, 12BA6 1st I.F., 12BA6 2nd I.F. & BFO, 12AV6 1st AUDIO, DETECTOR, AVC, & ANL, 6AQ5 AUDIO OUTPUT, AND 2 SILICON DIODE POWER RECTIFIERS. THE POWER SOURCE IS 120 VOLTS AC.

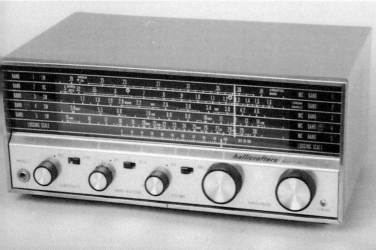

S-118, S-118 MARK II

S-119   SKYBUDDY II   1961-62 $49.95 factory-wired
S-119K $39.95 kit

THREE TUBES AND THREE BANDS COVERING 535KHz TO 16.4MHz, 455KHz I.F. FEATURES INCLUDE BUILT-IN SPEAKER, A FERRITE ROD ANTENNA FOR STANDARD BROADCAST, AND A BFO. THIS RADIO IS A "COMMEMORATIVE" UNIT CELEBRATING THE 100th MODEL PRODUCED SINCE THE S-19 SKY BUDDY. IT WAS ALSO THE FIRST RADIO SOLD BY THE COMPANY TO BE AVAILABLE AS A KIT (S-119K) THE POWER SOURCE IS 120 VOLTS AC. TUBES USED: 6BE6 OSCILLATOR & MIXER, 6BA6 I.F. & BFO, 6CM8 1st AUDIO & AUDIO OUTPUT, AND A SILICONE DIODE POWER RECTIFIER.

S-119, S-119K SKYBUDDY II

S-120

S-120   NONE   1961-64 $69.95

FOUR TUBES AND FOUR BANDS COVERING 540KHz TO 31MHz WITH A 455KHz I.F., FEATURES INCLUDE BAND SPREAD, BFO, FERRITE ROD LOOP ANTENNA FOR BROADCAST BAND, REAR MOUNTED 45" TELESCOPING WHIP ANTENNA FOR THE SHORT-WAVE BANDS, AND BUILT-IN SPEAKER. THE S-120 REPLACES THE S-38 SERIES AS THE ENTRY LEVEL SET. POWER SOURCE IS 120 VOLTS AC OR DC. TUBES USED: 12BE6 OSCILLATOR & MIXER, 12BA6 I.F., 12AV6 AVC & 1st AUDIO, 50C5 AUDIO OUTPUT, AND A SELENIUM RECTIFIER. MODELS SW-500 AND WR-1000 ARE THE SAME RADIO IN A DIFFERENT CASE.

S-120A   NONE   1967-69 $59.95

THIS 9-TRANSISTOR 6-DIODE SOLID-STATE RADIO COVERS 550KHz TO 30.2MHz IN 4 BANDS. THE I.F. IS 455KHz. FEATURES INCLUDE BFO, BAND SPREAD, BUILT-IN FERRITE ROD ANTENNA FOR THE BROADCAST BAND, AND BUILT-IN SPEAKER. THE POWER SOURCE IS 120 VOLTS AC, OR 12 VOLTS DC. IT IS TOTALY DIFFERENT THAN THE S-120 AND SHOULD HAVE BEEN GIVEN A NEW MODEL NUMBER. IT WAS MANUFACTURED IN JAPAN.

S-120A

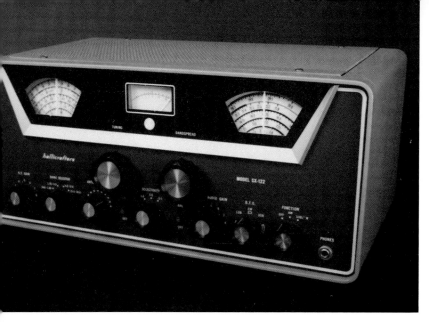

SX-122   NONE   1962-64 $295.00

AN 11-TUBE 4-BAND DUAL CONVERSION SET COVERING 540KHz TO 1600KHz & 1.75MHz TO 34MHz. THE I.F. IS 50KHz & 1650KHz. FEATURES INCLUDE A PRODUCT DETECTOR, BFO, ANL, SELECTABLE SIDEBAND, VARIABLE SELECTIVITY FROM 500Hz TO 5KHz IN 3 STEPS, CALIBRATED BAND SPREAD FOR 80-10 METERS, CRYSTAL FILTER, AND S-METER. OPTIONAL PLUG-IN CRYSTAL CALIBRATOR MODEL HA7, OPTIONAL EXTERNAL SPEAKER MODEL R-48A. POWER SOURCE IS 120 VOLTS AC. WITH THE CRYSTAL CALIBRATOR INSTALLED THE SET HAS 12 TUBES. TUBES USED: 6DC6 R.F. AMPLIFIER, 6AU6 1st MIXER, 6DC6 1650KHz I.F., 6BL8 2nd MIXER & CRYSTAL OSCILLATOR, 6BA6 50KHz I.F., 6BE6 BFO & PRODUCT DETECTOR, 6C4 1st CONVERSION OSCILLATOR, 6BN8 AVC AMPLIFIER, AVC RECTIFIER, & AM DETECTOR, 6GW8 1st AUDIO & AUDIO OUTPUT, OA2 VOLTAGE REGULATOR, AND 5Y3 RECTIFIER. THE OPTIONAL CRYSTAL CALIBRATOR USES A 6AU6.

SX-122R   NONE   1962   NONE

THE SX-112R IS ELECTRONICALLY IDENTICAL TO THE SX-122. THE ONLY DIFFERENCE IS IN THE FRONT PANEL, WHICH IS FOR RACK MOUNTING. THE SX-122R NEVER WENT INTO PRODUCTION. THE UNIT SHOWN HERE IS SERIAL NUMBER THREE, THE LAST OF ONLY THREE BUILT.

SX-122R. *See the Contents page.*

SX-122A   NONE   1967-69 $395.00

I CAN SEE NO DIFFERENCES BETWEEN THE SX-122 AND SX-122A WITH EXCEPTION OF THE OPTIONAL 100KHz CRYSTAL CALIBRATOR USED, WHICH IS THE HA-19. THERE MAY ALSO BE SOME MINOR VALUE CHANGES IN SOME CONPONENTS.

S-125   STAR QUEST   1970-72 $59.95

THE S-125 IS IDENTICAL TO THE S-120A. FOR TECHNICAL SPECIFICATIONS AND FEATURES SEE THE S-120A. MADE IN JAPAN.

S-125 STAR QUEST

S-129

S-129   NONE   1965-67 $164.50

SEVEN TUBES AND FOUR BANDS COVERING 535KHz TO 1610KHz AND 1.725MHz TO 31.5MHz. THE I.F. IS 1650KHz. FEATURES INCLUDE A PRODUCT DETECTOR, BFO, ANL, CALIBRATED BAND SPREAD AND ANTENNA TRIMMER. THE POWER SOURCE IS 120 VOLTS AC.

OPTIONAL EXTERNAL SPEAKER MODEL R-50 OR R-51. TUBES USED: 6DC6 R.F. AMPLIFIER, 6EA8 OSCILLATOR & MIXER, TWO 6BA6 AS 1st & 2nd I.F., 6AL5 AM DETECTOR & ANL, 6BE6 BFO & PRODUCT DETECTOR, 6GW8 1st AUDIO & AUDIO OUTPUT, AND A SILICON DIODE RECTIFIER.

SX-130   NONE   1965-67 $179.95

THE SX-130 HAS ALL THE FEATURES OF THE S-129 PLUS A CRYSTAL FILTER, VARIABLE SELEC-
TIVITY (BROAD & SHARP), AND S-METER. ALL OTHER SPECIFICATIONS INCLUDING TUBES
ARE THE SAME AS THE S-129.

SX-130

SX-133   NONE   1967-69 $249.50

SEVEN TUBES AND FOUR BANDS COVERING 535KHz TO 1610KHz AND
1.725MHz TO 31.5MHz. THE I.F. IS 1650KHz. FEATURES INCLUDE CALI-
BRATED BAND SPREAD FOR THE 80 THROUGH 10 METER AMATEUR
BANDS AND THE 49, 31, 25, AND 19 METER INTERNATIONAL SHORT-
WAVE BANDS, BFO, PRODUCT DETECTOR, ANL, ANTENNA TRIMMER,
CRYSTAL FILTER, S-METER, AND VARIABLE SELECTIVITY (BROAD & SHARP).
OPTIONAL 100KHz CRYSTAL CALIBRATOR MODEL HA-19, OPTIONAL
EXTERNAL SPEAKER MODEL R-50 OR R-51. TUBES USED: 6DC6 R.F. AM-
PLIFIER, 6EA8 OSCILLATOR & MIXER, 6EA8 1st I.F. & CRYSTAL FILTER, 6BA6
2nd I.F., 6AL5 AM DETECTOR & ANL, 6BE6 BFO & PRODUCT DETECTOR,
6GW8 1st AUDIO & AUDIO OUTPUT, AND A SILICON DIODE RECTIFIER.
THE POWER SOURCE IS 120 VOLTS AC.

SX-133

SX-140, SX-140K

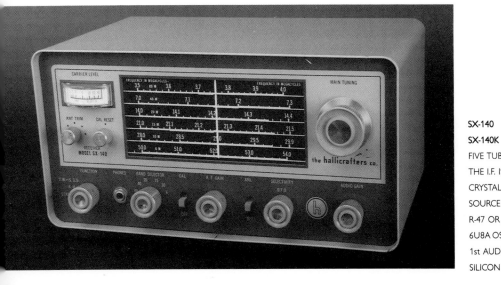

SX-140   NONE   1961-64 $124.95 factory-wired
SX-140K $104.95 kit

FIVE TUBES & HAM BANDS ONLY COVERING 80 THROUGH 6 METERS.
THE I.F. IS 1650KHz. FEATURES INCLUDE A BFO, ANL, CRYSTAL FILTER,
CRYSTAL CALIBRATOR, S-METER, AND ANTENNA TRIMMER. THE POWER
SOURCE IS 120 VOLTS AC. OPTIONAL EXTERNAL SPEAKER SUCH AS THE
R-47 OR R-48. TUBES USED: 6AZ8 R.F. AMPLIFIER & CRYSTAL MARKER,
6U8A OSCILLATOR & MIXER, 6BA6 1st I.F., 6T8A AVC, DETECTOR, ANL, &
1st AUDIO, 6AW8A S-METER AMPLIFIER AND AUDIO OUTPUT, AND 2
SILICON DIODES AS RECTIFIER.

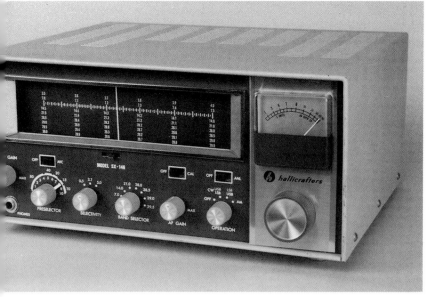

SX-146

SX-146   NONE   1965-69 $249.95

NINE TUBES, HAM BANDS ONLY COVERING 80 THROUGH 10 METERS. THE 10 METER BAND IS DIVIDED INTO FOUR 500KHz SEGMENTS FROM 28MHz TO 30MHz. THE I.F. IS 9MHz. FEATURES INCLUDE A BFO, PRODUCT DETECTOR, 2.1KHz CRYSTAL LATTICE FILTER, ANL, FLYWHEEL TUNING, AND S-METER. OPTIONS INCLUDE A 100KHz CRYSTAL CALIBRATOR, ADITIONAL PLUG-IN CRYSTAL FILTERS FOR 500Hz & 5KHz, AND EXTERNAL SPEAKER MODEL R-47 OR R-48A. IF THE CRYSTAL CALIBRATOR OPTION IS INSTALLED THE SET WILL HAVE 10 TUBES. POWER SOURCE IS 120 VOLTS AC. TUBES USED: 6JD6 R.F. AMPLIFIER, 12AT7 MIXER & CATHODE FOLLOWER, TWO 6AU6A AS 1st & 2nd I.F., 12AT7 AM DETECTOR, AVC RECTIFIER, & PRODUCT DETECTOR, 12AT7 UPPER & LOWER SIDEBAND OSCILLATORS, 6GW8 1st AUDIO AND AUDIO OUTPUT, 6BA6 VFO, 6EA8 CRYSTAL HETERODYNE OSCILLATOR & PRE-MIXER, 6AU6 100KHz CRYSTAL CALIBRATOR (MODEL HA-19 IF INSTALLED), AND A SILICON DIODE POWER RECTIFIER. THE PART #S OF THE OPTIONAL 500Hz & 5KHz CRYSTAL FILTERS ARE 049-000321 & 049-000319 RESPECTIVELY AND THE COST WAS $24.95 EACH.

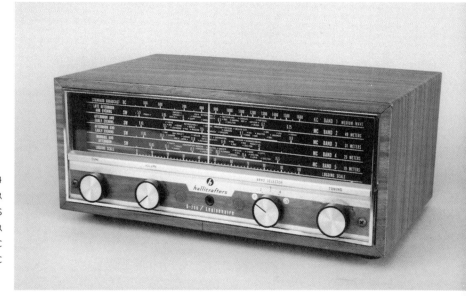

S-200 LEGIONNAIRE

S-200   LEGIONNAIRE   1965 $59.95

FOUR TUBES AND FIVE BANDS COVERING 550KHz TO 1620KHz, AND 4 SHORT-WAVE SPREAD BANDS COVERING THE 19, 25, 31, AND 49 METER INTERNATIONAL BROADCAST BANDS. THE I.F. IS 455KHz. FEATURES INCLUDE BUILT-IN SPEAKER, AND FERRITE ROD LOOP ANTENNA FOR THE STANDARD BROADCAST BAND. POWER SOURCE IS 120 VOLTS AC OR DC. TUBES USED: 12BE6 OSCILLATOR & MIXER, 12BA6 I.F., 12AV6 AVC & 1st AUDIO, 50C5 AUDIO OUTPUT, AND A SELENIUM RECTIFIER.

S-210

S-210   NONE   1966 $79.95

SIX TUBES AND SIX BANDS COVERING THE STANDARD AM & FM BROADCAST BANDS AND THE 49, 31, 25, AND 19 METER SHORT-WAVE BANDS. THE AM & FM I.F. FREQUENCIES ARE 455KHz & 10.7MHz. FEATURES INCLUDE BUILT-IN SPEAKER, BUILT-IN FERRITE ROD AND LINE CORD ANTENNAS, AND FM AFC. THERE ARE PROVISIONS FOR HEADPHONE AND EXTERNAL SPEAKER CONNECTIONS. POWER SOURCE IS 120 VOLTS AC OR DC. TUBES USED: 12DT8 FM OSCILLATOR & R.F. AMPLIFIER, 12BE6 AM OSCILLATOR & MIXER, TWO 12BA6 AS 1st & 2nd I.F., 12AX7 1st AUDIO, 35C5 AUDIO OUTPUT, AND A SILICON DIODE RECTIFIER.

S-214 NONE 1967 $89.95

A 10-TRANSISTOR 9-DIODE SOLID-STATE RECEIVER COVERING THE STANDARD AM & FM BROADCAST BANDS PLUS THE 49, 31, 25, AND 19 METER INTERNATIONAL SHORT-WAVE BANDS. THE AM & FM I.F. FREQUENCIES ARE 455KHz & 10.7MHz. WITH BUILT-IN SPEAKER, FM AFC, FERRITE ROD LOOP, LINE CORD, & TELESCOPING WHIP ANTENNAS. POWER SOURCE IS 120 VOLTS AC. MADE IN JAPAN.

S-214

S-240 NONE 1967 $109.95

ELEVEN TRANSISTORS, TEN DIODES, FIVE BANDS COVERING THE STANDARD AM & FM BROADCAST BANDS PLUS SHORT-WAVE FROM 1.9MHz TO 30.1MHz. THE AM/SW & FM I.F. FREQUENCIES ARE 455KHz & 10.7MHz. FEATURES INCLUDE BUILT-IN SPEAKER, FM AFC, BFO, FINE-TUNING CONTROL, DUAL CONVERSION, S-METER, FERRITE ROD, LINE CORD, AND TELESCOPING WHIP ANTENNAS. POWER SOURCE 120 VOLTS AC. MADE IN JAPAN.

SX-1000A NONE 1960 NO PRICE SET

THIS UNUSUAL ITEM IS NOT A WORKING RADIO. IT IS A MODEL SHOP MOCK-UP OF THE ENGINEER'S CONCEPT OF HOW A MECHENICAL DIGITAL VERSION OF THE SX-115 MIGHT LOOK IF PRODUCED. THE VFO, S-METER, AND MECHENICAL DIGITAL READ-OUT MECHANISM ARE FUNCTIONAL, BUT ALL OF THE OTHER CONTROLS ARE FALSE, BEING KNOBS ON SHAFTS THAT ARE GLUED TO THE PANEL. ITEMS LIKE THIS WOULD ALSO HAVE BEEN USED FOR PRE-PRODUCTION ADVERTISING PURPOSES. APPARENTLY THERE WERE MANY PROBLEMS WITH THIS MODEL, AS IT WAS NEVER PRODUCED.

S-240

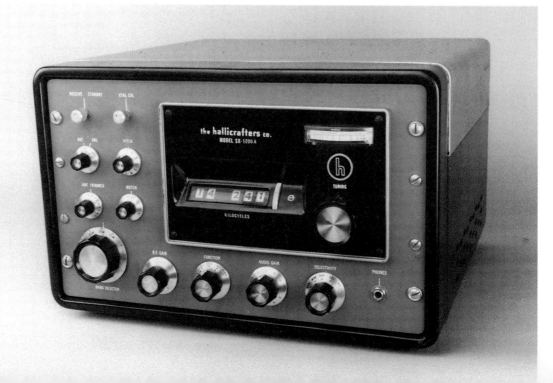

SX-1000A

HT SERIES TRANSMITTERS
AND TRANSCEIVERS

MODEL	NAME	DATE	ORIGINAL PRICE

HT-1   NONE   1937-38 $195.00

THE FIRST OF A LONG LINE OF TRANSMITTERS TO BE PRODUCED BY THE COMPANY. THIS 14-TUBE, CRYSTAL-CONTROLLED, 3-BAND UNIT OPERATES ON ANY FREQUENCY IN THE 40, 20, AND 10 METER BAND DEPENDING ON THE PLUG-IN CRYSTAL INSTALLED. IT IS COMPLETELY BAND-SWITCHABLE BETWEEN THE THREE BANDS, EACH BAND HAVING ITS OWN SET OF PRE-TUNED COILS. THERE ARE ALSO THREE SETS OF ANTENNA TERMINALS SO THAT EACH BAND HAS ITS OWN ANTENNA WHICH IS SWITCHED INTO THE CIRCUIT ALONG WITH THE COILS AND CRYSTALS FOR THE BAND IN OPERATION. THERE ARE 3 PANEL METERS TO MONITOR VARIOUS TUBE PARAMETERS, SUCH AS GRID CURRENT AND PLATE VOLTAGE. THE R.F. AND MODULATOR SECTIONS EACH HAVE A SEPERATE POWER SUPPLY. TRANSMITTING MODE IS EITHER AM OR CW. INPUT TO THE ANTENNA IS 50 WATTS AM AND 100 WATTS CW ON ALL BANDS EXCEPT 10 METERS WHERE THE POWER LEVELS DECREASE SLIGHTLY. THE UNIT IS MODULATED BY FOUR 6L6 TUBES, THE HIGH VOLTAGE RECTIFIERS ARE A PAIR OF 866 TUBES, AND THE FINAL AMPLIFIER IS A SINGLE 814 (RK-47) TUBE. THE POWER SOURCE IS 120 VOLTS AC.

HT-1

HT-2   NONE   1937-38 $175.00

THE HT-2 IS THE SAME BASIC UNIT AS THE HT-1 BUT IS INTENDED FOR CW TRANSMITTING MODE ONLY, AND THUS IS WITH-OUT THE 7-TUBE MODULATOR SECTION. THE OTHER FEATURES, FUNCTIONS, AND SPECIFICATIONS ARE THE SAME AS THE HT-1.

HT-3   NONE   1938 $175.00

A 50-WATT 14-TUBE MARINE RADIO TELEPHONE (TRANSCEIVER). THREE FIXED CRYSTAL FREQUENCIES ARE AVAILABLE IN THE MARINE BAND (2.1MHz TO 2.9MHz) FOR THE TRANSMITTER, AND THE RECEIVER IS VFO TUNED WITH TWO BANDS, 550KHz TO 1700KHz AND 1.9MHz TO 3.1MHz. THE POWER SOURCE IS 12 OR 32 VOLTS DC DEPENDING ON CHOICE OF DYNOMOTOR AND VIBRAPAK UNITS. COMMUNICATION IS ACCOMPLISHED WITH THE TELEPHONE-TYPE HAND SET IN TRANSCEIVE MODE AND THE RECEIVERS BUILT-IN SPEAKER FOR RECEIVING BROADCAST BAND SIGNALS. TUBES USED: TRANSMITTER - 6F6 CRYSTAL OSCILLATOR, FOUR 6L6 AS MODULATORS, AND TWO RK-39 IN PUSH-PULL CLASS C AS THE FINAL AMPLIFIER. RECEIVER - 6K7 R.F. AMPLIFIER, 6K8 OSCILLATOR & MIXER, 6K7 I.F., 6Q7 2nd DETECTOR & AVC, 6F5 1st AUDIO, AND 6K6 AUDIO OUTPUT.

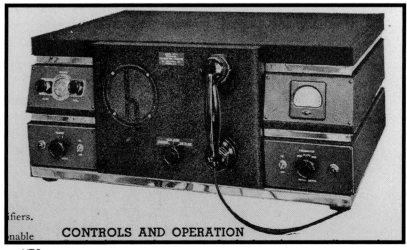

HT-3

HT-4	NONE	1938-45	from $695.00 (HT-4)
HT-4A, B, C, D, E F			to $1041.00 (HT-4F)
BC-610			
BC-610A, B, C, D, E, F			

THE HT-4 IS PROBLBLY THE MOST NOTORIOUS TRANSMITTER OF ITS TIME BECAUSE OF ITS MANY MILITARY APPLICATIONS DURING WORLD WAR II. A 450-WATT CW, 325-WATT AM CRYSTAL-CONTROLLED UNIT FOR OPERATION ON ANY FREQUENCY IN THE 160 THROUGH THE 10 METER BANDS WITH THE PROPER USER-INSTALLED PLUG-IN CRYSTALS AND TUNING UNITS. THERE ARE A TOTAL OF 16 TUBES, AND THE POWER SOURCE IS 120 VOLTS AC. TUBES USED: 6V6 CRYSTAL OSCILLATOR, 6L6 DOUBLER, TWO RK-39 AS INTERMEDIATE AMPLIFIER, TWO 2A3 AS AUDIO DRIVERS, TWO RK-38 (100TH) AS CLASS B MODULATORS, TWO 866 HIGH VOLTAGE RECTIFIERS, TWO 5Z3 AS EXCITER, BIAS & AUDIO UNIT RECTIFIERS, THREE VR-150 AS VOLTAGE REGULATORS, AND RK-63 (250TH) AS THE CLASS C FINAL POWER AMPLIFIER. THE WEIGHT OF THE HT-4 IS 390.5 POUNDS. THE MILITARY NUMBER FOR THE HT-4 IS BC-610. THE "A" THROUGH "F" MODELS ARE THE SAME BASIC UNIT WITH RELATIVELY MINOR COMPONENT AND COSMETIC DIFFERENCES. SHOWN HERE ARE THE HT-4B AND THE BC-610E.

BC-610E

HT-4B

HT-5	NONE	1938-45	from $56.50 (HT-5)
HT-5A-F			to $69.50 (HT-5F)
BC-614			
BC-614A-F			

THE HT-5 IS REALLY NOT A TRANSMITTER, BUT RATHER AN AUDIO SPEECH AMPLIFIER DESIGNED AS AN ACCESSORY UNIT TO THE HT-4. IT IS USED AS A PRE-AMPLIFIER TO DRIVE THE MODULATOR OF THE HT-4. POWER SOURCE IS 120 VOLTS AC. THE MILITARY MUMBER IS BC-614, AND AGAIN THERE ARE RELATIVELY MINOR COMPONENT AND COSMETIC CHANGES BETWEEN THE HT-5 AND THE "A" THROUGH "F" MODELS. TUBES USED: 80 RECTIFIER, TWO 6J5 IN PUSH-PULL AUDIO OUTPUT, 6J5 VOLTAGE AMPLIFIER, AND 6SQ7 MICROPHONE PRE-AMPLIFIER. SHOWN HERE ARE THE HT-5 AND THE BC-614E.

HT-5

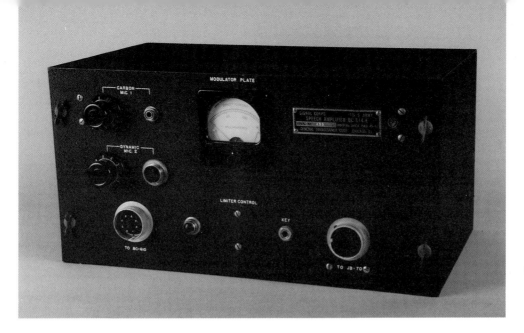

BC-614E

| HT-6 | NONE | 1939-45 | $99.00 |

25 WATTS AM OR CW, EIGHT TUBES, 160 THROUGH 6 METERS, WITH THE PROPER SET OF PLUG-IN COILS AND CRYSTALS, ANY 3 SETS MAY BE INSTALLED AT ONE TIME AND ARE BAND-SWITCHABLE. THE POWER SOURCE IS 120 VOLTS AC. PROVISION IS MADE FOR USE OF OTHER EXTERNAL POWER SOURCES THROUGH THE ACCESSORY SOCKET ON THE REAR APRON OF THE CHASSIS. TUBES USED: TWO 5Z3 RECTIFIERS, TWO 6L6 MODULATOR POWER AMPLIFIERS, 6SC7 MODULATOR DRIVER, 6SQ7 MICROPHONE PRE-AMPLIFIER, 6L6 OSCILLATOR, AND 807 CLASS C FINAL POWER AMPLIFIER.

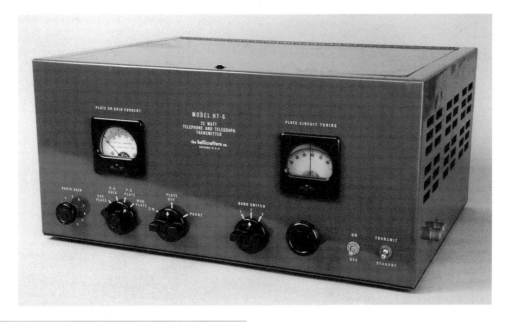

HT-6

| HT-7 | NONE | 1939 | $29.50 |

THE HT-7 IS A SELF-CONTAINED CRYSTAL-CONTROLLED FREQUENCY STANDARD OR CRYSTAL CALIBRATOR. IT WILL PUT OUT A "MARKER" EVERY 10KHz, 100KHz, OR 1MHz DEPENDING ON CONTROL SETTINGS. ITS FREQUENCY RANGE IS 1MHz TO 30MHz. ITS PRIMARY FUNCTION IS FOR USE IN ALIGNING RECEIVERS AND CHECKING FREQUENCY ACCURACY OF TRANSMITTERS. TUBES USED: 80 RECTIFIER, 6F6 HARMONIC AMPLIFIER, 6N7 MULTIVIBRATOR, AND 6L7 R.F.OUTPUT. POWER SOURCE IS 120 VOLTS AC, OR 120-240 VOLTS AC WITH UNIVERSAL POWER TRANSFORMER.

HT-7

The HT-7

Early HT-7's had the serial number stamped on the rear chassis apron. Later units had a metal serial number plate riveted to the bottom cover.

HT-8   THE CRUISING   1939 $290.00

A 25-WATT 12-TUBE MARINE RADIO TELEPHONE. THE TRANSMITTER AND RECEIVER ARE CRYSTAL-CONTROLLED WITH 5 SWITCHABLE FREQUENCIES AVAILABLE FROM 2.1MHz TO 6.6MHz. THE RECEIVER HAS A 6th CRYSTAL POSITION FOR RECEIVING MARINE WEATHER STATIONS. THE POWER SOURCE IS 120 VOLTS AC, OR 12 VOLTS DC DEPENDING ON THE USER'S CHOICE OF POWER SUPPLIES. THE AC SUPPLY USES A 5Z3 RECTIFIER, THE DC SUPPLY USES A VIBRAPAK AND DYNOMOTOR. THE RECEIVER I.F. IS 455KHz. TUBES USED: RECEIVER: 6SK7 R.F. AMPLIFIER, 6SJ7 OSCILLATOR & MIXER, 6SA7 1st I.F., 6SK7 2nd I.F., 6SQ7 DETECTOR & 1st AUDIO, 6H6 ANL, AND 6K6 AUDIO OUTPUT. TRANSMITTER: TWO 6L6 IN PUSH-PULL AS THE MODULATOR & SPEECH AMPLIFIER, 6L6 OSCILLATOR, AND 807 FINAL AMPLIFIER.

HT-9 BLACK   NONE   1939 $350.00
HT-9 GRAY   NONE   1944

A 14-TUBE 75-WATT AM, 100-WATT CW UNIT COVERING 1.5MHz TO 18MHz AND 28MHz TO 30MHz DEPENDING ON WHICH PLUG-IN TUNING UNITS, COILS & CRYSTALS ARE INSTALLED. UP TO 3 SETS OF COILS, CRYSTALS & TUNING UNITS MAY BE INSTALLED AT A TIME AND ARE BAND SWITCHABLE. THE HT-9 BLACK IS THE PRE-WAR VERSION, AND THE HT-9 GRAY IS THE LATE WAR VERSION. OTHER THAN THE COLOR AND STYLE OF KNOBS AND METERS I SEE NO OTHER DIFFERENCES BETWEEN THE TWO UNITS. TUBES USED: 6L6 R.F. OSCILLATOR, 6L6 R.F. BUFFER, 5Z3 LOW VOLTAGE RECTIFIER, 6SJ7 1st AUDIO, 6J5 AUDIO DRIVER FOR THE MODULATOR, FOUR 6L6 IN PUSH-PULL PARALLEL AS MODULATOR, 80 LOW VOLTAGE RECTIFIER, 5Z3 LOW VOLTAGE RECTIFIER, TWO 866A AS HIGH VOLTAGE RECTIFIERS, AND A SINGLE 814 AS THE FINAL R.F. POWER AMPLIFIER. THE POWER SOURCE IS 120 VOLTS AC.

HT-8 THE CRUISING

HT-9 BLACK

HT-9 GRAY

HT-11   THE ENSIGN   1939-41   from $159.00 (1939)

HT-11A-E   1942-45   to $267.50 (1945)

A 12-WATT 11-TUBE MARINE RADIO TELEPHONE (TRANSCEIVER). THE TRANSMITTER IS CRYATAL CONTROLED FOR ANY THREE FREQUENCIES BETWEEN 1.5MHz AND 2.9MHz, BAND SWITCHABLE, AND THE RECEIVER IS VFO TUNED IN TWO BANDS FROM 550KHz TO 1.6MHz AND 2.1MHz TO 2.9MHz. THE POWER SOURCE CAN BE 120 VOLTS AC, 6 OR 12 VOLTS DC DEPENDING ON THE USERS CHOICE OF POWER SUPPLY. TUBES USED–RECEIVER: 6SK7 R.F. AMPLIFIER, 6K8 OSCILLATOR & MIXER, 6SK7 I.F., 6SQ7 DETECTOR & 1st AUDIO, 6K6 AUDIO OUTPUT. TRANSMITTER: TWO 6V6 IN PUSH-PULL AS MODULATOR & SPEECH AMPLIFIER, 6V6 OSCILLATOR, AND A SINGLE 807 R.F. POWER AMPLIFIER. THERE ARE MINOR VALUE CHANGES OF SOME COMPONENTS BETWEEN THE HT-11 AND THE "A" THROUGH "E" MODELS. SHOWN HERE IS THE HT-11 AND HT-11E. THE OUTBOARD POWER SUPPLIES ARE NOT SHOWN.

HT-11

HT-11D

HT-12   UNKNOWN   1940-42   from $475.00 to $605.00

A 50-WATT 18-TUBE MARINE RADIO TELEPHONE (TRANSCEIVER), 10 CRYSTAL CONTROLED CHANELS FOR ANY FREQUENCY IN THE 2MHz TO 3MHz RANGE. TWO OF THESE CHANELS CAN BE IN THE 3MHz TO 6.7MHz RANGE WHEN SPECIAL-ORDERED BY THE USER. A SEPERATE 120 VOLT AC POWER SUPPLY COMES STANDARD WITH THE UNIT, AND A 12, 32, OR 110 VOLT DC SUPPLY CAN BE ORDERED AS AN OPTION. TUBES USED: TRANSMITTER: 6J5 INPUT AUDIO AMPLIFIER, FOUR 6L6 IN PUSH-PULL PARALLEL AS MODULATORS, 6L6 OSCILLATOR, AND TWO 807 FINAL POWER AMPLIFIERS. RECEIVER: 6SK7 R.F. AMPLIFIER, 6SA7 MIXER, 6SJ7 OSCILLATOR, 6SK7 I.F., 6SQ7 2nd DETECTOR & AVC, 6SF5 1st AUDIO. 6K6 AUDIO OUTPUT, AND TWO 5Z3 AND A 6X5 AS RECTIFIERS WITH THE AC POWER SUPPLY. THE SELLING PRICE VARIES WITH CHOICE OF POWER SUPPLIES.

HT-12

HT-14 THE COMMODORE

HT-14　　　**THE COMMODORE**　　1945-46　　　$1061.00
BC-669
BC-669A

A 20-TUBE 45-WATT MARINE RADIO TELEPHONE (TRANSCEIVER), 6 CRYSTAL-CONTROLLED CHANNELS FOR ANY FREQUENCY FROM 1.68MHz TO 4.45MHz WITH SIMULATANEOUS RECEIVER & TRANSMITTER BAND-SWITCHING. THE RECEIVER CAN BE EITHER CRYSTAL OR VFO CONTROLLED. POWER SOURCE CAN BE 120 VOLTS AC, 12, 32, OR 110 VOLT DC DEPENDING ON USER-SPECIFIED POWER SUPPLY. TUBES USED: TRANSMITTER: 6L6 OSCILLATOR, 12J5 SPEECH AMPLIFIER, FOUR 6L6 MODULATORS, AND TWO 807 AS THE FINAL R.F. AMPLIFIER. RECEIVER: 6SK7 R.F AMPLIFIER, 6SA7 MIXER, 6J5 OSCILLATOR, 6SK7 I.F., 6H6 2nd DETECTOR, AVC & ANL, 6SK7 1st AUDIO, 6K6 AUDIO OUTPUT, AND WITH THE AC POWER SUPPLY 80 AS RECEIVER RECTIFIER, AND FOUR 5Z3 AS TRANSMITTER RECTIFIERS. SELLING PRICE VARIES SLIGHTLY WITH CHOICE OF POWER SUPPLY. THERE WERE MINOR VARIATIONS BETWEEN THE MILITARY MODELS (BC-669 & BC-669A) AND THE HT-14.

HT-17　　　**NONE**　　　1947　　$49.50

A 25-WATT CRYSTAL-CONTROLLED CW TRANSMITTER COVERING 80 THROUGH 10 METERS WITH THE PROPER PLUG-IN P.A. TANK COILS AND CRYSTALS. THE UNIT COMES WITH A PILOT LAMP-TYPE TUNING INDICATOR & A SET OF 40 METER COILS. THE TUNING INDICATOR LIGHT COULD BE EASILY REPLACED BY THE OPTIONAL TUNING METER MODEL SM-17 FOR $6.50. ADDITIONAL COIL SETS FOR THE OTHER BANDS WERE PRICED AT $7.50 PER SET. ON THE HIGHER BANDS THE POWER DROPS OFF SOMEWHAT AND IS AROUND 12 WATTS ON 10 METERS. THE POWER SOURCE IS 120 VOLTS AC. TUBES USED: 5Y3 RECTIFIER, 6V6 OSCILLATOR, AND 807 R.F. POWER AMPLIFIER. THE UNIT SHOWN HERE HAS A TUNING METER, BUT IT IS NOT THE HALLICRAFTERS PART.

HT-17

HT-18 (SMOOTH)

HT-18　　　**NONE**　　　1947-49　　$110.00

A 4-WATT VFO-EXCITER CALIBRATED ON SEVEN BANDS FROM 3.5MHz TO 29.7MHz OR CAN BE CRYSTAL-CONTROLLED. BAND SWITCHABLE, OUTPUT MODES OF AM, CW, OR NBFM ON ALL BANDS. BUILT-IN PREAMP FOR HIGH-IMPEDANCE MICROPHONE. POWER SOURCE IS 120 VOLTS AC. 7 TUBES. SOME HAD A SMOOTH GRAY METAL DIAL ESCUTCHEON, SOME HAD A QUILTED BRIGHT METAL DIAL ESCUTCHEON. BOTH VERSIONS ARE SHOWN HERE. TUBES USED: 5Y3 RECTIFIER, OD3/VR-150 & OC3/VR-105 AS VOLTAGE REGULATORS, 6BA6 SPEECH AMPLIFIER, 6BA6 MODULATOR, 6BA6 OSCILLATOR, AND A 6L6 AS THE FINAL R.F. AMPLIFIER.

The HT-18

There were two production runs of the HT-18. The first run had a 'quilted' bright aluminum dial escutcheon, and the B+ was always on the plate of the 6L6 even in the 'check' mode. The second run had a smooth aluminum dial escutcheon painted silver gray, and the B+ was removed from the 6L6 during 'check'.

HT-18 (QUILTED)

HT-19	NONE	1948	359.50

A 10-TUBE 125-WATT CW OR NBFM UNIT WITH PROVISION FOR AM MODE. BAND SWITCHABLE EXCEPT FOR THE FINAL TANK COILS WHICH MUST BE CHANGED MANUALLY. BUILT-IN VFO CALIBRATED FOR 80 THROUGH 10 METERS, OR CAN BE CRYSTAL-CONTROLLED. FOR AM MODE AN EXTERNAL MODULATOR IS REQUIRED, BUT THE MICROPHONE PRE-AMPLIFIER IS BUILT-IN. POWER SOURCE IS 120 VOLTS AC. TUBES USED: 5Y3 LOW VOLTAGE RECTIFIER, TWO 866 HIGH VOLTAGE RECTIFIERS, OD3 & OC3 VOLTAGE REGULATORS, 6BA6 OSCILLATOR, 6BA6 FM MODULATOR, 6BA6 SPEECH AMPLIFIER, 6L6 BUFFER, AND A 4-65A FINAL R.F. AMPLIFIER. THIS TRANSMITTER ALSO HAS A BUILT-IN COOLING FAN.

HT-19

HT-20

HT-20	NONE	1950-53	$449.50

AN 11-TUBE 100-WATT BAND-SWITCHABLE AM-CW TRANSMITTER COVERING ANY 10 FREQUENCIES FROM 1.7MHz TO 30MHz WITH 10 USER-SELECTED CRYSTALS INSTALLED. PROVISION IS ALSO AVAILABLE FOR THE UNIT TO BE VFO OPERATED. OTHER FEATURES INCLUDE AN 8 POSITION METER SWITCH FOR MONITORING ALL FUNCTIONS, BUILT-IN COOLING FAN & LOW PASS FILTER, AND A GREAT DEAL OF SHIELDING AND SPECIAL CONSTRUCTION TO PREVENT TVI (TELEVISION INTERFERENCE). TUBES USED: TWO 5R4 HIGH VOLTAGE RECTIFIERS, 5U4 LOW VOLTAGE RECTIFIER, 6BL7 BIAS RECTIFIER, TWO 807 MODULATORS, 6K6 DRIVER, 6SL7 AUDIO PRE-AMPLIFIER, 6AG7 CRYSTAL OSCILLATOR, 6L6 BUFFER MULTIPLIER, AND A 4D32 FINAL R.F. POWER AMPLIFIER.

HT-21 LDS   LITTLE FONE   1952-57 $225.00 - $300.00
HT-21 LWS   with options
HT-21 HWS

A 22-TUBE PORTABLE BATTERY-OPERATED, SINGLE-FREQUENCY, CRYS-
TAL-CONTROLLED FM TRANSCEIVER OPERATING IN THE 25MHz TO
50MHz RANGE. FEATURES INCLUDE A DOUBLE CONVERSION RECEIVER,
TELEPHONE-TYPE HAND SET, SQUELCH CONTROL, AND SUB-MINIATURE
"PENCIL" TUBES. THERE IS A CHOICE OF .5 OR 1 WATT OUTPUT, AND
DRY CELL OR RECHARGABLE WET CELL BATTERIES. THE LETTERS AFTER
THE MODEL NUMBER INDICATE THE POWER LEVEL, DRY OR WET CELL
BATTERIES, AND SQUELCH (L=LOW POWER, H=HIGH POWER, D=DRY
CELL, W=WET CELL, AND S=SQUELCH). OPTIONS INCLUDE SHOUL-
DER STRAPS; BATTERY CHARGER; SHOULDER, LIP, OR THROAT MIC; AND
WALL MOUNT BRACKETS. THE SELLING PRICE DEPENDS ON THE OP-
TIONS CHOSEN.

HT-21 LDS AND HT-21 HWS LITTLE FONE

HT-22 LDS   LITTLE FONE   1952-57 $225.00 - $300.00
HT-22 LWS   with options
HT-22 HWS

THE HT-22 HAS ALL THE SAME FEATURES AND OPTIONS AS THE HT-21
BUT HAS 23 TUBES AND OPERATES IN THE 152MHz TO 174MHz FRE-
QUENCY RANGE. THE PRICE DEPENDS ON THE OPTIONS.

The HT-21

Between 1952 and 1957, Hallicrafters was in some way related
to Doolittle Radio, Inc. of Chicago. Doolittle produced a PJZ-1A
portable transceiver that was identical to the HT-21 series,
including the cabinet lettering and name "Littlefone."

HT-23   LITTLE FONE   1952-57 $450.00
HT-24   LITTLE FONE   1952-57

THE HT-23 IS THE 25MHz TO 50MHz BASE STATION TRANSCEIVER FOR THE HT-21 POR-
TABLE UNITS. 23 SUB-MINIATURE "PENCIL" TUBES PLUS VOLTAGE REGULATOR, AUDIO,
AND RECTIFIER. SINGLE FREQUENCY CRYSTAL-CONTROLLED, WITH SQUELCH. POWER
SOURCE IS 120 VOLTS AC. THE HT-24 IS THE BASE STATION FOR THE HT-22 152MHz TO
174MHz PORTABLE UNITS AND HAS THE SAME FEATURES AND FUNCTIONS AS THE HT-23.
SHOWN HERE IS THE HT-24.

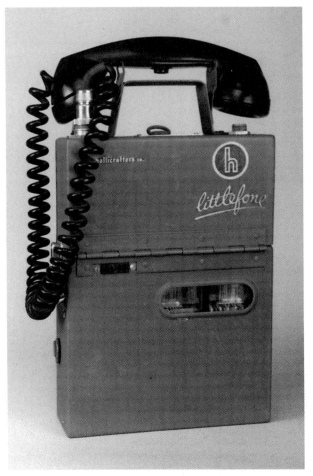

HT-22 HWS LITTLE FONE

HT-24 LITTLE FONE

| HT-25 | LITTLE FONE | 1952-57 | $475.00 |
| HT-26 | LITTLE FONE | 1952-57 | |

THE MOBILE VERSION OF THE HT-21 PORTABLE, 1 WATT OUTPUT, WITH 6 OR 12 VOLT DC VIBRATOR POWER SUPPLY FOR VEHICLE INSTALATION. OTHER FEATURES ARE THE SAME AS THE HT-21. THIS UNIT COMES COMPLETE WITH WHIP ANTENNA, HAND MICROPHONE, MOUNTING BRACKETS AND ALL NECESSARY HARDWARE. THE HT-26 IS THE MOBILE VERSION OF THE HT-22, WITH THE SAME FEATURES AS THE HT-25.

| HT-30 | NONE | 1954-56 | $349.50 |

THIS 22-TUBE TRANSMITTER/EXCITER FEATURES A FILTER-TYPE SSB GENERATOR, 35 WATTS P.E.P. CW & SSB, 9 WATTS AM ON THE 80, 40, 20, & 10 METER BANDS. FULL BAND-SWITCHING, SELECTABLE SIDE BAND, FULL METERING, BUILT-IN CALIBRATED VFO, 1 FIXED FREQUENCY CRYSTAL SPACE, AND VOX. IT IS THE FIRST SIDE BAND TRANSMITTER BUILT BY THE COMPANY. THE DRIVER TUBE IS A 12BY7 AND THE FINAL AMPLIFIER USES A PAIR OF 6146. THE POWER SOURCE IS 120 VOLTS AC. THE COMPANION UNITS ARE THE HT-31 LINEAR AMPLIFIER AND THE SX-100 RECEIVER.

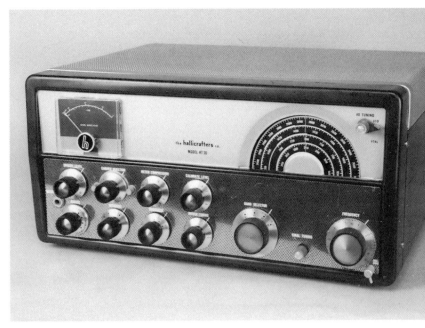

HT-30

HT-26 LITTLE FONE

| HT-31 | NONE | 1954-56 | $395.00 |

A 330-WATT P.E.P. 4-TUBE AM, SSB, CW LINEAR AMPLIFIER COVERING 80, 40, 20, AND 10 METERS. REQUIRES A 10-WATT INPUT FOR RATED OUTPUT. THE OUTPUT WILL BE SLIGHTLY LOWER ON 10 METERS. COMPLETLY BAND SWITCHABLE, BUILT-IN COOLING FAN, LO-PASS FILTERS, AND TVI SUPPRESSION. THE FINAL AMPLIFIER TUBES ARE A PAIR OF 811-A ZERO BIAS TRIODES, AND THE RECTIFIERS ARE TWO 866-A. POWER SOURCE IS 120 VOLTS AC. THE COMPANION TRANSMITTER/EXCITER IS THE HT-30.

HT-31

HT-32

HT-32   NONE   1957-58 $675.00

THIS 20-TUBE AM-CW-SSB TRANSMITTER/EXCITER HAS AN OUTPUT OF 70 TO 100 WATTS SSB & CW, AND 17 TO 25 WATTS AM ON THE 80 THROUGH 10 METER BANDS. FEATURES INCLUDE FULL BAND SWITCHING, METERING, FILTER-TYPE SSB, VOX, CW BREAK-IN KEYING, TVI SUPPRESSION, A BUILT-IN COLLING FAN, AND A CALI-BRATED VFO. THE POWER SOURCE IS 120 VOLTS AC. A 12BY7 IS USED AS A DRIVER, AND A PAIR OF 6146 AS THE FINAL R.F. AMPLIFIER. THE COMPANION UNITS ARE THE HT-33 LINIER AMPLIFIER AND THE SX-101 RECEIVER.

HT-32A   NONE   1958-59 $695.00

THE HT-32A LOOKS SIMILAR TO AND HAS ALL THE SAME FEATURES AND FUNCTIONS AS THE HT-32 PLUS PROVISION FOR A PHONE PATCH, FSK, AND PUSH-TO-TALK MICROPHONE CIRCUIT. THE COMPANION UNITS ARE THE HT-33A LINEAR AMPLIFIER AND THE SX-101A RECEIVER.

HT-32A

HT-32B

HT-32B   NONE   1960-64 $725.00

THE HT-32B HAS ALL THE FEATURES AND SPECIFICATIONS OF THE "A" MODEL. THERE IS A SLIGHT COSMETIC DIFFERENCE WITH THE ADDITION OF "WINDOWS" IN THE FRONT PANEL FOR BAND NUMBER READOUT ABOVE THE BAND SWITCH AND LOGGING SCALE ABOVE THE FREQUENCY KNOB AS SEEN IN THIS PHOTO TAKEN FROM THE TECHNICAL MANUAL. THE COMPANION UNITS ARE THE HT-33B LINEAR AMPLIFIER AND THE SX-115 RECEIVER.

HT-33

HT-33 NONE 1957-58 $775.00

A 7-TUBE 1000-WATT AM-CW-SSB 80 THROUGH 10 METER LINEAR AMPLIFIER REQUIRING ONLY 8 WATTS OF DRIVE POWER. FEATURES INCLUDE CERAMIC TUBES, PI-NETWORK OUTPUT SYSTEM, FULL METERING, BUILT-IN COOLING FAN, FULL BAND SWITCHING, AND CLASS AB1 OPERATION. TUBES USED: TWO OB2 & ONE OA2 AS SCREEN VOLTAGE REGULATORS, TWO 866A RECTIFIERS, AND TWO 4CX300A AS THE FINAL R.F. AMPLIFIERS. THE POWER SOURCE IS 120 VOLTS AC. THE HT-33 IS THE COMPANION AMPLIFIER TO THE HT-32 TRANSMITTER/EXCITER.

HT-33A NONE 1958-59 $795.00

A 7-TUBE 1000-WATT AM-CW-SSB 80 THROUGH 10 METER LINEAR AMPLIFIER REQUIRING 50 TO 60 WATTS DRIVE POWER. FEATURES INCLUDE A BUILT-IN COOLING FAN, A 20-AMP CIRCUIT BREAKER/ON-OFF SWITCH, FULL METERING, TVI SUPPRESSION, FULL BAND SWITCHING, AND CLASS AB1 OR AB2 OPERATION. POWER SOURCE IS 120 VOLTS AC AT 2350 WATTS. TUBES USED: FOUR OA2 AS VOLTAGE REGULATORS, TWO 3B28 HIGH VOLTAGE RECTIFIERS, AND A SINGLE PENTA-LAB PL-172 R.F. POWER AMPLIFIER. THE COMPANION UNIT TO THE HT-32A TRANSMITTER/EXCITER.

Line

HT-33A

HT-33B

HT-33B NONE 1960-64 $995.00

THE HT-33B HAS ALL THE SAME FUNCTIONS AND FEATURES AS THE HT-33A PLUS A SEPERATE R.F. OUTPUT METER, A REDESIGNED FRONT PANEL, AND TWO MORE OA2 VOLTAGE REGULATORS, MAKING IT A 9-TUBE UNIT. IT IS THE COMPANION TO THE HT-32B TRANSMITTER/EXCITER.

HT-36 NONE 1958

A 25-TUBE AM-CW-SSB TRANSMITTER/EXCITER WITH CONTINUOUS FREQUENCY COVERAGE FROM 2.2MHz TO 30MHz WITH A CRYSTAL-CONTROLLED VFO AND SPACE FOR 12 SWITCH SELECTABLE CRYSTALS. THE VFO WILL OPERATE 100KHz ON EITHER SIDE OF THE CRYSTAL FREQUENCY. THE POWER OUTPUT IS 70 TO 100 WATTS CW OR SSB, AND 17 TO 25 WATTS AM. FEATURES INCLUDE CRYSTAL FILTER-TYPE SIDE BAND GENERATOR, VOX, FULL METERING, SELECTABLE SIDE BAND, BUILT-IN COOLING FAN, SPEECH PROCESSING, CW BREAK-IN KEYING, AND A BUILT-IN 2" OSCILLOSCOPE FOR MONITORING OF LINEARITY OF ALL STAGES BETWEEN THE SIDE BAND GENERATOR AND THE FINAL AMPLIFIER. TUBES USED: 12AT7 SPEECH AMP., 12AT7 BALANCED MODULATOR, 12AT7 CRYSTAL OSCILLATOR BUFFER AMP., 6BA7 MIXER & SIDE BAND OSCILLATOR, 12AT7 1st I.F., 6AL5 ENVELOPE DETECTOR, 6AK6 VFO, 12AT7 1st BALANCED MIXER, 6C4 I.F., 12AT7 2nd MIXER & OSCILLATOR, 6AU6 9.4MHz I.F., 6X8 2nd BALANCED MIXER, 12AT7 HF CRYSTAL OSCILLATOR, 6360 DRIVER, TWO OA2 VOLTAGE REGULATOR, 5R4 HIGH VOLTAGE RECTIFIER, 5U LOW VOLTAGE RECTIFIER, 6AU6 HORIZONTAL AMPLIFIER, 2BP1 OSCILLOSCOPE TUBE, 12AT VOX & ANTI-TRIP AMP., 6AL5 VOX & ANTI-TRIP RECTIFIER, 12AT7 VOX & ANTI-TRIP RELA TUBE, AND A PAIR OF 6146 AS THE FINAL R.F. POWER AMPLIFIER. THE BIAS RECTIFIER AND OSCILLOSCOPE TRACE BLANKER ARE SILICON DIODES. THE POWER SOURCE IS 120 VOLT AC. THIS UNIT NEVER WENT INTO PRODUCTION. ONLY THREE HAND-BUILT WORKING ENGINEERING PROTOTYPES WERE BUILT AS SAMPLES AND WERE GIVEN TO THE ARMY NAVY, AND AIR FORCE FOR POSSIBLE CONTRACTS. NO CONTRACT WAS EVER OBTAINED I FEEL FORTUNATE TO HAVE ACQUIRED THE ONE SHOWN HERE. I HAVE NO INFORMA TION ON WHAT THE SELLING PRICE WOULD HAVE BEEN.

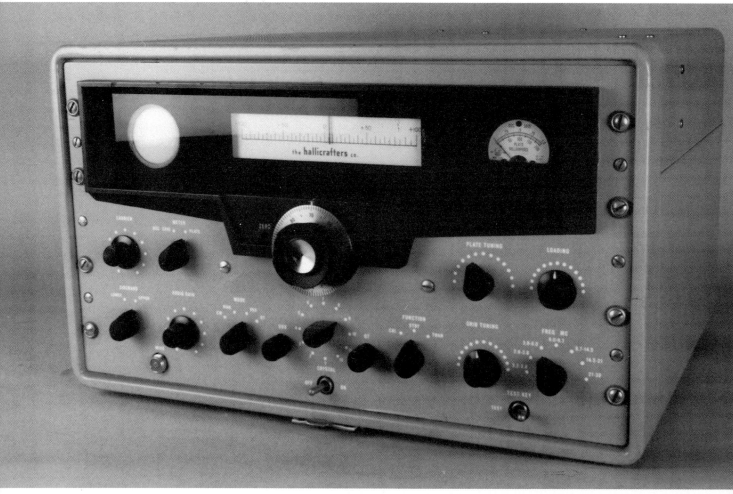

HT-36

HT-37 NONE 1959-62 $495.00

THIS 18-TUBE AM-CW-SSB 80 THROUGH 10 METER TRANSMITTER/EXCITER HAS A POWER OUTPUT OF 70 TO 100 WATTS CW OR SSB, AND 17 TO 25 WATTS AM. FEATURES INCLUDE PHASING-TYPE SIDE BAND GENERATOR, OUTPUT METER, VOX, FULL BAND SWITCHING, AND VFO. THE POWER SOURCE IS 120 VOLTS AC, THE DRIVER TUBE IS A 12BY7 AND THE FINAL AMPLIFIER IS A PAIR OF 6146s. THE COMPANION UNITS WOULD BE THE HT-41 LINEAR AMPLIFIER AND THE SX-111 RECEIVER.

HT-37

HT-40	NONE	1961-63	$109.95 factory wired
HT-40K			$89.95 kit
HT-40	MARK-1	1964	$139.95 Mark-1

THE HT-40 IS AN ENTRY LEVEL TRANSMITTER WITH A POWER OUTPUT OF 75 WATTS CW, AND CONSIDERABLY LOWER ON AM. THE FREQUENCY COVERAGE IS 80 THROUGH 6 METERS, CRYSTAL-CONTROLLED. THERE IS PROVISION FOR CONNECTION OF A EXTERNAL VFO SUCH AS THE HA-5. THE UNIT HAS 4 TUBES AND THE POWER SOURCE IS 120 VOLTS AC. IT COULD BE PURCHASED AS A KIT OR FACTORY-WIRED. TUBES USED: 6CX8 OSCILLATOR & BUFFER, 12AX7 MICROPHONE PRE-AMP & 1st AUDIO, 6DE7 2nd AUDIO & MODULATOR, AND A 6DQ5 AS THE R.F. FINAL POWER AMPLIFIER. THE RECTIFIER & VOLTAGE DOUBLER ARE SILICON DIODES. THE COMPANION RECEIVER IS THE SX-140. I SEE NO NOTICEABLE DIFFERENCE IN THE MARK-1 EXCEPT THE PRICE.

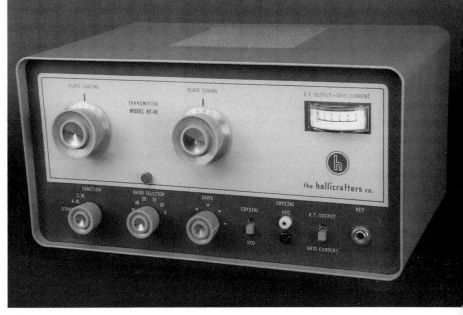

HT-40 PRODUCTION MODEL

HT-40 ENGINEERING PROTOTYPE

HT-41	NONE	1961	$395.00

A 4-TUBE AM-CW-SSB LINEAR AMPLIFIER FOR 80 THROUGH 10 METERS. THE PLATE INPUT POWER IS 1200 WATTS P.E.P SSB, 700 WATTS CW, AND 350 WATTS AM WITH A DRIVER INPUT POWER OF 60 WATTS, LESS FOR A DRIVER POWER OF 20 WATTS. FULL METERING AND BAND SWITCHING, BUILT-IN COOLING FAN. REQUIRES 20 TO 60 WATTS DRIVER POWER. TUBES USED: TWO 866AX HIGH VOLTAGE RECTIFIERS, AND TWO 7094 AS THE FINAL R.F. AMPLIFIER RUNNING IN GROUNDED-GRID CLASS "B" OPERATION. THE POWER SOURCE IS 120 VOLTS AC AT 1500 WATTS. THE COMPANION TRANSMITTER/EXCITER IS THE HT-37.

HT-41

HT-44   NONE   1962 $379.50 transmitter   WHEN USED WITH THE COMPANION SX-117 RECEIVER. THE POWER SUPPLY (MODEL PS-
                                              $99.95 AC power supply   150-120) IS ON A SEPERATE CHASSIS AND HAS A BUILT-IN SPEAKER, ALSO FOR USE WITH

A 17-TUBE AM-CW-SSB TRANSMITTER/EXCITER COVERING 80 THROUGH 10 METERS. THE SX-117. THE DRIVER TUBE IS A 12BY7, AND THE FINAL R.F. POWER AMPLIFIER IS A PAIR
POWER OUTPUT IS 100-130 WATTS P.E.P. SSB, 100-130 WATTS CW, AND 25 TO 35 WATTS OF 6DQ5. THE COMPANION UNITS ARE THE THE HT-45 LINEAR AMPLIFIER AND THE HA-8
AM. FEATURES INCLUDE VOX, CW BREAK-IN KEYING, PTT MICROPHONE CIRCUITRY, AALC, "SPLATTER GUARD" MODULATION MONITOR.
AND FRONT PANEL CONTROL OF SLAVE (TRANCEIVE) OR INDEPENDANT TRANSMITTER

HT-44 WITH PS-150-120 POWER SUPPLY

HT-45   NONE   1963-64 $299.95 amplifier   NONE   "LOUDENBOOMER"   1963-64
                                              $199.95 AC power supply   THE LOUDENBOOMER IS A LINEAR AMPLIFIER ELECTRONICALLY IDENTICAL TO THE HT-

THE HT-45 IS A 2000-WATT P.E.P SSB, 1000-WATT CW 80 THROUGH 10 METER LINEAR 45. THE ONLY DIFFERENCES ARE THE STYLE OF KNOBS, TYPE OF METER, AND FRONT
AMPLIFIER. FEATURES INCLUDE FULL METERING, BAND SWITCHING, AND BUILT-IN COOL- PANEL TRIM. IT WAS PRODUCED BY RADIO INDUSTRIES OF KANSAS CITY, KANSAS. RADIO
ING FAN. THE P-45-AC POWER SUPPLY IS ON A SEPERATE CHASSIS. THE ONLY TUBE USED INDUSTRIES WAS A SUBSIDIARY OF THE HALLICRAFTERS CO. I HAVE NO PRICE INFORMA-
IS A SINGLE 3-400Z IN A ZERO-BIAS GROUNDED-GRID CIRCUIT. THE POWER SUPPLY USES TION ON THE LOUDENBOOMER BUT SUSPECT IS SOLD FOR SLIGHTLY LESS THAN THE HT-
TWO 866A HIGH VOLTAGE RECTIFIERS. THE COMPANION TRANSMITTER/EXCITER IS THE 45. THE PHOTO SHOWN HERE IS FROM THE TECHNICAL MANUAL.
HT-44.

HT-45

LOUDENBOOMER

LOUDENBOOMER POWER SUPPLY

HT-46   NONE   1965 $295.00

A 70-100-WATT P.E.P. CW-SSB, 80-10 METER TRANSMITTER/EXCITER. FEA-
TURING FULL METERING, AALC, PTT, TRANSCEIVER OPERATION WHEN
USED WITH THE SX-146 RECEIVER, 6-POLE CRYSTAL LATTICE SSB FILTER,
AND VOX WITH THE OPTIONAL HA-16 VOX UNIT INSTALLED. THERE
ARE A TOTAL OF 9 TUBES INCLUDING A 12BY7 DRIVER AND A 6HF5
FINAL R.F. AMPLIFIER. THE RECTIFIERS ARE SOLID-STATE. THE COMPAN-
ION RECEIVER IS THE SX-146 AND JUST ABOUT ANY LINEAR AMPLIFIER
HAVING A 50 OHM INPUT IMPEDENCE SUCH AS THE HT-45. THE POWER
SOURCE IS 120 VOLTS AC.

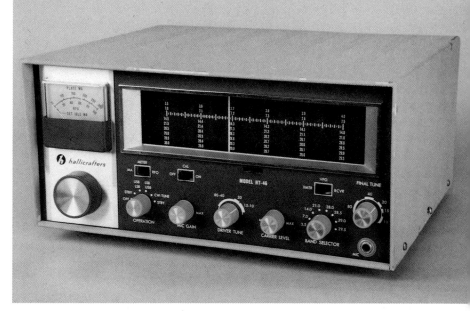

HT-46

SR SERIES TRANSCEIVERS

MODEL	NAME	DATE	ORIGINAL PRICE
SR-34	NONE	1958	$495.00 SR-34
SR-34AC			$395.00 SR-34AC

A 16-TUBE 6 TO 8-WATT AM-CW 6 & 2 METER TRANSCEIVER. THE TRANSMITTER IS CRYS-
TAL-CONTROLLED WITH 4 SWITCH SELECTABLE CRYSTALS, OR OPTIONAL EXTERNAL VFO.
THE RECEIVER IS DOUBLE CONVERSION WITH SEPERATE OSCILLATOR, MIXER, & R.F. STAGES
FOR EACH BAND. THE UNIT MAY BE OPERATED IN "CROSS BAND" MODE. OTHER FEA-
TURES INCLUDE S-METER, SQUELCH, ANL, BFO, BUILT-IN 120 VOLT AC POWER SUPPLY
AND TRANSISTORIZED 6 & 12 VOLT DC POWER SUPPLY FOR MOBILE OR PORTABLE USE. A
6N7 IS USED AS THE AUDIO OUTPUT AND MODULATOR AND A 6360 AS THE FINAL R.F.
AMPLIFIER. THE SR-34AC IS THE SAME RADIO WITHOUT THE BUILT-IN 6 & 12 DC POWER
SUPPLY OR THE COVER AND HANDLE ON THE CABINET. IT IS FOR 120 VOLT AC BASE
OPERATION ONLY.

SR-34 (WITH COVER)

DETAIL OF CONTROLS HIDDEN BEHIND PANEL
FLAP.

SR-34AC

| SR-42 | NONE | 1964 | $199.95 |
| SR-42A | | 1964-65 | $219.95 |

A 11-TUBE 12-WATT AM 2-METER TRANSCEIVER. THE TRANSMITTER IS CRYSTAL-CON-TROLLED WITH 4 SWITCH-SELECTABLE CRYSTALS AND PROVISION FOR CONNECTING AN OPTIONAL EXTERNAL VFO (MODEL HA-26). THE RECEIVER IS DOUBLE CONVERSION AND VFO TUNED, WITH S-METER, AND ANL. THE BUILT-IN UNIVERSAL POWER SUPPLY WILL RUN ON 120 VOLTS AC, OR 6 & 12 VOLTS DC. FOR MOBILE OPERATION THE THE OPTIONAL MR-40 MOBILE MOUNTING KIT AND HA-3 IGNITION NOISE-SUPPRESSOR KIT ARE REQUIRED. A 12AQ5 IS USED AS THE AUDIO OUTPUT AND MODULATOR AND THE FINAL R.F. AMPLIFIER IS A 7551. THE MAJOR DIFFERENCE BETWEEN THE SR-42 AND THE SR-42A IS THE ADDITION OF A SQUELCH CONTROL AND RELATED CIRCUITRY IN THE "A" MODEL.

SR-42

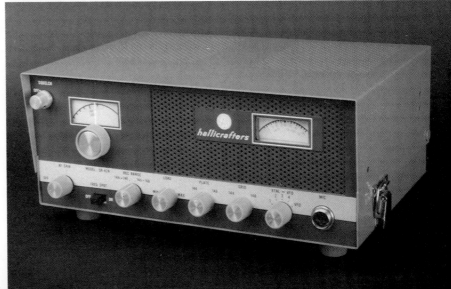

SR-42A

| SR-46 | NONE | 1964 | $199.95 |
| SR-46A | | 1964-65 | $219.95 |

THE SR-46 AND SR-46A HAVE ALL THE SAME FEATURES AND FUNCTIONS AS THE SR-42
AND SR-42A EXCEPT THE FREQUENCY COVERAGE IS FOR THE 6 METER BAND AND THE
SET HAS 10 RATHER THAN 11 TUBES.

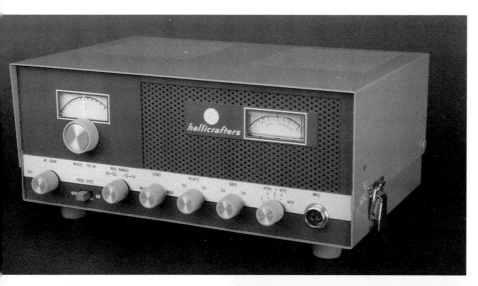

SR-46

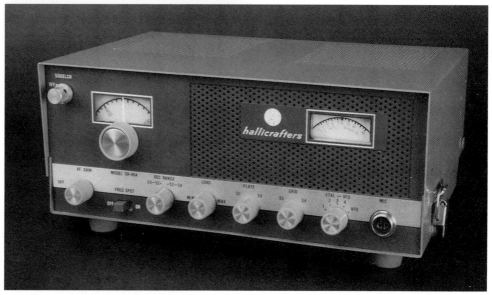

SR-46A

SR-75 (FRONT VIEW)

| SR-75 | NONE | 1950-51 | $79.95 |

THE SR-75 IS A S-38B RECEIVER WITH A BUILT-IN 10-WATT CRYSTAL-CON-
TROLLED 80 THROUGH 10 METER CW TRANSMITTER. THIS IS A ENTRY
LEVEL "NOVICE" CLASS UNIT. THE TRANSMITTING FREQUENCY DEPENDS
ON THE PLUG-IN CRYSTAL AND COILS INSTALLED. THE TRANSMITTER'S
CONTROLS ARE LOCATED ON THE REAR APRON OF THE CHASSIS AS
SHOWN HERE. THE POWER SOURCE IS 120 VOLTS AC & TWO 1.5-VOLT
"D" CELLS TO OPERATE THE KEYING RELAY. THE TRANSMITTER WILL
ALSO OPERATE ON THE 11 METER BAND. TUBES USED: 117Z6 RECTIFIER
& VOLTAGE DOUBLER, 12SA7 MIXER & OSCILLATOR, 12SK7 I.F., 12SQ7
2nd DETECTOR, AVC, & 1st AUDIO, 12BA6 AS THE TRANSMITTER'S OS-
CILLATOR, AND A 50L6 AS THE AUDIO OUTPUT AND R.F. FINAL AMPLI-
FIER. THE RECEIVER'S FREQUENCY COVERAGE IS 550kHz TO 31MHz IN 4
BANDS. SOME UNITS HAD A LIGHT GRAY DIAL BEZEL. OTHERS, LIKE
THE ONE SHOWN HERE, WERE THE SAME COLOR AS THE CASE.

SR-75 (REAR VIEW)

SR-150 NONE   1961-63 $650.00 without power supply
or options

A 19-TUBE CW-SSB 80 THROUGH 10 METER TRANSCEIVER. TRANSMITTER POWER INPUT IS 150 WATTS P.E.P. SSB & 125 WATTS CW. THE TRANSMITTER & RECEIVER ARE VFO CONTROLLED. OTHER FEATURES INCLUDE RECEIVER INCRIMENTAL TUNING (RIT) ALLOWING THE RECEIVER TO BE TUNED 2KHz ON EITHER SIDE OF THE TRANSMITTER FREQUENCY, DUAL CONVERSION, VOX, PTT, CW BREAK-IN, 100KHz CRYSTAL CALIBRATOR, PRODUCT DETECTOR, COMBINATION S-METER & R.F. OUTPUT METER, AND CRYSTAL-LATTICE FILTER. THERE IS A CHOICE OF POWER SUPPLIES, BOTH ARE ON SEPARATE CHASSIS. THE PS-150-120 WITH BUILT-IN SPEAKER FOR 120 VOLT AC USE ($99.95) AND THE PS-150-12 FOR 12-VOLT DC MOBILE USE ($109.50). OTHER OPTIONS INCLUDE THE MR-150 MOBILE MOUNT ($39.95). THE TRANSMITTER USES A 12BY7 DRIVER AND TWO 12DQ6B/12GW6 AS R.F. FINAL POWER AMPLIFIERS.

SR-160 NONE   1961-63 $395.00

THE SR-160 HAS ALL THE SAME FEATURES, OPTIONS, FUNCTIONS, AND SPECIFICATIONS AS THE SR-150 BUT IS A 3-BAND UNIT COVERING 80, 40, AND 20 METERS.

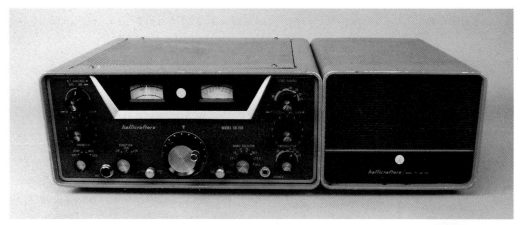

SR-150 WITH PS-150-120 POWER SUPPLY

PS-150-12, MOBILE POWER SUPPLY

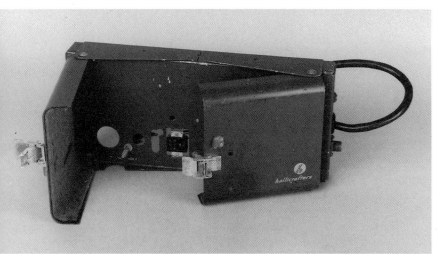

MR-150 MOBILE MOUNTING BRACKET

SR-400   CYCLONE   1965-69 $799.95 w/o power supply or options

A 20-TUBE 80 THROUGH 10 METER SSB-CW TRANSCEIVER WITH INPUT POWER OF 400 WATTS P.E.P. SSB & 360 WATTS CW, THE OUTPUT POWER IS 200 WATTS P.E.P SSB AND 200 WATTS CW. FEATURES INCLUDE VOX, PTT, AALC, PRODUCT DETECTOR, 1650KHz CRYSTAL LATTICE FILTER, CW SIDE-TONE, CRYSTAL CALIBRATOR, DUAL CONVERSION RECEIVER, COMBINATION R.F. OUTPUT & S-METER, NOISE BLANKER, AND RIT WITH A 3KHz OFFSET. THERE IS A CHOICE OF SEPARATE POWER SUPPLIES. THE PS-500-AC FOR 120-VOLT AC OPERATION ($119.95), AND THE PS-500-DC FOR 12-VOLT MOBILE USE ($159.95). OPTIONS INCLUED THE HA-20 EXTERNAL VFO FOR FUNCTIONS LIKE CROSS-BAND OPERATION, AND THE MR-400 MOBILE MOUNTING KIT ($49.95). THE DRIVER TUBE IS A 12BY7 AND THE FINAL R.F. AMPLIFIER IS A PAIR OF 6HF5.

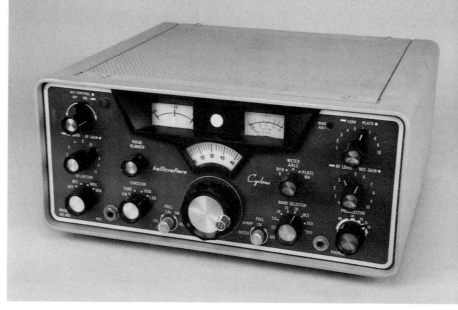

SR-400 CYCLONE

SR-400 WITH PS-500-AC POWER SUPPLY

400A   CYCLONE III   1969 $895.00 w/o power supplies

E SR-400A HAS THE SAME FUNCTIONS, FEATURES, AND SPECIFICA-
)NS AS THE SR-400 WITH THE FOLLOWING EXCEPTIONS. THE POWER
PUT IS 550 WATTS P.E.P SSB & 350 WATTS CW. POWER OUTPUT IS 275
ATTS P.E.P SSB AND 175 WATTS CW. THE HA-60 COOLING FAN IS FAC-
RY-INSTALLED TO HANDLE THE ADDITIONAL COOLING NEEDED
TH THE INCREASED POWER. THERE IS A PHONE PATCH INPUT. THE
IVER TUBE IS A 7558 AND TWO 6KD6 TUBES AS THE FINAL R.F. AM-
FIER.

Figure 1. Model SR-400A Transceiver.

PS-500-DC MOBILE POWER SUPPLY

SR-500 CONSOLE

SR-500   CONSOLE   1955 $1495.00

THIS UNIT CONSISTS OF THE HT-30, HT-31, AND SX-100 BUILT INTO A DESK-TYPE RACK, WITH INTERCONNECTING CABLES.

SR-500   TORNADO   1965 $395.00 without power supplies

A 17-TUBE 3-BAND SSB-CW TRANSCEIVER COVERING 80, 40, & 20 METERS. POWER INPUT IS 500 WATTS P.E.P SSB & 300 WATTS CW. SINGLE CONVERSION RECEIVER. OTHER FEATURES INCLUDE AALC, CRYSTAL CALIBRATOR, PRODUCT DETECTOR, CRYSTAL-LATTICE FILTER, RIT WITH A 3KHz OFFSET, & R.F. OUTPUT/S-METER. OPTIONS INCLUDE THE HA-16 VOX ADAPTOR, MR-160 MOBILE MOUNTING KIT, AND CHOICE OF POWER SUPPLY (PS-500-AC OR PS-500-DC). THE DRIVER TUBE IS A 12BY7, AND TWO 8236 TUBES AS THE FINAL R.F. AMPLIFIER.

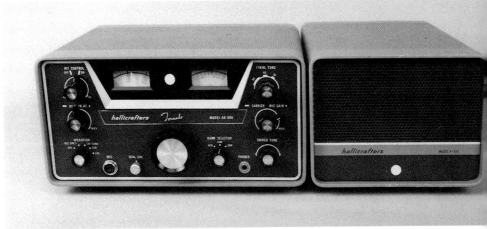

SR-500 TORNADO with PS-500-AC

SR-540   NONE ("the Eastwood")   1965 $699.00

I HAVE NO TECHNICAL DATA ON THIS RADIO. BY CLOSE INSPECTION IT WOULD APPEAR TO BE SOME VARIATION OF THE SR-400. THE TUBES USED, CONTROLS, COMPONENT LAYOUT, FUNCTIONS AND APPEARENCE SEEM IDENTICAL TO THE SR-400 AND IT USES THE SAME POWER SUPPLIES AND OPTIONS. THE UNIT SHOWN HERE WAS USED BY WARNER BROTHERS AS PART OF THE COMMUNICATIONS TRAILER IN THE 1994 MOVIE "A PERFECT WORLD," STARRING CLINT EASTWOOD AND KEVIN COSTNER.

SR-540 "THE EASTWOO

R-750	CYCLONE	1965	$695.00 without
			power supply

50-WATT CW-SSB, 80 TO 10 METERS, VFO, RIT, VOX, NOISE BLANKER, FILTER-TYPE SSB. USED THE PS-750-AC POWER SUPPLY (129.00).

R-2000	HURRICANE	1965-1972	$1095.00 without
			power supply

NINETEEN TUBES AND TWENTY-ONE DIODES, POWER INPUT 2000 WATTS P.E.P SSB, 900 WATTS CW. POWER OUTPUT 1000 WATTS P.E.P SSB & 500 WATTS CW. FIVE BANDS COVERING 80 THROUGH 10 METERS. OTHER FEATURES INCLUDE NOISE BLANKER, VOX, BREAK-IN CW KEY-ING, PTT, AALC, FULL METERING, RIT, DUAL CONVERSION RECEIVER, CW SIDE TONE, 2.1KHz CRYSTAL LATTICE FILTER, AND TWO-SPEED COOLING FAN. THE P-2000 POWER SUPPLY IS A SEPARATE UNIT AND CONTAINS THE SPEAKER AND THE FINAL AMPLIFIER PLATE VOLTAGE AND CURRENT METERS. THE POWER SUPPLY WAS PRICED SEPARATELY AT $450.00. TWO 8122 TUBES WERE USE AS THE FINAL R.F. POWER AMPLIFIER, AND A 12BY7 AS THE DRIVER. THE HA-20 VFO WAS AN OPTIONAL ACCESSORY FOR SEPERATE CONTROL OF THE TRANSMIT-TER AND RECEIVER FREQUENCIES.

SR-2000 HURRICANE

FPM SERIES TRANS-CEIVERS

MODEL	NAME	DATE	ORIGINAL PRICE
FPM-200	NONE	1961	$2660.00

THIS MOSTLY SOLID-STATE TRANSCEIVER WAS WAY AHEAD OF ITS TIME. ITS HYBRID CIRCUITRY CONSISTED OF 41 TRANSISTORS, 49 DIODES IN-CLUDING 14 POWER RECTIFIERS, AND 5 TUBES. THE POWER OUTPUT IS 70 TO 100 WATTS P.E.P SSB, 60 TO 90 WATTS CW, AND 15 TO 20 WATTS AM OVER ITS FREQUENCY RANGE OF 80 THROUGH 10 METERS. THE RECEIVER ALSO HAS A POSITION FOR RECEIVING WWV AT 10MHz. OTHER FEATURES INCLUDE TWO SEPARATE VFOs ENABLING THE UNIT TO BE RUN AS A TRANSCEIVER WITH THE SAME TRANSMIT AND RE-CEIVE FREQUENCY, OR AS AN INDEPENDENT TRANSMITTER AND RE-CEIVER FOR SPLIT-FREQUENCY OPERATION WITHIN ANY BAND COV-ERED. IT ALSO HAS A 100KHz CRYSTAL CALIBRATOR, CRYSTAL LATTICE FILTER, COMBINATION R.F. OUTPUT & S-METER, CW SIDETONE, VOX, DUAL CONVERSION RECEIVER, ANL, AND BUILT-IN COOLING FAN. THE POWER SOURCE IS 12 VOLTS DC NEGATIVE GROUND, OR 120 VOLTS

P-2000 POWER SUPPLY FOR THE HURRICANE

AC WITH THE SEPARATE P-200 AC POWER SUPPLY WHICH PUTS OUT 12 VOLTS DC AT 20 AMPS AND CONTAINS THE RECEIVER'S SPEAKER. THE UNIT COMES WITH THE P-200 POWER SUPPLY AND THE MR-200 MOBILE MOUNTING KIT. TUBES USED: TWO OB2 VOLTAGE REGULA-TORS, A 12BY7 DRIVER, AND TWO 6146 AS THE FINAL R.F. AMPLIFIER. THESE UNITS WERE MOSTLY EXPERIMENTAL, WITH A LIMITED PRODUC-TION RUN OF LESS THAN 200 UNITS. FOR MOST PEOPLE THE COST WAS PROHIBITIVE.

FPM-200 WITH P-200 POWER SUPPLY

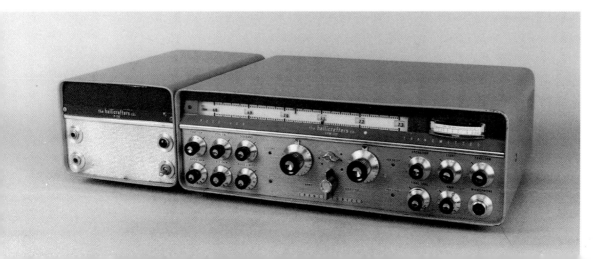

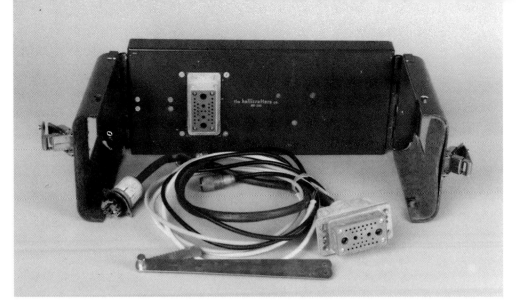

MR-200 MOBILE MOUNTING BRACKET

FPM-300 PRODUCTION MODEL

FPM-300   NONE   1972-74 $595.00

THIS 80 THROUGH 10 METER CW-SSB TRANSCEIVER USES HYBRID CIR-
CUITRY CONSISTING OF 3 ICs, 19 BI-POLAR TRANSISTORS, 14 FET TRAN-
SISTORS, 3 BRIDGE RECTIFIERS, 7 ZENER & 17 REGULAR DIODES, AND 2
TUBES. THE TRANSMITTER POWER INPUT IS 250 WATTS P.E.P SSB AND
180 WATTS CW. OTHER FEATURES INCLUDE VOX, PTT, 6-POLE 9MHz
CRYSTAL LATTICE FILTER, 25KHz CRYSTAL CALIBRATOR, AALC, SEMI-
AUTOMATIC CW BREAK-IN, MULTI-PURPOSE METER, AND BUILT-IN 12
VOLT DC AND 120 VOLT AC POWER SUPPLY. OPTIONS INCLUDE THE
HA-60 COOLING FAN AND THE MR-300 MOBILE MOUNTING KIT.
THE TUBES USED ARE A 12BY7 DRIVER AND A 6KD6 FINAL R.F. AMPLI-
FIER. SHOWN HERE ARE THE PRODUCTION MODEL AND THE WORK-
ING PRE-PRODUCTION ENGINEERING PROTOTYPE UNIT.

FPM-300   SAFARI   1974-77 $625.00
MARK II

THE MARK II HAS ALL THE SAME FEATUIRES, FUNCTIONS, AND SPECIFI-
CATIONS OF THE FPM-300. THERE ARE VALUE CHANGES IN SOME OF
THE SMALLER COMPONENTS AND NUMBER OF DIODES USED. THE
MAJOR DIFFERENCE IS IN THE TYPE OF PRINTED CIRCUIT SWITCHES
USED, WHICH WERE CHANGED BECAUSE OF PROBLEMS WITH THE
ORIGINAL TYPE IN THE FIRST PRODUCTION RUN. THE COSMETIC
APPEARENCE IS IDENTICAL TO THE FPM-300. "MARK II" IS STAMPED ON
THE REAR APRON OF THE CHASSIS.

FPM-300 PROTOTYPE

HA SERIES
ACCESSORY UNITS

MODEL	NAME	DATE	ORIGINAL PRICE
HA-1	"T.O. KEYER"	1960	$79.95
HA-1A	"T.O. KEYER"	1969	$119.00

AN ELECTRONIC MORSE CODE KEYER EMPLOYING "DIGITAL" CIRCUITRY TO FORM PERFECT CODE CHARACTERS AND MARK-SPACE RATIOS AT ANY SPEED OVER THE RANGE OF THE UNIT, WHICH IS FROM 10 TO 65 WORDS PER MINUTE. FEATURES INCLUDE BUILT-IN TONE GENERATOR AND SPEAKER. THERE ARE 6 TUBES, INCLUDING 2 VOLTAGE REGULATORS. POWER SOURCE IS 120 VOLTS AC. THERE ARE SOME VALUE CHANGES IN SOME OF THE COMPONENTS IN THE "A" MODEL; OTHERWISE IT IS THE SAME UNIT.

MODEL	NAME	DATE	ORIGINAL PRICE
HA-2	NONE	1962	$349.50 for either model,
HA-6	NONE	1962	without power supply

THE HA-2 TWO-METER TRANSVERTER IS A TWO-WAY CONVERTER DESIGNED TO CONVERT ANY 10 METER TRANSMITTER AND RECEIVER FOR USE ON 2 METERS. ANY MODE OF TRANSMISSION (SSB-AM-CW, ETC) CAN BE USED. THE UNIT REQUIRES AN EXTERNAL 120-VOLT AC POWER SUPPLY MODEL P-26 ($99.50). THERE ARE 8 TUBES INCLUDING THE 5894 FINAL AMPLIFIER. THE MAXIMUM EXCITATION INPUT IS 25 WATTS, AND THE POWER OUTPUT IS 60 WATTS P.E.P SSB, CW, FM, ETC, AND 15 WATTS AM. THE HA-6 HAS ALL THE SAME FUNCTIONS, FEATURES, AND SPECIFICATIONS OF THE HA-2 BUT IS FOR USE ON 6 METERS. THE P-26 POWER SUPPLY CAN RUN BOTH UNITS AT THE SAME TIME.

HA-1 "T.O. KEYER"

HA-2

HA-6

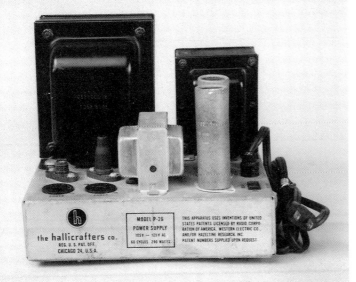

P-26 POWER SUPPLY FOR HA-2 AND HA-6

| HA-3 | NONE | 1962-63 | $13.50 |

HA-3A

AUTOMOTIVE NOISE-SUPPRESSION KIT FOR CANCELLING IGNITION AND ALTERNATOR NOISE. FOR USE WITH MOBILE INSTAILATION OF TRANSCEIVERS LIKE THE SR-150, SR-160 CB-3, CB-5, ETC.

| HA-4 | "T.O. KEYER" | 1961 | $59.95 |

AN ELECTRONIC MORSE CODE KEYER EMPLYOING "DIGITAL" CIRCUITRY TO FORM PERFECT CODE CHARACTERS AND MARK-SPACE RATIOS AT ANY SPEED OVER THE 8 TO 5 WORD PER MINUTE RANGE OF THE UNIT. IT IS THE TRANSISTORIZED VERSION OF TH HA-1 WITH 8 TRANSISTORS AND 10 DIODES. FOR 120 VOLTS AC.

HA-4 "T.O. KEYER"

HA-5

| HA-5 | NONE | 1962 | $79.95 |

A 4-TUBE HETERODYNE-TYPE VFO CALIBRATED FOR THE 80 THROUGH 2 METER AMATEUR BANDS. FOR USE ON 6 & 2 METERS OPTIONAL CRYSTALS ARE REQUIRED. THE UNIT IS DESIGNED TO BE A CRYSTAL SUBSTITUTE FOR ANY AMATEUR TRANSMITTER COVERING 80 THROUGH 2 METERS SUCH AS THE HT-40. THE POWER SOURCE IS 120 VOLTS AC. TUBES USED: 6U8A VARIABLE OSCILLATOR & CRYSTAL OSCILLATOR, 6BA7 MIXER, 6AQ OUTPUT AMPLIFIER, OA2 VOLTAGE REGULATOR AND 2 SILICON RECTIFIERS.

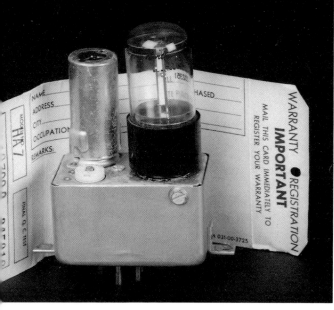

HA-7

HA-7　　　　NONE　　　　　　　　1959-62　　$19.95

A PLUG-IN CRYSTAL CALIBRATOR, ONE TUBE, 100KC MARKERS, FOR USE WITH THE SX-100, SX-101, SX-101A, AND SX-122. THE TUBE IS A 6AU6 AND THE UNIT GETS ALL ITS POWER FROM THE RADIO IT IS INSTALLED IN.

HA-8　　　　SPLATTER GUARD　　　1962-63　　$24.95

A MODULATION LEVEL INDICATOR FOR MONITORING TRANSMITTERS. THE INDICATOR IS A "MAGIC EYE" TUBE. THE UNIT MAY BE USED ON ANY SYSTEM WITH A 50 OHM TRANS-MISSION LINE, A POWER LEVEL OF 40 TO 1000 WATTS, AND FREQUENCIES FROM 3MHz TO 30MHz. IT MAY ALSO BE USED ON 6 AND 2 METERS BUT THE VSWR MAY INCREASE TO 1.5 TO 1. ALTHOUGH IT CAN BE USED WITH ANY UNIT MEETING THE CRITERIA IT WAS DESIGNED FOR USE WITH THE HT-44. THE POWER SOURCE IS 120 VOLTS AC. THE EYE TUBE IS A EM-84/6FG6.

HA-9　　　　NONE　　　　　　　　1961-64　　$9.95

METER KIT FOR INSTALATION ON THE CB-3, CB-3A, CB-7 AND CB-17.

HA-10　　　　NONE　　　　　　　　1962-63　　$24.95

LOW AND MEDIUM FREQUENCY RF CONVERTER COVERING 85KHz TO 3MHz IN 4 BANDS. IS SPECIFICALLY DESIGNED TO BE USED WITH THE SX-117 RECEIVER.

HA-11　　　　NONE　　　　　　　　1961-64　　UNKNOWN

2-TUBE NOISE SUPPRESSOR KIT DESIGNED AS AN ACCESSORY TO BE USED ON THE CB-2, CB-3, CB-3A, AND CB-7 CITIZENS-BAND TRANSCEIVERS TO REDUCE IGNITION AND ALTER-NATOR NOISE. IT COMES IN KIT FORM AND DERIVES ITS POWER FROM THE UNIT IT IS INSTALLED IN. TUBES USED: 12AX7 & 6AL5.

HA-8 SPLATTER GUARD

HA-10

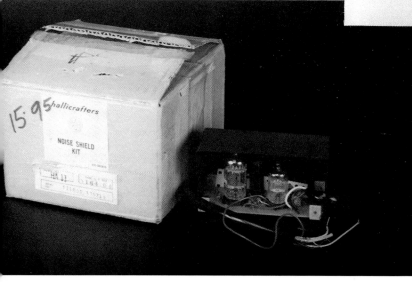

HA-11

HA-12, HA-12A

HA-12   NONE   1961-64   UNKNOWN
HA-12A

A ENCODER-DECODER FOR USE WITH THE CB-3A. IT IS USED FOR SE-LECTIVE CALLING AND RECEIVING WHEN TWO OR MORE UNITS HAVE THE SYSTEM INSTALLED. IT OPERATES ON A TONE BURST SYSTEM AND DERIVES ITS POWER FROM THE UNIT IT IS INSTALLED IN. THE HA-12A IS A ENCODER ONLY.

HA-13   NONE   1961-64 $14.95

VFO KIT FOR USE WITH THE CB-3A, & CB-17. MOUNTS IN THE SAME CABINET.

HA-14   NONE   1961-64   UNKNOWN

CARRYING CASE AND BATTERY RE-CHARGE UNIT FOR USE WITH THE CB-5.

HA-15   NONE   1961-64   UNKNOWN

CB ACCESSORY. THE NATURE OF THIS UNIT UNKNOWN TO ME AT THIS TIME.

HA-16   NONE   1961-64 $44.95

PLUG-IN VOX ADAPTOR FOR USE WITH THE SR-160, SR-500, AND HT-46.

HA-13

HA-16

HA-18,18A   NONE   1969 $9.95

A SOLID-STATE BATTERY OPERATED CODE PRACTICE OSCILLATOR WITH KEY.

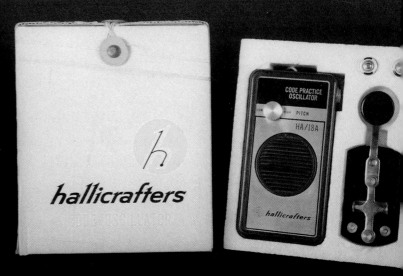

HA-18, HA-18A

HA-19   NONE   1969 $29.95

PLUG-IN CRYSTAL CALIBRATOR WITH 100KHz MARKER FOR USE IN THE SX-122A & SX-133.

HA-20   NONE   1965-69 $199.95

A DELUXE 80 THROUGH 10 METER VFO WITH BUILT-IN VSWR BRIDGE AND METER. IT IS DESIGNED AS AN ACCESSORY UNIT TO BE USED WITH THE SR-400, SR-400A, SR-750, AND SR-2000 WHERE SEPERATE TRANSMITTER AND RECEIVER FREQUENCIES ARE NEEDED ON THE SAME BAND. SELF-CONTAINED 120 VOLT AC POWER SUPPLY, AND 3 TUBES CONSISTING OF A 12AT7, 12BA6, AND OA2.

HA-26   NONE   1964-65 $59.95

THIS IS AN EXTERNAL 6 AND 2 METER VFO DESIGNED AS AN ACCESSORY UNIT TO BE USED AS A CRYSTAL SUBSTITUTE FOR THE TRANSMITTER SECTIONS OF THE SR-42, SR-42A, SR-46, AND SR-46A. IT DERIVES ITS POWER FROM THE TRANSCEIVER AND CAN BE USED IN BASE OR MOBILE OPERATION. THE SET HAS ONE TUBE, A 6U8A.

HA-20

HA-26

HA-32   NONE   1964   UNKNOWN

A HEAVY DUTY ANTENNA ROTATOR CONSISTING OF THE ROTATOR ASSEMBLY AND THE CONTROL HEAD. A GREAT FEATURE OF THIS UNIT IS ITS ABILITY FOR CONTINUOUS ROTATION IN EITHER DIRECTION. THIS IS ACCOMPLISHED BY USE OF A ROTARY COAXIAL JOINT IN THE ROTATOR ASSEMBLY. NO MORE BROKEN OR TWISTED COAX CABLE! THE UNIT WAS BUILT BY RADIO INDUSTRIES INC. (A DIVISION OF HALLICRAFTERS). THE POWER SOURCE IS 120 VOLTS AC. SHOWN HERE IS THE CONTROL HEAD.

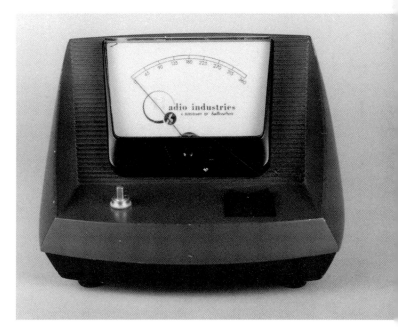

HA-32

HA-36   NONE   1969-70 $12.50

THE 120-VOLT AC ADAPTOR FOR USE WITH THE CR-44 AND CR-44A TRANSISTOR PORTABLE RADIOS.

HA-60   NONE   1965-74 $39.95

A 6.4-CFM COOLING FAN FOR USE ON THE SR-400, SR-400A, SR-750, SR-2000, FPM-300, AND FPM-300 MARK II. POWER SOURCE IS 120 VOLTS AC.

HA-700   NONE   1977 $44.95

ANTENNA, BASE STATION, 6db GAIN, COLLINEAR, 5/8 WAVE, 135-174MHz AND 144-148MHz, RATED AT 500 WATTS.

HA-800   NONE   1977 $29.95

ANTENNA, MOBILE, 3db GAIN, 5/8 WAVE, 132-174MHz, RATED AT 200 WATTS.

HA-900   NONE   1977 $29.95

ANTENNA, MOBILE, 5/8 WAVE, 144-148MHz, RATED AT 200 WATTS.

HA-985   NONE   1977 $32.95

ANTENNA, SAME AS HA-900 ONLY HAS A MAGNETIC MOUNT.

MISCELLANEOUS ACCESSORY UNITS

MODEL	NAME	DATE	ORIGINAL PRICE

A-80C   NONE   1977   **UNKNOWN**

WHIP ANTENNA FOR PORTABLE USE ON 164-174Mhz, WITH PL-259 CONNECTOR.

A-82   NONE   1977   **$29.95**

ANTENNA, MOBILE, 3db GAIN, 5/8 WAVE, 132-174MHz, RATED AT 200 WATTS.

AT-2   NONE   1940-45   **UNKNOWN**

ANTENNA TUNER (TRANSMATCH) FOR USE WITH TWO-WIRE TRANSMISSION LINES. PI-SECTION NETWORK, PLUG-IN INDUCTORS, WITH ANTENNA CHANGEOVER RELAY FOR SEPARATE RECEIVING AND TRANSMITTING ANTENNAS. USED WITH THE HT-4 SERIES.

AT-3   NONE   1940-45   **UNKNOWN**
(BC-939)

ANTENNA TUNER (TRANSMATCH) FOR USE WITH A SINGLE-WIRE ANTENNA. 1.5-18 MHz, SELF-CONTAINED (NO PLUG-INS). ALSO USED WITH THE HT-4 SERIES. THE BC-939 IS THE MILITARY VERSION FOR USE WITH THE BC-610.

AT-2

AT-3 (BC-939)

B-42   NONE   1946-55   **$7.50**

THE ADJUSTABLE TILT BASE FOR USE WITH THE SX-42, SX-62, S-47, & T-54. THIS ACCESSORY IS VERY DIFFICULT TO FIND.

BA-100   NONE   1967   **$14.95**

AN OMNI-DIRECTIONAL 27 TO 50MHz 1/4 WAVE GROUND PLANE ANTENNA FOR USE AS AN EXTERNAL ANTENNA WITH THE CRX-100 SERIES MONITORS.

BA-101   NONE   1967   **$9.95**

AN OMNI DIRECTIONAL 108 TO 174MHz 1/4 WAVE GROUND PLANE ANTENNA FOR USE AS AN EXTERNAL ANTENNA WITH THE CRX-100 SERIES MONITORS.

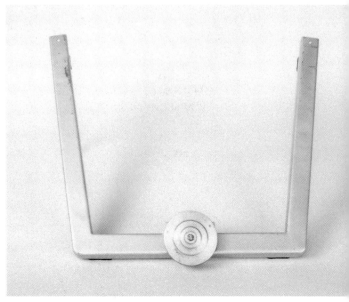

B-42

BC-13 NONE 1969-74 UNKNOWN

NI-CAD BATTERY CHARGER FOR USE WITH THE OPS/FM SERIES TRANSCEIVERS.

BL-20 NONE 1969 UNKNOWN

THE COOLING FAN ASSEMBLY FOR USE ON THE SBT-20 SERIES TRANSCEIVERS.

CN-1 NONE 1946 $15.00

A FM RF CONVERTER TO CONVERT THE EARLY 40 TO 60MHz FM RECEIVERS TO THE "NEW" 88 TO 108MHz FM BROADCAST BAND. IT USES ONE TUBE (A 7N7), SEVERAL RESISTORS AND CAPACITORS, AND DERIVES ITS POWER FROM THE RADIO IT IS INSTALLED IN.

CTS-2 NONE 1970 UNKNOWN
CTS-4

A SOLID-STATE, CONTINUOUS-TONE SQUELCH UNIT FOR USE AS A SUB-AUDIBLE TONE ENCODER/DECODER FOR HALLICRAFTERS UHF-FM TRANSCEIVERS. THERE ARE "A" THROUGH "E" MODELS FOR VARIOUS TONE FREQUENCIES. THE CTS-2 IS SPECIFICALLY DESIGNED FOR USE ON THE PC-210 AND PC-230 TRANSCEIVERS.

H-3 NONE 1967 $4.95

LOW-IMPEDENCE, GENERAL-PURPOSE HEAD PHONES

HCG-3 NONE 1967-68 $495.00
HCG-5 1972-77

A HAND-CRANK GENERATOR USED FOR CHARGING 12 TO 14 VOLT NI-CAD BATTERIES AND FOR OPERATING THE SBT-20 TRANSCEIVER UNDER EMERGENCY CONDITIONS WHEN THE INTERNAL BATTERY HAS FAILED. THE HCG-5 IS FOR THE SBT-22 SERIES.

MC-1 NONE 1968 UNKNOWN

A MULTIPLE BATTERY CHARGER FOR USE WITH THE HC-100 TRANSCEIVERS THAT WILL CHARGE TWO HC-100s WITHOUT REMOVING THE BATTERIES FROM THE UNIT, AND 2 SPARE BATTERY PACKS.

MC-401S NONE 1971 UNKNOWN
MC-412S, 412SR

NICKEL-CADMIUM BATTERY CHARGERS USED FOR CHARGING THE BA-400LS AND BA-400SS BATTERY PACKS USED IN THE HC-400 PORTABLE UHF-FM TRANSCEIVER.

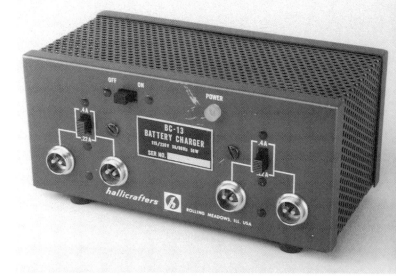

BC-13

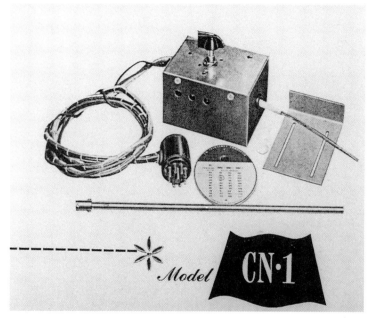

CN-1

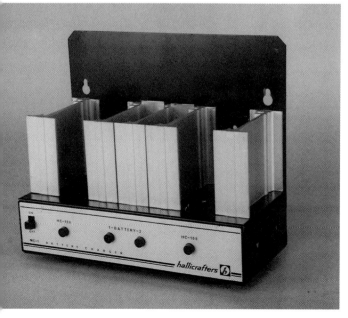

MC-1

Model HCG-3 Hand Crank Generator

HCG-3

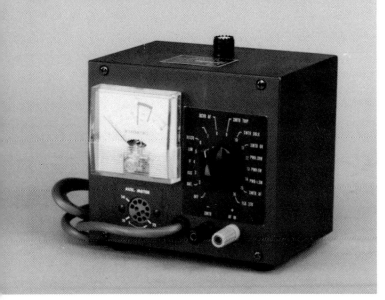

OPS/TS-20

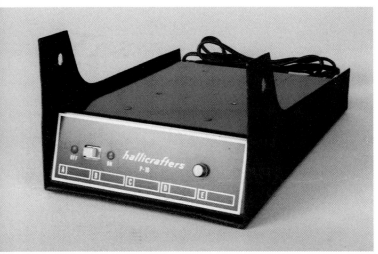

P-10

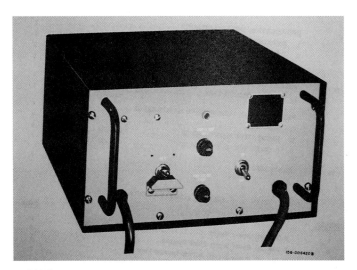

P-20-A

OPS/TS-20   NONE   1969   UNKNOWN

A TEST SET FOR USE IN TROUBLESHOOTING AND ALIGNMENT OF THE OPS/FM-1 AND THE OPS/FM-5 TRANSCEIVERS.

P-10   NONE   1966   UNKNOWN

THE BASE STATION POWER SUPPLY FOR SMALL CB UNITS LIKE THE CB-20 AND CB-24. 120-VOLT AC INPUT, 12-VOLT DC OUTPUT.

P-20A   NONE   1968   UNKNOWN

THE BASE STATION POWER SUPPLY FOR THE SBT-20 SERIES TRANSCEIVER, THE INPUT IS 120 OR 240 VOLTS AC, THE OUTPUT IS 12.6 VOLTS DC, REGULATED TO .06 VOLTS FROM 0 TO 8 AMPS.

PS-20   NONE   1967 $35.00

GENERAL PURPOSE CB BASE STATION POWER SUPPLY FOR USE WITH THE CB-20 & OTHERS. 120 VOLTS AC INPUT, 12 VOLTS DC OUTPUT.

RA-45   NONE   1965 $30.00

A HAND-HELD MICROPHONE WITH PUSH TO TALK BUTTON, FOR USE AS AN EXTERNAL MICROPHONE ON THE HC, FM, & SBT SERIES TRANSCEIVERS.

RCM-100   NONE   1971-77   UNKNOWN
RCB-100 $425.00

THESE ARE REMOTE CONTROL "HEADS" FOR REMOTE OPERATION OF THE SBT-100. RCM IS FOR MOBILE USE ($325.00) & RCB IS FOR BASE STATION USE

RM-10   NONE   1971   UNKNOWN

THIS UNIT USED WITH THE LT-10 LINE TERMINATOR WILL PROVIDE 2-WAY VOICE PLUS PUSH-TO-TALK OPERATION USING A BALANCED TELEPHONE PAIR OVER DISTANCES UP TO 5 MILES. IT IS DESIGNED TO BE USED WITH THE FM-5G AND THE FM-10. FOR USE WITH OTHER HALLICRAFTERS FM RADIO SETS A DIFFERENT LINE TERMINATOR MUST BE USED: LT-5 FOR THE FM-5B; LT-200 FOR THE PC-200 SERIES. SELF-CONTAINED, USES 8 "D" CELLS.

PS-20

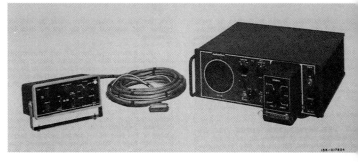

RCM-100, RCB-100

| SM-20 | NONE | 1939-45 | $10.00 |

SM-21

SM-22

THE EXTERNAL S-METER FOR USE WITH THE S-20, S-20R, S-21, S-22, AND S-22R RECEIVERS. THE ONLY DIFFERRENCE BETWEEN THE MODELS IS THE COLOR AND FINISH OF THE CASE, WHICH WAS THE SAME AS THE RECEIVER'S CABINET. SHOWN HERE IS THE SM-21.

| SM-40 | NONE | 1946-55 | $15.00 |

THE EXTERNAL S-METER FOR USE WITH THE S-40, S-40A, AND S-40B.

| SP-44 | SKYRIDER PANORAMIC | 1946 | $99.50 |

A 2" PANORAMIC ADAPTOR DESIGNED FOR USE WITH ANY RECEIVER WITH A 455KHz IF FREQUENCY. IT CAN BE USED TO MONITOR MODULATION, DISTORTION, CARRIER SHIFT, OR OTHER TRANSMISSION PARAMETERS. IT WILL SHOW BAND ACTIVITY 100KHz EITHER SIDE OF THE CENTER FREQUENCY THE RECEIVER IS TUNED TO. THE POWER SOURCE IS 120 VOLTS AC, AND IT HAS 10 TUBES, TWO 6X5 RECTIFIERS, 2AP1 CRT, 6SN7 SAW TOOTH GENERATOR AND AMPLIFIER, VR-105 VOLTAGE REGULATOR, 6AC7 REACTOR, 6SQ7 DE-TECTOR & VIDEO AMPLIFIER, 6SG7 I.F., 6SA7 MIXER & OSCILLATOR, AND 6SG7 R.F. AMPLI-FIER. THE SAME UNIT (PCA-2 T-200) WAS PRODUCED BY PANORAMIC RADIO CORPORA-TION OF NEW YORK. THE ONLY DIFFERENCE IS THE STYLE OF THE KNOBS AND THE FIN-ISH ON THE CASE. BOTH UNITS ARE SHOWN HERE.

| VP-2 | NONE | 1941-42 | UNKNOWN |

THIS UNIT IS THE VIBRATOR POWER SUPPLY FOR OPERATING THE S-27 AND SX-28 FROM A 6-VOLT DC SOURCE. IT SUPPLIES THE HIGH VOLTAGE TO THE RADIO WHICH IS PRODUCED BY THE VIBRATOR AND POWER TRANSFORMER AND THEN RECTIFIED BY TWO 6X5 TUBES. THE TUBE FILAMENTS OF THE RADIO ARE POWERED DIRECTLY FROM THE 6-VOLT SOURCE.

SM-21

SM-40

SP-44 SKYRIDER PANORAMIC

VP-2

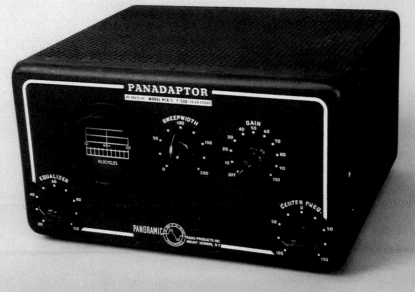

PCA-2, T-100 SKYRIDER PANORAMIC

TS-22

CRX SERIES RECEIVERS

MODEL	NAME	DATE	ORIGINAL PRICE
CRX-1	NONE	1962-63	$99.95

A 9-TUBE SINGLE-BAND DUAL-CONVERSION FM RECEIVER COVERING 30MHz TO 50MHz. THE IF FREQUENCIES ARE 455KHz & 4.5MHz. FEATURES INCLUDE A VERNIER TUNING DRIVE, SPACE FOR 2 SWITCH SELECTABLE FIXED FREQUENCY CRYSTALS, & BUILT-IN SPEAKER. THE POWER SOURCE IS 120 VOLTS AC. TUBES USED: 12BA6 R.F. AMPLIFIER, 6BL8 1st MIXER & OSCILLATOR, 6BA6 2nd MIXER, 6BL8 3rd MIXER & CRYSTAL OSCILLATOR, 12BA6 1st IF, 6BA6 2nd IF, 6DT6 LIMITER, 6BL8 SQUELCH & 1st AUDIO, AND 12AQ5 AUDIO OUTPUT. THE RECTIFIERS ARE SILICON DIODES.

CRX-1

CRX-2   NONE   1962-63 $109.95

A 10-TUBE SINGLE-BAND DUAL-CONVERSION FM RECEIVER COVERING
151MHz TO 174MHz WITH IF FREQUENCIES OF 455KHz AND 10.7MHz.
FEATURES INCLUDE BUILT-IN SPEAKER, VERNIER TUNING DRIVE, AND
SPACE FOR 2 SWITCH-SELECTABLE FIXED-FREQUENCY CRYSTALS. TUBES
USED: 6ER5 R.F. AMPLIFIER, 6BL8 1st MIXER & OSCILLATOR, 6BL8 2nd
MIXER & IF, 6BL8 3rd MIXER & CRYSTAL OSCILLATOR, 12BA6 IF, 12AT7
CRYSTAL OSCILLATOR, 12BA6 IF, 6DT6 DETECTOR, 6BL8 SQUELCH & 1st
AUDIO, 12AQ5 AUDIO OUTPUT, AND 2 SILICON RECTIFIERS. 120 VOLTS
AC POWER.

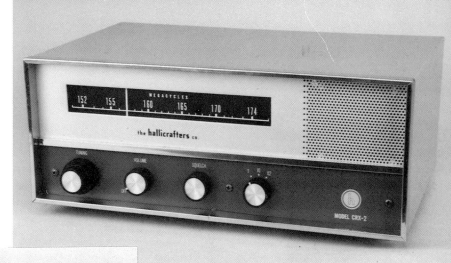

CRX-2

CRX-2A

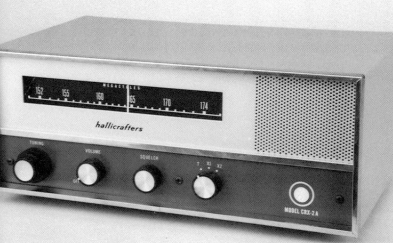

CRX-2A   NONE   1963-64 $109.95

THE CRX-2A HAS ALL THE FUNCTIONS, FEATURES, AND APPEARANCE
OF THE CRX-2. THE DIFFERENCES ARE IN SOME OF THE TUBES USED. A
6EA8 1st MIXER & OSCILLATOR, 12BZ6 IF, AND A 12AX7 SQUELCH AND
1st AUDIO.

CRX-3   NONE   1962-63 $99.95

A 7-TUBE ONE BAND DUAL CONVERSION AM RECEIVER COVERING
108MHz TO 135MHz. THE IF FREQUENCIES ARE 455KHz & 10.7MHz. BUILT-
IN SPEAKER, VERNIER TUNING DRIVE, VFO TUNED OR SPACE FOR 2
SWITCHABLE FIXED-FREQUENCY CRYSTALS. THE POWER SOURCE IS 120
VOLTS AC. TUBES USED: 6ER5 R.F. AMPLIFIER, 6BL8 1st MIXER & OSCILLA-
TOR, 6BL8 2nd MIXER & OSCILLATOR, 6BA6 IF, 12AT7 CRYSTAL OSCILLA-
TOR, 6EA8 SQUELCH & 1st AUDIO, AND 6AQ5 AUDIO OUTPUT.

CRX-4

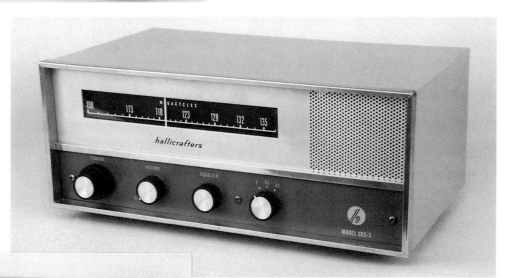

CRX-3

CRX-4   CIVIC PATROL   1964 $79.95

A 7-TUBE 1 BAND FM RECEIVER COVERING 30MHz TO 50MHz. THE IF
FREQUENCY IS 10.7MHz. FEATURES INCLUDE BUILT-IN SPEAKER AND
SQUELCH CONTROL. THE POWER SOURCE IS 120 VOLTS AC. TUBES
USED: 12AW6 R.F. AMPLIFIER, 12AT7 MIXER & OSCILLATOR, TWO 12BA6
AS 1st & 2nd IF, 12AL5 DETECTOR, 12AX7 1st AUDIO & SQUELCH, AND A
50C5 AUDIO OUTPUT. THE RECTIFIER IS A SILICON DIODE.

CRX-5   CIVIC PATROL   1964 $79.95

THE CRX-4 HAS ALL THE FUNCTIONS AND FEATURES OF THE CRX-3, BUT COVERS THE 152MHz TO 173MHz BAND AND HAS 8 TUBES. TUBES USED: 12AT7 DUAL R.F. AMPLIFIER, 12AT7 MIXER & OSCILLATOR, TWO 12BA6 AS 1st & 2nd IF, 12AL5 DETECTOR, 12AX7 SQUELCH, 12AW6 1st AUDIO, AND 35C5 AUDIO OUTPUT. THE RECTIFIER IS A SINGLE SILICON DIODE.

CRX-100   PORTAMON   1967-69 $39.95
CRX-101
CRX-102

A COMPACT HAND-HELD SOLID-STATE PORTABLE MONITOR TUNABLE FROM 27MHz TO 50MHz. NINE TRANSISTORS AND THREE DIODES. FEATURES INCLUDE BUILT-IN TELESCOPING WHIP ANTENNA, SPEAKER, ANL, 1 RF STAGE AND 3 IF STAGES. THE POWER SOURCE IS A SINGLE 9-VOLT BATTERY. THE RECEPTION MODE IS AM. OPTIONS INCLUDE A CARRYING CASE, AND AC ADAPTOR FOR OPERATION FROM 120 VOLTS AC. THE CRX-101 AND CRX-102 HAVE THE SAME FUNCTIONS, FEATURES, OPTIONS, AND SPECIFICATIONS EXCEPT THE 101 COVERS 108MHz TO 135MHz AM RECEPTION, AND THE 102 COVERS 144MHz TO 174MHz FM RECEPTION. ALL OF THESE UNITS WERE MADE IN JAPAN.

CRX-103   CIVIC MONITOR   1967-69 $49.95
CRX-103A

A SOLID-STATE TABLETOP UNIT FOR AM RECEPTION IN THE 30-50MHz BAND. ELEVEN TRANSISTORS AND FIVE DIODES. FEATURES INCLUDE BUILT-IN SPEAKER, ANL, SQUELCH CONTROL, 1 RF & 3 IF STAGES. THE POWER SOURCE IS 120 VOLTS AC. I SEE NO SIGNIFICANT DIFFERENCES IN THE "A" MODEL. MADE IN JAPAN.

CRX-5

(LEFT TO RIGHT) CRX-101, CRX-100, CRX-102, CRX-107

CRX-104   CIVIC MONITOR   1967-69 $49.95
CRX-105
CRX-105A

THE CRX-104, 105, AND 105A HAVE ALL THE FEATURES AND APPEARANCE OF THE CRX-103 EXCEPT FREQUENCY COVERAGE. THE 104 IS AM RECEPTION IN THE 108MHz TO 138MHz BAND, THE 105 IS FOR FM RECEPTION IN THE 150MHz TO 174MHz BAND, I SEE NO SIGIFICANT DIFFERENCES BETWEEN THE 105 AND THE "A" MODEL.

CRX-105

CRX-103A

CRX-106   PORTAMON   1969-70 $39.95
CRX-107

A COMPACT SOLID-STATE HAND-HELD PORTABLE MONITOR TUNABLE FROM 27MHz TO 50MHz, AM RECEPTION. TWELVE TRANSISTORS AND FOUR DIODES. FEATURES INCLUDE SQUELCH CONTROL, EARPHONE JACK, ANL, BUILT-IN SPEAKER AND TELESCOPING WHIP ANTENNA. THE POWER SOURCE IS A SINGLE 9-VOLT BATTERY. OPTIONS INCLUDE A CARRYING CASE AND 120-VOLT AC ADAPTOR. THE CRX-107 HAS ALL THE SAME FEATURES, FUNCTIONS, AND SPECIFICATIONS OF THE CRX-106 EXCEPT IT IS FOR FM RECEPTION IN THE 144MHz TO 174MHz BAND. BOTH UNITS ARE SIMILAR IN APPEARENCE TO THE CRX-100 AND 101 AND WERE ALSO MADE IN JAPAN.

R AND PM SERIES SPEAKERS

A number of the early speakers used by Hallicrafters were not issued model numbers. For indentification purposes I have issued these items my own model number designation. Where I have done this there will be an * after the model number.

> ## Speaker Parts
> During the late 40's and early 50's Hallicrafters used some imported parts. Particularly speakers that were used in the consumer line of radios like the EC-113, 5R and 7R series which were made in France.

MODEL	NAME	DATE	ORIGINAL PRICE
DD-CS*	NONE	1937-38	$145.00

THE OPTIONAL CONSOLE BASE REFLEX SPEAKER FOR USE WITH THE DD-1. CONSISTING OF A JENSEN 15" PERMENANT MAGNET SPEAKER WITH A 5K OHM MATCHING TRANS-FORMER HOUSED IN A LARGE DECO WALLNUT CABINET WITH A PULL-OUT WRITING DESK AT TOP FRONT, AND SHELVES IN THE REAR FOR HOUSING THE POWER SUPPLY AND AUDIO CHASSIS OF THE DD-1. THE TUNER SITS ON TOP OF THE CABINET.

R-8-T*	NONE	1937-39	$12.00 (12" model, shown)
R-12-T*			$8.00 (identical 8" model)

THE OPTIONAL 8" OR 12" TABLETOP SPEAKER WITH 5K OHM MATCHING TRANSFORMER IN BLACK STEEL CABINET WITH WOOD GRILL FOR USE WITH THE DD-1, SX-16, 17, & SX-18.

R-8	NONE	1940-41	$19.50 (8" R-8 model)
R-12			$29.50 (larger R-12, shown)

8" OR 12" PM SPEAKER WITH 5K-OHM MATCHING TRANSFORMER IN A WOOD CONSOLE BASE-REFLEX CABINET PAINTED GRAY. THE 8" WAS FOR USE WITH THE SX-25. THE R-12 HAS A LARGER CABINET AND IS FOR USE WITH THE SX-28.

PM-8-S*	NONE	1937-39	$8.00 (8" model)
PM-12-S*			$12.00 (12" model)

8" OR 12" PM SPEAKER WITH 5K-OHM TRANSFORMER IN A BLACK STEEL TABLETOP CABI-NET, "SPOKES"-TYPE GRILLE. FOR USE WITH THE SX-10, 11, & 12 IN THE STEEL CASE, AND THE S-15.

R-12-T

R-12

PM-8-S

PM-12-S

PM-12-M

PM-12-M*   NONE   1937-39 $16.00

12" PM SPEAKER WITH 5K-OHM TRANSFORMER IN A MAHOGANY TABLETOP CABINET. THIS SPEAKER WAS USED WITH THE SX-10, 11, AND 12 TO MATCH THE OPTIONAL MAHOGANY WOOD CASE FOR THE RADIOS.

PM-23   NONE   1939-44 $15.00

10" PM SPEAKER WITH 5K-OHM TRANSFORMER IN A DECO TABLETOP STEEL CABINET. THIS SPEAKER WAS USED WITH THE SX-23, 24, 25, AND SX-28. SOME HAD THE CHROME "h" LOGO IN THE LOWER LEFT CORNER AS SHOWN HERE; MOST DID NOT.

R-42   REPRODUCER   1946-48 $29.50

8" PM SPEAKER WITH 5K OHM MATCHING TRANSFORMER IN A STEEL TABLETOP BASE-REFLEX CABINET. BUILT-IN SWITCHABLE CROSSOVER NETWORK FOR COMMUNICATIONS OR HI-FI RECEPTION. DESIGNED FOR USE WITH THE SX-42.

R-44   NONE   1947-48 $15.00

6" x 9" PM SPEAKER WITH 5K-OHM MATCHING TRANSFORMER IN A STEEL TABLETOP CABINET. BUILT-IN SWITCH SELECTABLE CROSSOVER NETWORK FOR COMMUNICATION OR HI-FI RECEPTION. FOR USE WITH THE SX-43.

R-42 REPRODUCER

PM-23

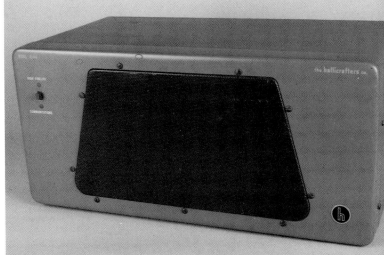

R-44

44B	NONE	1948-50	$24.95

AME AS THE R-44 EXCEPT NO TRANSFORMER (FOR 3.2-OHM USE).

45	REPRODUCER	1946-48	$29.50

AME AS THE R-42 EXCEPT FOR RACK MOUNTING RATHER THAN TABLETOP USE.

46	NONE	1950-54	$19.95

)" PM SPEAKER WITH 5K-OHM MATCHING TRANSFORMER IN A TABLETOP STEEL CABI-
ET. FOR USE WITH THE SX-62, SX-71, SX-73, SX-88, AND OTHERS.

46A	NONE	1954-55	$17.95

AME AS THE R-46 EXCEPT NO TRANSFORMER (FOR 3.2 OHM USE). USED WITH THE SX-
2A, SX-100, SX-101, SX-101A, AND OTHERS.

46B	NONE	1955-59	$7.95

AME AS THE R-46A EXCEPT THE CABINET IS ABOUT 4" SHALLOWER. FOR USE WITH THE
X-62B, SX-96, SX-99, SX-115, AND OTHERS.

R-45

-46

R-46A

R-46-B

R-47   NONE   1960-69 $14.95
PS-5

4" PM SPEAKER IN A COMPACT STEEL CASE, 3.2-OHM, FOR VOICE FREQUENCIES ONLY.
USED WITH THE SX-115, SX-122. SX-122A, S-129, SX-130, AND SX-133. SOME OF THE R-47s
HAD THE NAME & LOGO EMBOSSED IN THE CASTING, & SOME HAD A SMOOTH CASTING
WITH A DECAL NAME & LOGO. THE PS-5 HAS A BRACKET FOR HANGING ON A VEHICLE
WINDOW AND WAS FOR USE WITH THE HC-150. ALL THREE ARE SHOWN HERE.

The R-47

The R-47 speaker had two versions. On one the logo and
name were part of the case casting and were raised; on the
other the logo and name were painted on a smooth surface.

R-47, PS-5

R-48

R-48   NONE   1965-69 $19.95

5" X 7" PM SPEAKER, 3.2-OHM, TABLETOP STEEL CABINET, CROSSOVER
NETWORK WITH REAR MOUNTED VOICE/NORMAL SWITCH, FOR USE
WITH THE SX-111, SX-140 & OTHERS.

R-48A   NONE   1970-72 $24.95

SAME AS THE R-48 BUT VOICE/NORMAL SWITCH IS ON FRONT GRILLE.

RA-48   NONE   1965-69 $24.75

PERSONAL COMMUNICATIONS TYPE HEADPHONES, UNIVERSAL
IMPEDENCE.

R-49   NONE   1960-69 $7.95

4" PM SPEAKER SIMILAR TO THE R-47 BUT FOR MOBILE USE: A MOUNT-
ING BOLT ON TOP OF THE CASE INSTEAD OF A STAND ON THE BOT-
TOM, FOR UNDER-DASH MOUNTING.

R-48A

R-50 NONE 1965-69 $22.50

" X 7" PM SPEAKER, 3.2-OHM, STEEL TABLETOP CASE. FOR USE WITH THE S-129, SX-130, AND SX-133.

R-51 NONE 1965-69 $39.95

" X 6" PM SPEAKER, 3.2-OHM, STEEL TABLETOP CASE WITH A BUILT-IN 24-HOUR MECHANICAL DIGITAL CLOCK THAT RUNS ON 120 VOLTS AC. THIS SPEAKER IS ALSO FOR USE WITH THE S-129, SX-130 AND SX-133.

R-75 NONE 1947-48 $50.00 proposed price

0" PM SPEAKER WITH 5K-OHM TRANSFORMER AND BUILT-IN CROSSOVER NETWORK WITH REAR-MOUNTED SWITCH FOR LOW/HIGH, OR HI-FI RECEPTION. WOOD CONSOLE BASE REFLEX CABINET PAINTED SATIN BLACK WITH GRAY TRIM. FOR USE WITH THE SX-42, SX-43, AND OTHERS. THIS UNIT MAY NEVER HAVE BEEN PRODUCED. THE PHOTO IS FROM A LATE 1940s HALLICRAFTERS BROCHURE.

R-80 NONE 1947-48 $65.00 proposed price

THE R-80 HAS THE SAME FEATURES AS THE R-75 BUT ITS CABINET HAS DIFFERENT STYLING AND IS OF NATURAL WALNUT RATHER THAN PAINTED. FOR USE WITH THE SX-42, S-47, AND OTHERS. IT TOO MAY NOT HAVE BEEN A PRODUCTION MODEL. PHOTO FROM HALLICRAFTERS BROCHURE.

R-75

R-50

R-51

R-80

R-85

| R-85 | NONE | 1947-48 | $160.00 proposed price |

A 15" JENSEN COAXIAL SPEAKER WITH 500/600-OHM TRANSFORMER MOUNTED IN A LARGE BLOND MAHOGANY BASE REFLEX CONSOLE WOOD CABINET. THE FREQUENCY RESPONSE IS FLAT FROM 50Hz TO 12KHz. FOR USE WITH THE S-47 AS A TUNER AND THE S-49 AS THE AUDIO AMPLIFIER. AS WITH THE R-75 & R-80 THIS MAY NOT HAVE BEEN A PRODUCTION MODEL. THE PHOTO IS FROM A HALLICRAFTERS LATE 1940s ADVERTISING BROCHURE.

| RSP-1 | NONE | 1967 | $59.95 |

A HI-FI BOOK SHELF SPEAKER UNIT CONSISTING OF A 8" WOOFER AND A HORN TWEETER HOUSED IN A WALNUT FINISHED CABINET. IT IS FOR USE AS AN EXTENSION SPEAKER FOR THE S-214 AND S-240.

| R-EC2-3* | NONE | 1941-46 | UNKNOWN |

THE OPTIONAL EXTERNAL SPEAKER FOR USE WITH THE EC-2 & EC-3 RECEIVERS.

| R-CBS-1* | NONE | 1970s | UNKNOWN |

THIS SPEAKER IS FOR USE AS A MOBILE EXTENSION SPEAKER FOR SOME OF THE CB UNITS.

R-EC2-3

R-CBS-1

CB SERIES CITIZENS' BAND TRANSCEIVERS

MODEL	NAME	DATE	ORIGINAL PRICE
CB-1	LITTLE FONE	1959	$129.95

SINGLE CHANNEL, CRYSTAL-CONTROLLED, ELEVEN TUBES, BUILT-IN SPEAKER, EARPHONE JACK, SQUELCH CONTROL, EYE-TUBE MODULA-TION INDICATOR. ANY OF THE 23 AVAILABLE CB CHANNELS MAY BE USED WITH THE PROPER PLUG-IN CRYSTAL. THE POWER SOURCE IS 120 VOLTS AC. THE FINAL R.F. AMPLIFIER IS A 6AQ5.

CB-1 LITTLE PHONE

CB-2   **LITTLE FONE**   **1960**   **$189.95**

FOUR-CHANNEL, CLASS D, CRYSTAL-CONTROLLED TRANSMIT AND RECEIVE, WITH SWITCH-CONTROLLED TUNABLE RECEIVER. SEVEN TUBES, 6 OR 12 VOLT DC AND 120 VOLT AC SUPPLY BUILT IN. THE PLATE INPUT POWER TO THE 6AW8A FINAL AMPLIFIER IS 5 WATTS.

CB-2 LITTLE FONE

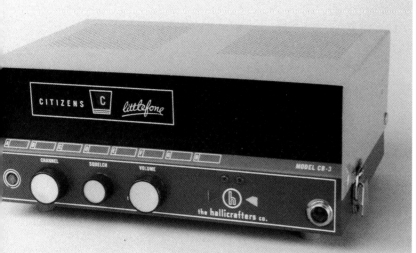

CB-3 LITTLE FONE

CB-3   **LITTLE FONE**   **1961**   **$149.95**

EIGHT-CHANNEL, CLASS D, CRYSTAL-CONTROLLED, PROVISION FOR S-METER AND VFO (HA-13 VFO & HA-9 "S"-METER) FOR THE RECEIVER, SEVEN TUBES, SQUELCH CONTROL, BUILT-IN 6 OR 12 VOLT DC AND 120 VOLT AC POWER SUPPLY. THE PLATE POWER INPUT TO THE 6AW8A FINAL AMPLIFIER IS 5 WATTS.

CB-3A   **LITTLE FONE**   **1962-63**   **$159.95**

THE CB-3A HAS ALL THE SAME FEATURES AND FUNCTIONS OF THE CB-3 PLUS A DOUBLE CONVERSION RECEIVER.

CB-4   **LITTLE FONE**   **1962**   **$89.95**

A COMPACT HAND-HELD 7-TRANSISTOR SINGLE CHANEL CRYSTAL-CONTROLLED UNIT. ANY OF THE 23 CB CHANELS MAY BE USED WITH THE PROPER PLUG-IN CRYSTALS. BUILT-IN TELESCOPING WHIP ANTENNA, 100 MILIWATT INPUT. THE POWER SOURCE IS A SINGLE 2-VOLT MERCURY BATTERY.

CB-4 LITTLE FONE

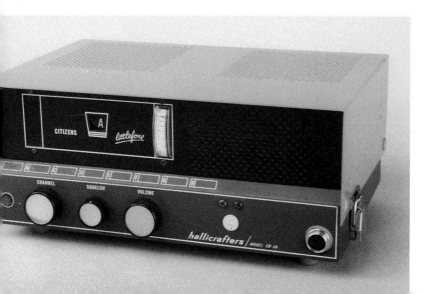

CB-3A LITTLE FONE

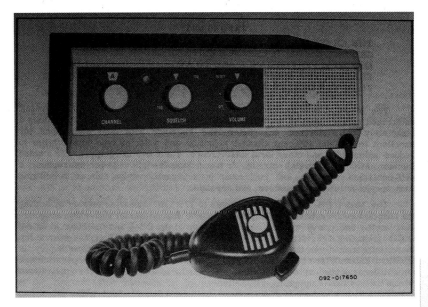

CB-5 LITTLE FONE

CB-5   LITTLE FONE   1962 $185.00
CB-5 MARK II

HYBRID CIRCUITRY, THREE TUBES, 18 TRANSISTORS, SIX-CHANNEL, CRYS-TAL-CONTROLLED, DOUBLE CONVERSION RECEIVER, SQUELCH CON-TROL, 5-WATT INPUT FROM THE TWO 3B4 FINAL AMPLIFIR TUBES. THE POWER SOURCE IS 12 VOLTS DC OR 120 VOLTS AC WITH OPTIONAL BASE POWER SUPPLY (PS-5-120)

CB-6   LITTLE FONE   1963-64 $99.50

A COMPACT HAND-HELD 9-TRANSISTOR SINGLE CHANEL CRYSTAL-CONTROLLED UNIT. ANY OF THE 23 CB CHANELS MAY BE USED WITH THE PROPER PLUG-IN CRYSTALS. BUILT-IN TELESCOPING WHIP AN-TENNA, 100 MILIWATT INPUT. THE POWER SOURCE IS 8 SIZE "AA" BAT-TERIES. SHOWN HERE WITH CARRYING CASE.

CB-7   LITTLE FONE   1965 $179.50

SIX CHANNELS, SEVEN TUBES, CRYSTAL-CONTROLLED TRANSMIT & RECEIVE, SQUELCH CONTROL, PROVISION FOR OPTIONAL S-METER (HA-9), RECEIVER VFO (HA-13), IGNITION NOISE SHIELD (HA-11), AND HA-12 OR 12A ENCODER/DECODER. BUILT-IN 12-VOLT DC & 120-VOLT AC POWER SUPPLY. THE POWER INPUT IS 5 WATTS WITH A 6CX8 FINAL AMPLI-FIER.

CB-6 LITTLE FONE

CB-7 LITTLE FONE

CB-8   NONE   1964   UNKNOWN

A COMPACT HAND-HELD 13-TRANSISTOR CRYSTAL-CONTROLLED UNIT WITH CARRYING CASE AND TELESCOPING WHIP ANTENNA. 1-WATT INPUT, POWER SOURCE IS A 12-VOLT RECHARGABLE NI-CAD BATTERY.

CB-8

CB-9   LITTLE FONE   1965 $179.50
SIX CHANNELS, SEVEN TUBES, HAS ALL THE FUNCTIONS, FEATURES, &
SPECIFICATIONS OF THE CB-7 WITH A DIFFERENT CONTROL AND PANEL
LAYOUT.

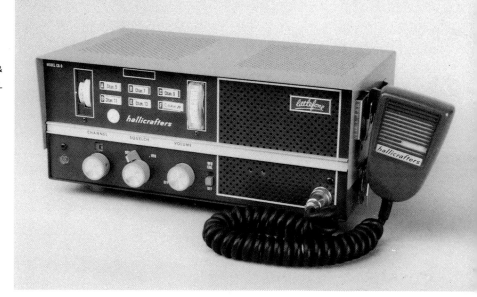

CB-9 LITTLE FONE

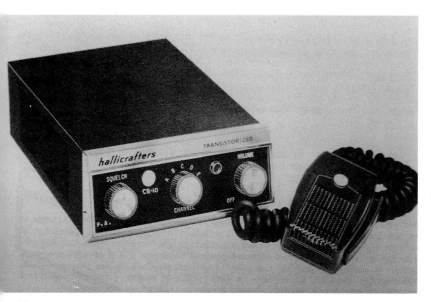

CB-10

CB-10   NONE   1964   UNKNOWN
FIVE CHANNELS, 14 TRANSISTORS, 8 DIODES, CRYSTAL-CONTROLLED,
SQUELCH CONTROL, PA SWITCH FOR PAGING, AUDIO OUTPUT IS 3.5
WATTS, TRANSMITTER INPUT IS 5 WATTS. POWER SOURCE IS 12 VOLTS
DC.

CB-11   LITTLEFONE   1964 $79.95
CB-11A
A COMPACT SINGLE-CHANNEL HAND-HELD CRYSTAL-CONTROLLED 9-
TRANSISTOR UNIT FOR ANY ONE OF 23 CHANNELS WITH PROPER
PLUG-IN CRYSTALS. BUILT-IN TELESCOPING WHIP ANTENNA, 100-MW
INPUT, USES 9-VOLT BATTERY, SOLD IN PAIRS AND COMES WITH EAR-
PHONES AND CARRYING STRAPS, MADE IN JAPAN. THE CB-11A HAS 10
TRANSISTORS. THE CB-11s SHOWN HERE WITH THEIR ORIGINAL BOX.

CB-11, CB-11A LITTLE FONE

CB-12   NONE   1965   UNKNOWN
TWELVE CHANNELS, 14 TRANSISTORS, 10 DIODES, CRYSTAL-CON-
TROLLED, SQUELCH CONTROL, PA SWITCH FOR PAGING, AUDIO OUT-
PUT IS 3.5 WATTS, TRANSMITTER INPUT IS 5 WATTS. THE POWER
SOURCE IS 12 VOLTS DC.

CB-14   NONE   1970 $159.95
23 CHANNELS, 20 TRANSISTORS, 11 DIODES, CRYSTAL-CONTROLLED,
WITH SQUELCH CONTROL, COMBINATION RF OUTPUT/S-METER, PA
SWITCH FOR PAGING. 2 WATTS AUDIO OUTPUT AND 5 WATTS TRANS-
MITTER INPUT. POWER SOURCE IS 13.8 VOLTS DC.

CB-12

CB-15   NONE   1965 $59.95
A COMPACT SINGLE CHANNEL HAND-HELD CRYSTAL-CONTROLLED
UNIT WITH BUILT-IN AM BROADCAST RECEIVER AND TELESCOPING
WHIP ANTENNA. NINE TRANSISTORS AND TWO DIODES. THE POWER
SOURCE IS FOUR SIZE "AA" BATTERIES. ANY OF THE 23 CB CHANNELS
MAY BE USED WITH PROPER PLUG-IN CRYSTALS. MADE IN JAPAN.

CB-14

CB-17   NONE   1965 $149.95
SEVEN TUBES, SIX-CHANNEL, CRYSTAL-CONTROLLED, 5-WATT INPUT, BUILT-IN 120-VOLT
AC AND 12-VOLT DC POWER SUPPLY, SQUELCH CONTROL. THE FINAL RF AMPLIFIER IS A
6CX8. THIS UNIT IS VERY SIMILAR TO THE CB-7. THE ONLY DIFFERENCE IS THE PANEL
DESIGN AND ANTENNA CONNECTOR. PROVISION FOR ADDING A RECEIVER VFO AND S-
METER (HA-13 & HA-9)

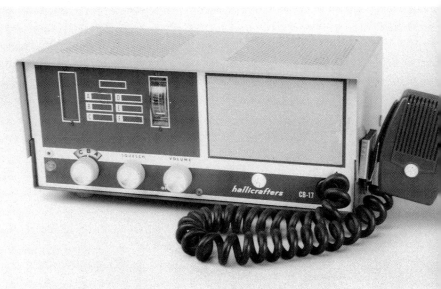

CB-15

CB-17

CB-18   NONE   1966   UNKNOWN

A 2-CHANNEL HAND-HELD SOLID-STATE CRYSTAL-CONTROLLED UNIT WITH SQUELCH CONTROL, PTT, BUILT-IN TELESCOPING WHIP ANTENNA, PROVISION FOR EXTERNAL ANTENNA WITH ANTENNA SWITCH, EARPHONE AND EXTERNAL MIC JACKS. COMES WITH TWO 6-VOLT NI-CAD "BUTTON" BATTERIES AND THE BC-18 BATTERY CHARGER. THE TRANS-MITTER POWER INPUT IS 2 WATTS. MADE IN JAPAN.

CB-19   NONE   1966 $159.95

SEVEN TUBES AND EIGHT CRYSTAL-CONTROLLED CHANNELS FOR THE TRANSMITTER, CRYSTAL- CONTROLLED RECEIVER OR BUILT-IN VFO. WITH S-METER, SQUELCH CONTROL, AND BUILT-IN 120-VOLT AC AND 12-VOLT DC POWER SUPPLY. THE FINAL RF AMPLIFIER IS A 6CX8 WITH 5 WATTS INPUT.

CB-20   NONE   1966 $ 99.95

FIVE-CHANNEL, CRYSTAL-CONTROLLED TRANSMIT AND RECEIVE, 12 TRANSISTORS AND 11 DIODES, WITH SQUELCH CONTROL. TRANSMITTER INPUT POWER IS 5 WATTS. THE POWER SOURCE IS 12 VOLTS DC.

CB-21   REACTER II   1967 $139.95

EIGHT-CHANNEL, SOLID-STATE, CRYSTAL-CONTROLLED TRANSMIT AND RECEIVE, SQUELCH CONTROL, AGC, AND ANL. THE POWER SOURCE IS 12 VOLTS DC.

CB-18

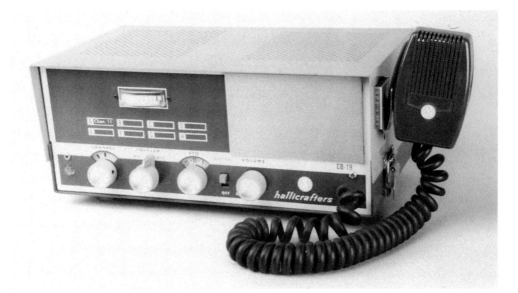

CB-19

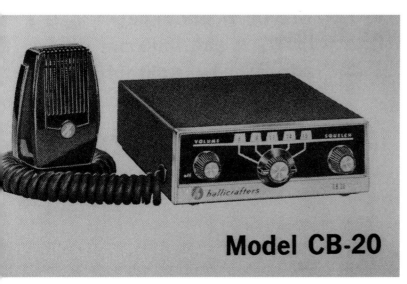

CB-20

CB-21 REACTER II

CB-24   NONE   1967-68 $199.95

A 23-CHANNEL SOLID-STATE CRYSTAL-CONTROLLED UNIT WITH COMBINATION RF OUT-
PUT/S-METER, SQUELCH CONTROL, PA SWITCH FOR PAGEING, & A DUAL CONVERSION
RECEIVER. THE POWER SOURCE IS 12 VOLTS DC.

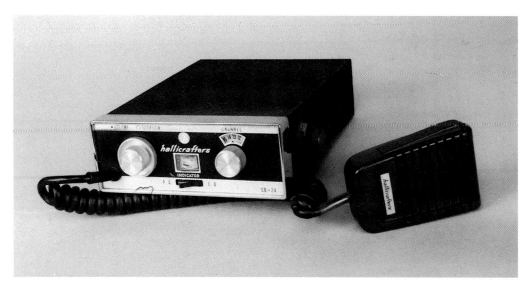

CB-24

CB-24 WITH P-10 POWER SUPPLY

CB-181   NONE   1967 $79.95

A SOLID-STATE 2-CHANNEL HAND-HELD PORTABLE UNIT WITH DUAL CONVERSION RE-
CEIVER AND 2 WATTS RF OUTPUT. 14 TRANSISTORS AND 4 DIODES. THE POWER SOURCE
IS 2 "AA" CELLS OR OPTIONAL RECHARGABLE NI-CAD CELLS.

In 1967 Hallicrafters had the contract to build CB radios for Sears. The following is a list of some of
the Sears Silvertone Models that correspond to Hallicrafters models:

SEARS 6552 & 6553 = CB-12 & P-12
SEARS 6554 & 6555 = CB-14 & P-14
SEARS 6550 = CB-17.

These Sears models are electronically identical to the Hallicrafters units; only knobs and trim differ.

CB-181

H SERIES TEST EQUIPMENT

In the 1960s electronic kit building was very popular. The entire "H" line of test equipment was sold in kit form, or wired. The "W" in the model number indicates factory wired. No "W" in the model number indicates the kit form. The kits were known as "Master Kits."

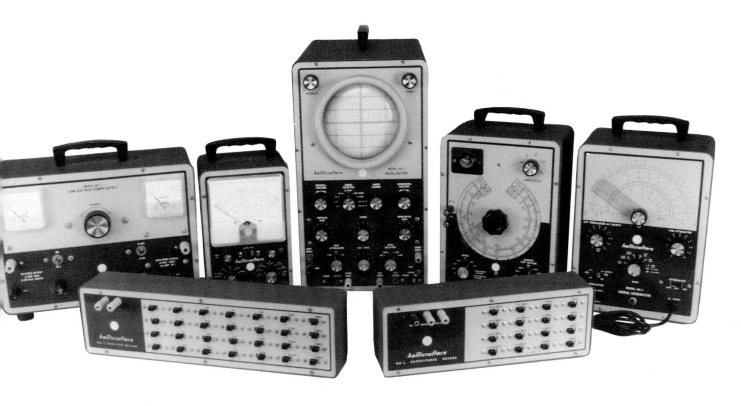

THE ENTIRE TEST EQUIPMENT PRODUCT LINE

MODEL	NAME	DATE	ORIGINAL PRICE
HCW-1	NONE	1964	**$49.95 factory-wired**
HC-1			**$29.95 kit**

A CAPACITANCE-RESISTANCE BRIDGE FOR DETERMINING THE VALUES OF UNKNOWN CAPACITORS AND RESISTORS, OR THE TOLERANCE OF KNOWN CAPACITORS OR RESISTORS. THE CAPACITANCE RANGE IS FROM 10 PF TO 5000 UF, AND RESISTANCE VALUES FROM 1/2-OHM TO 5-MEGOHM. LEAKAGE AND POWER FACTOR OF CAPACITORS CAN ALSO BE DETERMINED. THE INDICATOR IS A "EYE" TUBE AND THE POWER SOURCE IS 120 VOLTS AC.

HDW-1	NONE	1964	**$24.95 factory-wired**
HD-1			**$14.95 kit**

A CAPACITANCE DECADE BOX WITH RANDOM SELECTION OF 10,000 VALUES FROM .001 UF TO 1.0 UF IN STEPS OF 100 UUF WITH 10% ACCURACY. THE MAXIMUM CONTINUOUS VOLTAGE THAT CAN BE APPLIED IS 350 VOLTS.

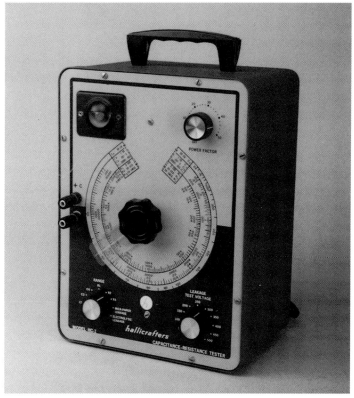

HCW-1, HC-1

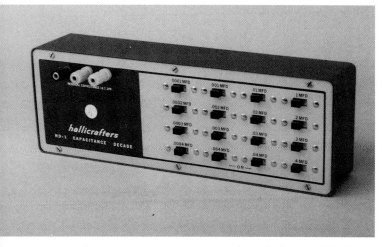

HDW-1, HD-1

| HDW-2 | NONE | 1964 | $24.95 factory-wired |
| HD-2 | | | $14.95 kit |

A RESISTANCE DECADE BOX WITH RANDOM SELECTION OF 10 MILLION RESISTANCES FROM 1-OHM TO 10 MEGOHMS. MAXIMUM POWER DISAPATION IS 1-WATT AND THE ACCURACY IS 10%.

| HGW-1 | NONE | 1964 | $64.95 factory-wired |
| HG-1 | | | $24.95 kit |

AN RF SIGNAL GENERATOR COVERING 50KHz TO 55MHz ON FUNDAMENTALS AND 50MHz TO 880MHz ON HARMONICS, WITH 400 CYCLE AUDIO MODULATION, 3-STEP RF ATTENUATOR, FIXED 30% AUDIO MODULATION, AN ACCURACY OF 1.5%, AND A FREQUENCY DRIFT OF PLUS OR MINUS 0.2% AFTER WARM-UP. USES A SINGLE 6EA8 TUBE AS RF AND AUDIO OSCILLATORS. THE POWER SOURCE IS 120 VOLTS AC.

| HMW-1 | NONE | 1964 | $59.95 factory-wired |
| HM-1 | | | $29.95 kit |

A VACUUM TUBE VOLT METER (VTVM) COVERING THE FOLLOWING RANGES: DC VOLTS FROM 0 TO 1500, AC VOLTS FROM 0 TO 1500 RMS, AC VOLTS 0 TO 4000 PEAK-TO-PEAK, OHMS FROM 0.2 TO 1000 MEG, MA FROM 1.5 TO 500. USES TWO TUBES, A 12AU7A AND 6AL5. POWER SOURCE IS 120 VOLTS AC.

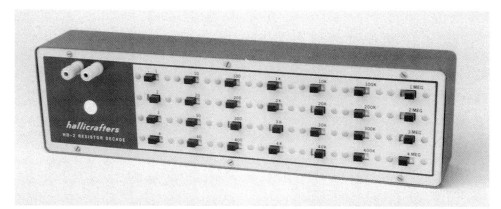

HDW-2, HD-2

HGW-1, HG-1

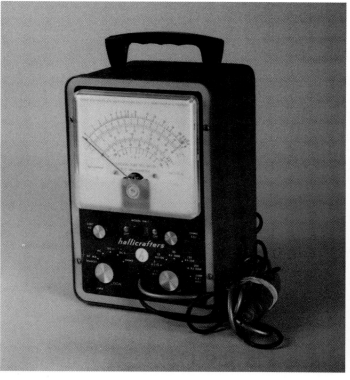

HMW-1, HM-1

| HOW-1 | NONE | 1964 | $164.95 factory-wired |
| HO-1 | | | $84.95 kit |

A 5" OSCILLOSCOPE WITH A VERTICAL BAND WIDTH OF 5MHz, SENSITIVITY OF 10 MILLI-VOLTS RMS PER CENTIMETER, AND A RISE TIME OF 0.08 MICROSECONDS. THE HORIZON-TAL RESPONSE IS 4Hz TO 400KHz WITH A SENSITIVITY OF 120 MILLIVOLTS PER CENTIME-TER. THERE ARE A TOTAL OF 11 TUBES INCLUDING THE 5UP1 CRT. THE POWER SOURCE IS 120 VOLTS AC.

| HPW-1 | NONE | 1964 | $74.95 factory-wired |
| HP-1 | | | $49.95 kit |

A LOW-VOLTAGE DUAL-OUTPUT VARIABLE DC POWER SUPPLY. THE FILTERED OUTPUT IS 0 TO 15 VOLTS AT 5 AMPS MAXIMUM. THE UN-FILTERED OUTPUT IS 0 TO 16 VOLTS AT 10 AMPS CONTINUOUS OR UP TO 20 AMPS INTERMITTANT. VOLTAGE AND CURRENT ARE MONITORED BY SEPARATE PANEL METERS. INPUT POWER IS 120 VOLTS AC.

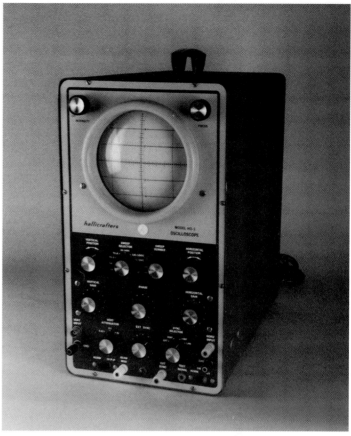

HOW-1, HO-1

HPW-1, HP-1

WR SERIES RECEIVERS

The prefix in the model number of this series "WR" is from the words World Range.

MODEL	NAME	DATE	ORIGINAL PRICE
WR-600	NONE	1961-64	$69.95
G & W			

4 TUBES AND 4 BANDS COVERING 540KHz TO 31MHz WITH A 455KHz I.F., FEATURES INCLUDE BAND SPREAD, BFO, FERRITE ROD LOOP AN-TENNA FOR BROADCAST BAND, AND A BUILT-IN SPEAKER. POWER SOURCE IS 120 VOLTS AC/DC. TUBES: 12BE6 OSCILLATOR & MIXER, 12BA6 I.F., 12AV6 AVC & 1st AUDIO, 50C5 AUDIO OUTPUT, AND A SELENIUM RECTIFIER. EXCEPT FOR THE COLOR OF THE CASE, THE DIAL BEZEL, AND KNOBS, THIS RADIO IS IDENTICAL TO THE S-120, SW-500, & WR-1000. "G" INDICATES A GRAY CASE AND "W" INDICATES A SIMULATED WOOD-GRAINED WALNUT CASE.

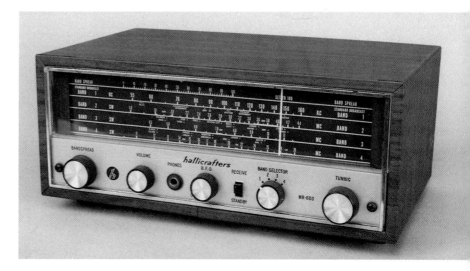

WR-600W

WR-700 ·   **NONE**   **1961-62**   **$57.50**

A 6-TUBE 2-BAND UNIT COVERING THE STANDARD AM & FM BROADCAST BANDS, HOUSED
IN A WOOD TABLE-TOP CABINET. FEATURES INCLUDE FM AFC WITH A DEFEAT SWITCH,
AND BUILT-IN AM ANTENNA. TUBES: 12DT8, TW0 12BA6, 12BE6, 12AV6, & 50C5. POWER
SOURCE IS 120 VOLTS AC.

WR-700

WR-800   **NONE**   **1965**   **UNKNOWN**

FOUR TUBES AND FOUR BANDS COVERING THE STANDARD AM BROADCAST BAND AND
SHORT-WAVE 1.8MHz TO 30MHz. WITH BFO AND BAND SPREAD. THIS UNIT IS SIMILAR IN
APPEARANCE TO THE S-120. THE POWER SOURCE IS 120 VOLTS AC. TUBES: 12BE6, 12BA6,
12AV6, 50C5, AND A SILICON DIODE RECTIFIER.

WR-1000   **NONE**   **1961-62**   **$69.95**

FOUR TUBES AND FOUR BANDS COVERING 540KHz TO 31MHz WITH A 455KHz IF. FEA-
TURES INCLUDE BAND SPREAD, BFO, BUILT-IN SPEAKER, FERRITE ROD ANTENNA FOR THE
BROADCAST BAND AND TELESCOPING WHIP ANTENNA FOR SHORT-WAVE. TUBES: 12BE6,
12BA6, 12AV6, 50C5, AND A SELENIUM RECTIFIER. THIS RADIO IS IDENTICAL TO THE S-120
EXCEPT FOR ITS WOOD CABINET.

WR-1000

WR-1500   NONE   1962 $99.95

FIVE TUBES AND FIVE BANDS COVERING 190KHz TO 30MHz. THE I.F. FREQUENCY IS 455KHz. FEATURES INCLUDE BAND SPREAD, BFO, ANL, BUILT-IN SPEAKER, AND BUILT-IN FERRITE LOOP ANTENNA FOR BANDS 1 & 2 (190KHz TO 1600KHz). TUBES USED: 6BL8 MIXER & OSCILLATOR, 12BA6 1st I.F., 12BA6 2nd I.F. & BFO, 12AV6 1st AUDIO, DETECTOR, AVC, & ANL, 6AQ5 AUDIO OUTPUT, AND 2 SILICON DIODE POWER RECTIFIERS. THE POWER SOURCE IS 120 VOLTS AC. EXCEPT FOR ITS WOOD CABINET THIS UNIT IS IDENTICAL TO THE S-118.

WR-1500

WR-2000

WR-2500

WR-2000   NONE   1962   UNKNOWN
WR-2500

FIVE TUBES AND FOUR BANDS COVERING THE STANDARD AM & FM BROADCAST BANDS AND SHORT-WAVE FROM 2MHz TO 18MHz. THE IF FREQUENCIES ARE 455KHz AM AND 10.7MHz FM. FEATURES INCLUDE BUILT-IN ANTENNAS FOR AM & FM, BUILT-IN SPEAKER WITH EXTERNAL SPEAKER JACK, AFC, AND RUGGED STEEL CABINET. TUBES: 6BL8 MIXER AND OSCILLATOR, 6BA6 1st IF, 6KL8 2nd IF, 6GW8A 1st AUDIO AND AUDIO OUTPUT, AND A SILICON DIODE RECTIFIER. THE POWER SOURCE IS 120 VOLTS AC. THE WR-2500 IS IDENTICAL EXCEPT FOR ITS WALNUT VENEER WOOD CABINET.

WR-3000   NONE   1962-64   UNKNOWN

A 6-BAND SOLID-STATE PORTABLE RADIO COVERING 185KHz TO 400KHz, 535KHz 1625KHz,
AND FOUR SHORT-WAVE BANDS FROM 2MHz TO 23MHz. THE IF FREQUENCY IS 455KHz.
FEATURES INCLUDE A ROTATING DRUM DIAL THAT DISPLAYS ONLY THE BAND IN USE,
TEN PLUG-IN TRANSISTORS, BUILT-IN FERRITE ROD AND TELESCOPING WHIP ANTENNAS,
BFO, SWITCHABLE DIAL LIGHT, & BAND SPREAD. THE POWER SOURCE IS EIGHT 1.5 VOLT
"D" CELLS FOR THE RADIO AND ONE FOR THE DIAL LAMP.

WR-3000

WR-3000

WR-3100   NONE   1964 $49.95

A 10-TRANSISTOR 3-BAND PORTABLE RECEIVER COVERING THE STANDARD AM & FM
BROADCAST BANDS AND SHORT-WAVE 3.8MHz TO 12.5MHz. THE IF FREQUENCIES ARE
455KHz AM & 10.7MHz FM. BUILT-IN FERRITE ROD AND TELESCOPING WHIP ANTENNAS.
THE POWER SOURCE IS FOUR "AA" CELLS OR AC ADAPTOR. MADE IN JAPAN.

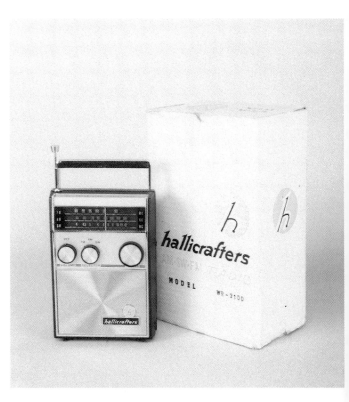

WR-3100

WR-3200

WR-3200 NONE   1965-66 $69.95

A 12-TRANSISTOR 4-DIODE 4-BAND PORTABLE RADIO COVERING THE STANDARD AM/FM BROADCAST BANDS AND SHORT-WAVE 1.6MHz TO 18.5MHz. FEATURES A PUSH-BUTTON BAND SWITCH, TWO ANTENNAS, AFC & TONE CONTROL. POWERED BY FOUR "AA" CELLS AND MADE IN JAPAN.

WR-4000 NONE   1965-66 $139.95

SIMILAR IN APPEARANCE TO THE WR-3000, THE WR-4000 IS A 14 TRANSISTOR 8 DIODE PORTABLE RECEIVER COVERING THE STANDARD AM & FM BROADCAST BANDS & 4 SHORT-WAVE BANDS FROM 2MHz TO 18.2MHz. FEATURES INCLUDE THE ROTATING DRUM DIAL DISPLAYING ONLY THE BAND IS USE, 4"x 6" SPEAKER, BUILT-IN FERRITE ROD & TELESCOPING WHIP ANTENNAS, BFO, EARPHONE JACK, SWITCHABLE DIAL LIGHT, AND BAND SPREAD. THERE ARE NO PLUG-IN COMPONENTS. THE POWER SOURCE IS EIGHT "D" CELLS FOR THE RADIO AND ONE "D" CELL FOR THE DIAL LIGHT.

WR-4000

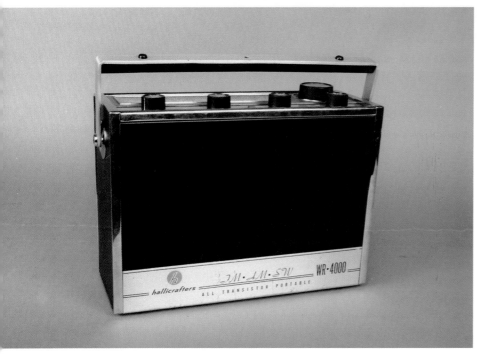

WR-4000

TW SERIES RECEIVERS

The model prefix "TW" is derived from the words "Trans-World."

TW-25

MODEL	NAME	DATE	ORIGINAL PRICE
TW-24	NONE	1954	UNKNOWN
TW-25			

A 4-TUBE SINGLE-BAND PORTABLE RADIO COVERING 535KHz TO 1620KHz, WITH A 455KC IF. BUILT-IN FERRITE ROD ANTENNA. THERE WERE THREE PRODUCTION RUNS. THE POWER SOURCE IS 120 VOLTS AC OR DC, AND BATTERY POWER FROM A 90 VOLT "B" BATTERY AND A 7.5 VOLT "A" BATTERY. TUBES: 1R5 OSCILLATOR & MIXER, 1U4 IF, 1U5 DETECTOR AND 1st AUDIO, 3V4 AUDIO OUTPUT, AND A SELENIUM RECTIFIER. THE DIFFERENCE BETWEEN MODELS IS THE COLOR OF THE CASE. TW-25 SHOWN.

TW-55	NONE	1954	UNKNOWN

A 4-TUBE SINGLE-BAND PORTABLE RADIO COVERING 535KHz TO 1620KHz WITH A 460KHz IF. BUILT-IN FERRITE ROD ANTENNA, SEPERATE PEDISTAL BASE CONTAINING THE 120 VOLT AC POWER SUPPLY. FOR PORTABLE OPERATION THE RADIO UNPLUGS FROM THE BASE AND IS POWERED BY A 45 VOLT "B" BATTERY AND A 1.5 VOLT "A" BATTERY. TUBES: 1R5 MIXER AND OSCILLATOR, 1T4 IF, 1S5 DETECTOR AND 1st AUDIO, AND A 3V4 AUDIO OUTPUT. THE SELENIUM RECTIFIERS FOR 120-VOLT AC USE ARE LOCATED IN THE BASE UNIT.

TW-100	NONE	1954-56	$29.50
TW-101			
TW-102			

A 4-TUBE SINGLE-BAND PORTABLE RADIO COVERING THE AM STANDARD BROADCAST BAND. THREE-WAY POWER SOURCE OF 120 VOLTS AC OR DC OR BATTERIES. BUILT-IN FERRITE ROD ANTENNA. TUBES: 1R5 OSCILLATOR & MIXER, 1U4 IF, 1U5 DETECTOR AND 1st AUDIO, 3V4 AUDIO OUTPUT, AND A SELENIUM RECTIFIER. THE DIFFERENCE BETWEEN THE TW-100, 101, AND 102 IS THE COLOR OF THE CASE.

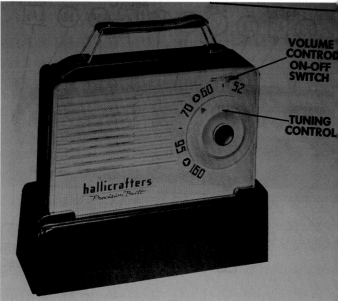

TW-55

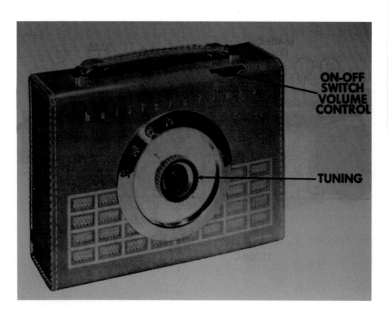

TW-100

(FRONT TO BACK) TW-203A, TW-202A, TW-201A

TW-200-A	NONE	1954-56	$29.50
TW-201-A			
TW-202-A			
TW-203-A			

A 4-TUBE SINGLE-BAND PORTABLE RADIO COVERING THE AM STANDARD BROADCAST BAND. BUILT-IN FERRITE ROD ANTENNA AND 3-WAY POWER SOURCE OF 120 VOLTS AC OR DC OR BATTERY POWER FROM A 67.5-VOLT "B" BATTERY AND A 7.5-VOLT "A" BATTERY. TUBES: 1R5 OSCILLATOR AND MIXER, 1U4 IF (455KHz), 1U5 DETECTOR & 1st AUDIO, 3V4 AUDIO OUTPUT, AND A SELENIUM RECTIFIER. THE DIFFERENCE BETWEEN THESE MODELS IS THE COLOR OF THE COWHIDE CASE. TW-200-A: "BRITISH TAN." 201-A: "DOVE GRAY." 202-A: "FOREST GREEN." 203-A: "CHERRY RED."

TW-500	WORLD-WIDE	1954	$99.95
TW-600			

A 5-TUBE 4-BAND PORTABLE RADIO COVERING 170KHz TO 415KHz AND 530KHz TO 18MHz. THE IF IS 455KHz, AND THE POWER SOURCE IS 120 VOLTS AC-DC, OR SELF-CONTAINED BATTERIES. FEATURES INCLUDE BUILT-IN SPEAKER, LOOP, AND TELESCOPING ANTENNAS AND A WORLD TIME MAP. THE CASE IS COVERED IN GREEN "LEATHERETTE." THE MODEL S-93 IS THE SAME RADIO WITH A GRAY CASE. TUBES USED: 3V4 AUDIO OUTPUT, 1U5 DETECTOR, AVC, AND 1st AUDIO, 1U4 IF, 1L6 CONVERTER (MIXER) AND OSCILLATOR, AND 1U4 R.F. AMPLIFIER. THE TW-600 IS IDENTICAL EXCEPT FOR ITS BROWN CASE.

TW-500 (LID CLOSED)

TW-1000 (OPEN)

TW-1000 (CLOSED)

TW-1000 WORLD-WIDE 1952-56 $149.95
TW-1000A
TW-2000

A 5-TUBE 8-BAND PORTABLE RADIO COVERING 180KHz TO 400KHz, 540KHz TO 1600KHz, 1.8MHz TO 3.9MHz, 3.9MHz TO 8MHz, AND FOUR SPREAD BANDS COVERING THE 31, 25, 19, AND 16 METER INTERNATIONAL SHORT-WAVE BANDS. OTHER FEATURES INCLUDE A "DYNAMIC" TURRET TUNER, BUILT-IN FERRITE ROD LOOP ANTENNA, REMOVABLE "SKYRIDER" ANTENNA FOR USE IN CARS, TRAINS, ETC., TELESCOPING WHIP ANTENNA FOR THE SHORT-WAVE BANDS, A 4-SWITCH TONE CONTROL SYSTEM ALLOWING 16 DIFFERENT TONE SETTINGS, AND HEADPHONE JACK. THE POWER SOURCE IS 120 VOLTS AC OR DC, OR SELF-CONTAINED BATTERY POWER. TUBES: 1U4 RF AMPLIFIER, 1L6 OSCILLATOR AND MIXER, 1U4 IF (455KHz), 1U5 DETECTOR AND 1st AUDIO, 3V4 AUDIO OUTPUT, AND A SELENIUM RECTIFIER FOR AC USE. THE TW-1000, 1000A, AND TW- 2000 ARE ELECTRICALLY IDENTICAL EXCEPT FOR WHERE THE LOOP ANTENNA IS MOUNTED. THE 1000 USES A CONVENTIONAL LOOP ANTENNA MOUNTED IN THE FRONT COVER. THE 1000A AND 2000 USE THE FERRITE LOOP MOUNTED ON THE CHASSIS. ALL THREE MODELS HAVE A 5"x 7" SPEAKER. THERE ARE SLIGHT PHYSICAL DIFFERENCES BETWEEN THE CABINETS. THE COLORS ARE BLACK, BROWN, AND BLUE.

TW-1000A (CLOSED)

TW-2000 (OPEN)

TW-2000 (CLOSED)

TW-1200   NONE   1979 $399.95

A SOLID-STATE MULTI-MODE 12-BAND PORTABLE RECEIVER COVERING 145-400KHz, 530-1600KHz, 1.6-4MHz, 4-8MHz, 8-12MHz, 12-18MHz, 18-30MHz, 66-86MHz, 88-108MHz, 144-174MHz, AND 430-470MHz. RECEPTION MODES ARE AM, FM, CW AND SSB DEPENDING ON THE BAND IN USE. OTHER FEATURES INCLUDE A WORLD TIME MAP, SEVERAL DIFFERENT BUILT-IN ANTENNA SYSTEMS FOR VARIOUS FREQUENCIES, DUAL CONVERSION, DUAL SPEED TUNING, BFO, SQUELCH CONTROL, RF GAIN CONTROL, COMBINATION BATTERY CONDITION AND S-METER, EARPHONE AND AUDIO OUTPUT JACKS. SUPPLIED ACCESSORIES INCLUDE EARPHONE, CIGARETTE LIGHTER POWER CORD, AC POWER CORD, EXTERIOR ANTENNA, AND AUDIO PATCH CORDS THE POWER SOURCE IS 120-240 VOLTS AC, 12 VOLTS DC OR 120 VOLTS DC OR BATTERY POWER WITH 8 "D" CELLS. THIS RADIO WAS MADE IN JAPAN AND WAS ONE OF THE FEW CONSUMER PRODUCTS SOLD BY THE COMPANY UNDER OWNERSHIP OF THE BRAKER CORPORATION OF GRAND PRAIRIE TEXAS. THIS SET IS ALSO KNOWN AS MODEL NUMBER R-1200.

TW-1200 (OPEN)

TW-1200 (CLOSED)

#R# SERIES RECEIVERS

MODEL	NAME	DATE	ORIGINAL PRICE
5R10	NONE	1951-53	$39.95
5R100			
5R100 A			
5R10A.			

FIVE TUBES AND FOUR BANDS COVERING 540KHz TO 31MHz. THE IF IS 455KHz. WITH
BAND SPREAD, EARPHONE CONNECTOR AND SPEAKER-PHONES SWITCH ON THE REAR
APRON OF THE CHASSIS. THE POWER SOURCE IS 120 VOLTS AC-DC. TUBES: 12SA7 OSCIL-
LATOR AND MIXER, 12SK7 IF, 12SQ7 DETECTOR AND 1st AUDIO, 50L6 AUDIO OUTPUT,
AND 35Z5 RECTIFIER. OTHER THAN THE FINISH ON THE CASES (SMOOTH "SMOKEY BLACK"
OR WRINKLE BLACK) AND A 12SG7 IF TUBE. I SEE NO DEFFERENCE BETWEEN THE 5R10,
5R100 AND THE "A" MODELS. THE ONLY DIFFERENCE BETWEEN 5R10A AND THE 5R100A
IS THE COLOR OF THE CASE. THE 5R10A IS "SMOKEY BLACK," AND THE 5R100A IS
"HAMMERTONE GREY." ALL ARE VERY SIMILAR TO THE S-38D.

5R-10

5R-100

5R11, 12   NONE   1951   UNKNOWN

5R13, 14

5R19, 20

5R21, 22

A 5-TUBE SINGLE-BAND TABLE-TOP RADIO COVERING 540KHz TO
1625KHz. THE IF IS 455KHz AND THE POWER SOURCE IS 120 VOLTS AC-
DC. TUBES USED: 12BE6 MIXER AND OSCILLATOR, 12BA6 IF, 12AV6 OR
12AT6 DETECTOR AND 1st AUDIO, 50B5 AUDIO OUTPUT, AND 35W4
RECTIFIER. THE ONLY DIFFERENCE BETWEEN THESE MODELS IS THE
COLOR AND STYLE OF THE CASE. THE 5R14 IS SHOWN HERE.

5R-14

The 5R11, 12, 13, & 14	

Hallicrafters built radios for the Coronado
Radio Corporation in 1951. Hallicrafters'
models 5R11, 12, 13, and 14, were Coronado
models 05RA33-43-8136A and 8137A.

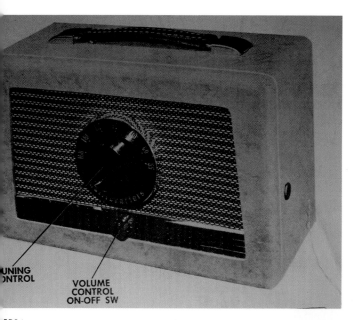

UNING
ONTROL

VOLUME
CONTROL
ON-OFF SW

5R24

5R17   NONE   1952   UNKNOWN

A 5-TUBE TABLE-TOP CLOCK RADIO COVERING THE AM BROADCAST BAND, 455KHz IF.
THIS RADIO IS ONE OF THE FIRST IN THE PRODUCT LINE TO FEATURE PRINTED CORUCITRY,
AND IS SIMILAR TO THE ATCL-7 "ATOM" CLOCK RADIO. FOR 120-VOLT AC USE. TUBES:
12BE6 OSCILLATOR, 12BA6 IF, 12AV6 1st AUDIO, AVC, & DETECTOR, 50C5 AUDIO OUTPUT,
AND 35W4 RECTIFIER.

5R24   NONE   1952   UNKNOWN

A 4-TUBE SINGLE-BAND PORTABLE RADIO COVERING THE STANDARD AM BROADCAST
BAND. THE IF IS 455KHz AND THE POWER SOURCE IS 120 VOLTS AC-DC OR BATTERY
POWER. TUBES USED: 1R5 OSCILLATOR & MIXER, 1U4 IF, 1U5 DETECTOR AND 1st AUDIO,
3V4 AUDIO OUTPUT, AND A SELENIUM RECTIFIER.

5R30, 31   CONTINENTAL   1951-52 $29.95

32, 33, 34

5R30A, 31A

32A, 33A, 34A

A 5-TUBE 2-BAND UNIT COVERING 540KHz TO 1620KHz AND 6MHz TO
18MHz WITH A 455KHz IF. MOLDED "BAKELITE" CASE. THE POWER
SOURCE IS 120 VOLTS AC-DC. TUBES USED: 12SA7 MIXER AND OSCILLA-
TOR, 12SK7 IF, 12SQ7 DETECTOR, AVC, AND 1st AUDIO, 50L6 AUDIO
OUTPUT, AND 35Z5 RECTIFIER. AN EXTERNAL ANTENNA IS REQUIRED
FOR RECEPTION ON BOTH BANDS. THE ONLY DIFFERENCE BETWEEN
THESE MODELS IS THE COLOR OF THE CASE AND KNOBS. THE "A"
MODEL IS THE SAME RADIO WITH EXCEPTION OF THE TUBES USED.
SOME "A" MODELS USED A COMBINATION OF OCTAL AND MINI-ATURE
TUBES (35Z5, 50C5, 12AV6, 12SK7, & 12SA7). SOME USED ALL MINIATURE
TUBES (35W4, 50C5, 12AV6, 12BA6, & 12BE6). AN EXTERNAL ANTENNA
WAS ALSO NEEDED.

5R30 CONTINENTAL

5R31 CONTINENTAL

5R33 CONTINENTAL

5R34 CONTINENTAL

5R35,36 **CONTINENTAL** **1955** **$34.95**
37,38,39

THESE MODELS HAVE THE SAME FUNCTIONS, FEATURES, SPECIFICATIONS AND APPEARANCE AS THE 5R30A THROUGH 5R34A WITH ONE CONVIENIENT EXCEPTION: THEY HAVE A BUILT- IN LOOP ANTENNA, WHICH ELIMINATES THE NEED FOR AN EXTERNAL ANTENNA.

5R40, 41, 42 **CONTINENTAL** **1953** **$29.95**
A 4-TUBE 2-BAND PORTABLE RADIO COVERING 535KHz TO 1620KHz & 5.8MHz TO 18.3MHz WITH A 455KHz IF. BUILT-IN LOOP ANTENNA FOR THE BROADCAST BAND. THE POWER SOURCE IS 120 VOLTS AC-DC OR BATTERY POWER WITH A 90 VOLT "B" AND 7.5 VOLT "A" BATTERY. TUBES USED: 1R5 OSCILLATOR AND MIXER, 1U4 IF, 1U5 DETECTOR AND 1st AUDIO, 3V4 AUDIO OUTPUT, AND A SELENIUM RECTIFIER. THE ONLY DIFFERENCE IN THESE MODELS IS THE COLOR OF THE SPEAKER GRILL, KNOBS, TRIM, AND DIAL.

5R40 CONTINENTAL

5R41 CONTINENTAL

5R42 CONTINENTAL

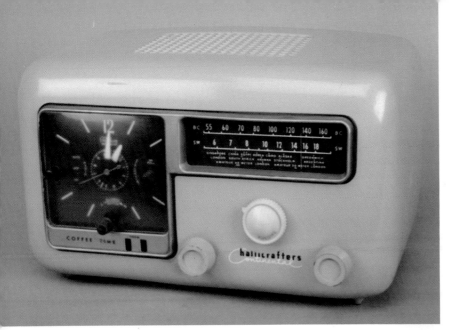

5R50, 51, 52   CONTINENTAL   1952 $39.9

A 5-TUBE 2-BAND CLOCK RADIO COVERING 540KHz TO 1620KHz & 6MHz TO 18MHz. IT IS ELECTRONICALLY IDENTICAL TO THE 5R30 SERIES, BUT WITH A TOP-MOUNTED SPEAKER. THE CLOCK HAS A TIMED APPLIANCE OUTLET FOR USE WITH A COFFEE MAKER. THE ONLY DIFFERENCE IN THESE MODELS IS THE COLOR OF THE MOLDED BAKELITE CASE.

5R60, 61   1955   UNKNOWN

A 5-TUBE SINGLE-BAND TABLETOP RADIO COVERING THE STANDARD AM BROADCAST BAND. THE IF IS 455KHz. WITH BUILT-IN LOOP ANTENNA. POWER SOURCE IS 120 VOLTS AC-DC. TUBES USED: 12BE6 OSCILLATOR AND MIXER, 12BA6 IF, 12AV6 DETECTOR AND 1st AUDIO, 50C5 AUDIO OUTPUT, AND 35W4 RECTIFIER. THE DIFFERENCE IN THESE MODELS IS THE COLOR OF THE PLASTIC CASE.

5R50 CONTINENTAL

5R70, 71   NONE   1956   UNKNOWN

A 5-TUBE SINGLE-BAND TABLETOP UNIT COVERING THE AM STANDARD BROADCAST BAND. THE VOLUME AND TUNING CONTROLS ARE LOCATED ON OTHER SIDE OF THE SIMULATED COWHIDE CASE. BUILT-IN FERRITE ROD ANTENNA AND FRONT-MOUNTED SPEAKER. TUBES: 12BE6 OSCILLATOR AND MIXER, 12BA6 IF (455KHz), 12AV6 DETECTOR AND 1st AUDIO, 50C5 AUDIO OUTPUT, AND 35W4 RECTIFIER. POWER SOURCE IS 120 VOLTS AC-DC. THE DIFFERENCE IN MODELS IS THE COLOR OF THE CASE.

5R72CL   NONE   1956   UNKNOWN
5R73CL

A 5-TUBE SINGLE-BAND TABLETOP CLOCK RADIO. THE CLOCK IS BUILT INTO THE FRONT OF THE CASE, THE SPEAKER IS SIDE-MOUNTED, AND THERE IS A TIMED APPLIANCE OUTLET ON THE REAR APRON. ALL OTHER SPECIFICATIONS ARE THE SAME AS THE 5R70 AND 71. THE DIFFERENCE IN MODELS IS THE COLOR OF THE CASE.

5R230   ATOM DELUXE   1953   UNKNOWN
231, 232

A COMPACT 5-TUBE 2-BAND TABLETOP RADIO COVERING 535KHz TO 1620KHz AND 1.79MHz TO 4.1MHz. THE IF IS 455KHz. BUILT-IN LOOP ANTENNA. THE BAND SWITCH IS LOCATED ON THE REAR COVER OF THE CASE. TUBES: 12BE6 OSCILLATOR AND MIXER, 12BA6 IF, 12AV6 DETECTOR AND 1st AUDIO, 50C5 AUDIO OUTPUT, AND 35W4 RECTIFIER. THE POWER SOURCE IS 120 VOLTS AC-DC. THE DIFFERENCE IN MODELS IS THE COLOR OF THE PLASTIC CASE. THE 230 IS MAROON, 231 IS WHITE, AND THE 232 IS "AIR FORCE BLUE." SHOWN HERE IS THE 5R232.

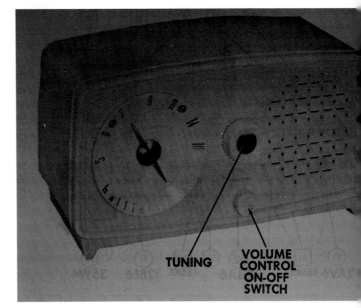

TUNING   VOLUME CONTROL ON-OFF SWITCH

5R60

5R73

5R232 ATOM DELUXE

7R11 CONTINENTAL

7R10, 11, 12   CONTINENTAL   1952-54   UNKNOWN

A 7-TUBE 2-BAND TABLETOP RECEIVER IN A MOLDED BAKELITE CASE, COVERING THE AM AND FM STANDARD BROADCAST BANDS. THE IF FREQUENCIES ARE 455KHz AND 10.7MHz. BUILT-IN SPEAKER, LOOP AND LINE CORD ANTENNAS. POWER SOURCE IS 120 VOLTS AC OR DC. TUBES: 6BJ6 RF, 12AT7 OSCILLATOR AND MIXER, TWO 12BA6 AS 1st AND 2nd IF, 12AL5 RATIO DETECTOR, 12AV6 AM DETECTOR AND 1st AUDIO, 50C5 AUDIO OUTPUT, AND A SELENIUM RECTIFIER. THE 7R10 IS "BLUE GREEN," 7R11 "COCOA BROWN," AND 7R12 "IVORY." THE 7R11 AND 7R12 ARE SHOWN HERE.

8R40   NONE   1950-55 $89.95
8R40C   UNKNOWN

EIGHT TUBES AND FOUR BANDS COVERING 540KHz TO 44MHz. THE IF IS 455KHz. WITH BAND SPREAD, VARIABLE PITCH BFO, RF GAIN CONTROL, AND HEADPHONE JACK. THE 8R40 IS A TABLETOP UNIT WITH BUILT-IN SPEAKER, AND THE 8R40C IS HOUSED IN A WOOD CONSOLE CABINET WITH A 8" SPEAKER AND 3-SPEED AUTOMATIC RECORD CHANGER. TUBES USED: 6SG7 RF, 6SA7 OSCILLATOR AND MIXER, TWO 6SK7 AS 1st AND 2nd IF, 6H6 DETECTOR & AVC, 6SC7 BFO & 1st AUDIO, AND 6K6 AUDIO OUTPUT. RUN #1 USED SELENIUM RECTIFIERS, LATER RUNS USED A 5Y3 RECTIFIER.

7R12 CONTINENTAL

8R40

139

H AND Z SERIES RECEIVERS

Most of the following facts and illustrations of the H, Z, J, and K series radios were obtained from the 1934 Silver-Marshall Manufacturing Company advertising brochure. Some of the items appear to be re-designed versions of earlier Silver-Marshall radios. In the early 1930s, Silver-Marshall Inc. was experiencing financial and legal difficulties. In late 1933 Bill Halligan and The Hallicrafters took over the manufacturing branch of Silver-Marshall Inc., reorganized it, and reopened as the Silver-Marshall Manufacturing Company. In early 1935 Bill Halligan changed the name of the company to Hallicrafters, and the association with Silver-Marshall was over. It was during late 1933 and 1934 that the H, Z, J, and K product line would have been produced, along with the S-1, S-2, and S-3. All of the radios listed in this section are superheterodyne unless otherwise stated. It is my opinion that none of the H, Z, J, or K series radios ever went into production.

H-5 HANDCRAFT

MODEL	NAME	DATE	ORIGINAL PRICE
H-5	HANDCRAFT	1933-34	$39.50

FIVE TUBES AND ONE BAND COVERING 550KHz THROUGH 1720KHz, HOUSED IN A WALNUT "CATHEDRAL" CABINET. THE POWER SOURCE IS 120 VOLTS AC. TUBES USED: TWO 58s, ONE 57, ONE 2A5 AUDIO OUTPUT, AND ONE 80 RECTIFIER.

MODEL	NAME	DATE	ORIGINAL PRICE
H-6	HANDCRAFT	1933-34	$39.50

SIX TUBES AND ONE BAND COVERING 550KHz THROUGH 1720KHz, HOUSED IN A DECO RECTANGULAR WALNUT TABLETOP CABINET. THE POWER SOURCE IS 120 VOLTS AC OR DC. TUBES USED: TWO 78s, ONE 6A7, ONE 6B7, ONE 43 AUDIO OUTPUT, AND ONE 25Z5 RECTIFIER.

MODEL	NAME	DATE	ORIGINAL PRICE
H-7	HANDCRAFT	1933-34	$59.50

SEVEN TUBES, TWO BANDS COVERING 150KHz THROUGH 1620KHz, KNOWN AS THE "AIRPORT" RECEIVER, AND HOUSED IN A GOTHIC CATHEDRAL-STYLE CABINET. THIS SET HAS A "UNIVERSAL" POWER TRANSFORMER FOR USE ON 120-240 VOLTS AC 25-60 CYCLES AND USES A 2A5 AS THE AUDIO OUTPUT TUBE.

H-6 HANDCRAFT

H-7 HANDCRAFT

H-8   HANDCRAFT   1933-34 $79.50 console
                                 $64.50 tabletop

EIGHT TUBES, TWO BANDS, AM BROADCAST AND SHORT-WAVE IN THE 3MHz RANGE.
THE EXACT SHORT-WAVE COVERAGE IS UNKNOWN. COMES IN CHOICE OF CATHEDRAL
OR CONSOLE CABINET. THE POWER SOURCE IS 120 VOLTS AC. TUBES USED: THREE 56s,
TWO 58s, ONE 57, A 2A5 AUDIO OUTPUT AND A 80 RECTIFIER. A 8" SPEAKER WAS USED
WITH BOTH CABINET STYLES.

H-8 HANDCRAFT, CATHEDRAL

HV   HANDCRAFT   1933-34 $99.50
EIGHT TUBES, FREQUENCY RANGE UNKNOWN, WITH 8" SPEAKER, HOUSED IN A WAL-
NUT VENEER GOTHIC CATHEDRAL CABINET. THE POWER SOURCE IS 32 VOLTS AC-DC.
TUBES USED: TWO 37s, THREE 39s, ONE 79, ONE 85, AND ONE 25Z5.

H-10   HANDCRAFT   1933-34 $99.50
TEN TUBES AND TWO BANDS COVERING THE AM STANDARD BROADCAST BAND AND
SHORTWAVE TO 3MHz. SPECIAL "VITATONE" CIRCUITRY GIVES THIS SET A WIDER AUDIO
FREQUENCY RANGE THAN MOST SETS OF ITS TIME. THE POWER SOURCE IS 120 VOLTS AC.
THE SET IS HOUSED IN A SIX-LEGGED CONSOLE CABINET. TUBES USED: THREE 56s, THREE
58s, ONE 57, TWO 2A5s IN PUSH-PULL AUDIO OUTPUT, AND ONE 80 RECTIFIER.

H-8 HANDCRAFT, CONSOLE

HW   HANDCRAFT   1933-34 $44.50
A 5-TUBE SINGLE-BAND BATTERY-OPERATED SET COVERING THE AM STANDARD BROAD-
CAST BAND AND HOUSED IN A CATHEDRAL CABINET. REQUIRES THREE 45-VOLT "B," ONE
-VOLT "A," AND ONE "C" BATTERY OF UNKNOWN VOLTAGE. TUBES USED: ONE 19, ONE
0, ONE 32, AND TWO 34s.

HW HANDCRAFT

H-10 HANDCRAFT

141

HARWICH has side panels that are simple, yet beautifully decorated by the grain of the wood itself --highlighted and curve-grained Walnut found occasionally in the stump of an old tree. Its dimensions are forty-three inches high, twenty-nine inches wide, and fifteen inches deep.

H-12 HANDCRAFT

H-12	HANDCRAFT	1933-34	$134.50 Harwich console
			$114.50 chassis and speaker

A 12-TUBE SINGLE-BAND AM BROADCAST RECEIVER FEATURING TWO RF AMPLIFIER STAGES RESISTANCE COUPLED 1st AUDIO STAGE, PUSH-PULL AUDIO OUTPUT STAGE DRIVING A 12" SPEAKER, AND A CHROMIUM-PLATED CHASSIS. THIS RADIO WAS AVAILABLE AS A CHASSIS AND SPEAKER ONLY, OR IN THE "HARWICH" SIX-LEGGED WALNUT CONSOLE CABINET. THE POWER SOURCE IS 120 VOLTS AC. TUBES USED: FIVE 56s, THREE 58s, ONE 57, TWO 2A5s AS AUDIO OUTPUT, AND ONE 80 RECTIFIER.

H-13	ROUND THE WORLD	1933-34	$139.50–$234.50

THE 1934 SILVER-MARSHALL MFG. CO. BROCHURE INDICATES THAT THE H-13 AND THE Z-13 (Z-DE LUXE) ARE THE SAME RADIO. HOWEVER, I HAVE A SEPERATE BROCHURE PUBLISHED BY THE HALLICRAFTERS AND DATED 1933 THAT DESCRIBES THE H-13 AS TOTALLY DIFFERENT FROM THE Z-13. THIS DESCRIPTION INDICATES TWO CHASSIES, ONE FOR THE TUNER AND ONE FOR THE POWER SUPPLY AND AUDIO AMPLIFIER. THE FEATURES LISTED INCLUDE A BFO, S-METER, ANTENNA TRIMMER, TONE CONTROL, "COLORGRAPH" BAND-IN-USE INDICATOR, AND A "COLORGRAPH" COLOR-CODED DIRECT READING CALIBRATED DIAL. THE FREQUENCY RANGE IS 520KHz TO 21MHz IN FOUR BANDS. IT USES THE 13" "AUDITORIUM" SPEAKER AND THE SAME CHOICES OF CABINETS AS THE Z-13, OR COULD BE PURCHASED WITHOUT A CABINET. THE TUBES USED ARE SIX 56s, FOUR 58s, ONE 5Z3 RECTIFIER, AND TW0 2A3s IN PUSH-PULL AS THE AUDIO OUTPUT (THIS IS THE ONLY DIFFERENCE IN THE TUBE LINE-UP FROM THE Z-13). SELLING PRICE VARIED DEPENDING ON CHOICE OF CABINETS AND PHONOGRAPH OPTION.

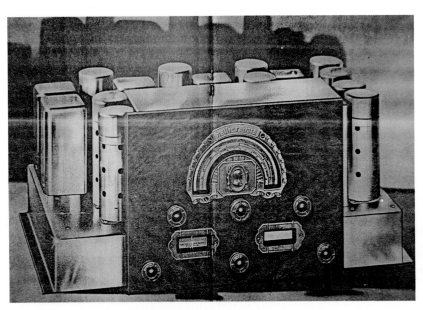

H-13 ROUND THE WORLD (DETAIL OF TUNER CHASSIS)

H-13 ROUND THE WORLD (COVER OF H-13 BROCHURE)

Z-10　　　ROUND THE WORLD　　1933-34　　$86.50–$119.50

SEVEN TUBES AND FOUR BANDS COVERING 525KHz TO 30MHz. FEATURES INCLUDE A BFO, AVC, CALIBRATED DIAL, AND A 5-WATT PUSH-PULL AUDIO AMPLIFIER WITH A FREQUENCY RESPONSE OF 30Hz TO 4KHz. THE Z-10 CAME WITH CHOICE OF A 10" OR 13" SPEAKER AND WAS SOLD AS A CHASSIS AND SPEAKER ONLY, OR IN A CHOICE OF TWO CONSOLE CABINETS. TUBES USED: ONE 2A7, ONE 2B7, ONE 58, ONE 56, TWO 2A5s FOR AUDIO OUTPUT,AND ONE 5Z3 RECTIFIER. THE STYLE OF DIAL ESCUTCHEON DEPENDS ON THE CHOICE OF CABINETS AS DOES THE SELLING PRICE.

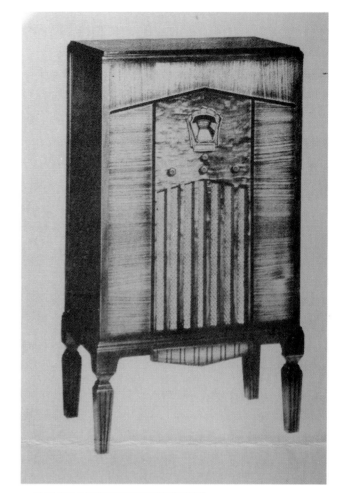

Z-10　ROUND THE WORLD "CATALINA"

Z-10　ROUND THE WORLD "JONQUIL"

Z-10　ROUND THE WORLD "WELLFLEET"

Z-13 ROUND THE WORLD "GLENDALE"

Z-13   ROUND THE WORLD   1933-34 $139.50–$294.50
Z-DE LUXE   ALL WAVE

THIRTEEN TUBES AND FOUR BANDS COVERING THE STANDARD AM BROADCAST BAND TO ABOUT 30MHz. THE IF PEAK IS 472.5KHz. THIS SET FEATURES A BFO, TUNING METER, AVC, A PUSH-PULL AUDIO OUTPUT, AND A SQUELCH CIRCUIT. IT WAS SOLD WITH A CHOICE OF A 12" OR 13" SPEAKER, AS A CHASSIS AND SPEAKER ONLY, OR IN A CHOICE OF FOUR DIFFERENT CONSOLE CABINET STYLES—THE "GLENDALE," THE "ETON," THE "JONQUIL," AND THE "ROBINETTE" (WHICH CAME WITH A PHONOGRAPH). TUBES USED: SIX 56s, FOUR 58s, TWO 2A5s AS AUDIO OUTPUT, AND ONE 5Z3 RECTIFIER. THE POWER SOURCE IS 120 VOLTS AC. THE PRICE DEPENDED ON CHOICE OF CABINETS AND SPEAKERS.

Z-13 ROUND THE WORLD "ETON"

J   AIR-FLIGHT   1933-34 $89.50

A 6-TUBE AUTO RADIO COVERING THE STANDARD BROADCAST BAND. THE MAIN CHASSIS CONSISTS OF THE RADIO, POWER SUPPLY, AND SPEAKER. MOUNTS ON THE FLOOR OR ON THE FIREWALL OF THE VEHICLE. A SEPARATE CONTROL HEAD, WITH THE DIAL, VOLUME, AND TUNING CONTROLS, IS MOUNTED ON THE STEERING COLUMN OR UNDER THE DASH. EXTERNAL SPARK PLUG SUPPRESSORS AND GENERATOR CAPACITORS WERE SUPPLIED WITH THIS UNIT TO REDUCE IGNITION NOISE. THE POWER SOURCE IS 6 VOLTS DC. TUBES USED: ONE 75, TWO 6E7s, ONE 6A7, ONE 89, AND ONE 6Z4.

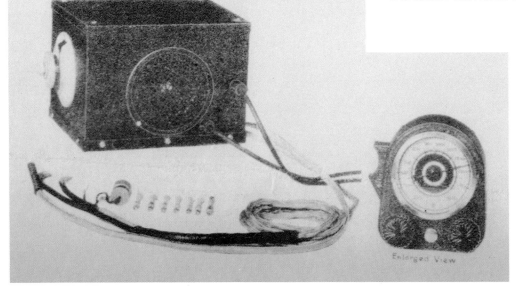

J AIR-FLIGHT

AIR-FLIGHT   1933-34 $89.50

A 6-TUBE AUTO RADIO SIMILAR TO THE MODEL J IN A DIFFERENT CASE, WITH A DIFFERENT STYLE CONTROL HEAD, AND BUILT-IN SPARK PLUG NOISE SUPPRESSION. THE POWER SOURCE IS 6 VOLTS DC. THE TUBE TYPES USED ARE UNKNOWN.

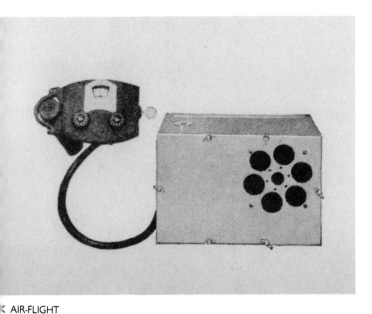

AIR-FLIGHT

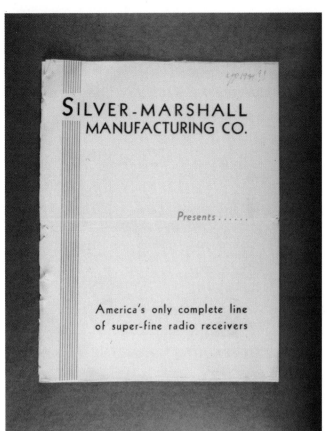

The cover of a 1934 Silver-Marshall/Hallicrafters catalogue.

In 1933, Wiley Post (1900-1935) became the first man to make a solo flight around the world. The actual flight took him 7 days, 18 hours, and 49 minutes—but his preparation for it had taken nine years! Wiley had lost his eye in an oil drilling accident in 1924; with the insurance money he bought an old airplane, and learned to fly. He then began winning air derbies, and made a round-the-world flight with Harold Gatty (see The Gatty Expedition) in 1931. In 1935, Wiley was killed in a plane crash with Will Rogers, in Alaska.

EC AND EX SERIES RECEIVERS

With the "divorce" of Hallicrafters from the Silver-Marshall Manufacturing Company in progress, a new relationship with the Echophone Radio Co. was begun. This relationship would see the two companies merge in 1935, with Hallicrafters as the dominant partner. The Echophone name and product line were all but forgotton until the middle and late years of the war, when the following product line was started. Some of the Echophone radios became affectionately known as "the poor man's Hallicrafters" because of the generally lower selling price. With exception of the first few models, the EC and EX product lines were general consumer products oriented toward home entertainment rather than towards communications. The Echophone line was produced from aproximately 1940 throuth 1953.

EC, EC-1 ECHOPHONE COMMERCIAL

MODEL	NAME	DATE	ORIGINAL PRICE
EC	ECHOPHONE	1941	$29.50
EC-1	COMMERCIAL		

SIX TUBES AND THREE BANDS COVERING 545KHz TO 30.5MHz WITH A 455KHz IF. FEATURES INCLUDE BAND SPREAD, BFO, BUILT-IN SPEAKER, EARPHONE CONNECTIONS, SPEAKER-PHONES SWITCH AND A RECEIVE-STANDBY SWITCH. THE POWER SOURCE IS 120 VOLTS AC-DC. TUBES USED: 12K8 OSCILLATOR AND MIXER, 12SK7 IF, 12SQ7 DETECTOR AND 1st AUDIO, 12J5 BFO, 35L6 AUDIO OUTPUT, AND A 35Z5 RECTIFIER.

EC-1A	ECHOPHONE	1941-46	$19.95
EC-1B	COMMERCIAL		

A 6-TUBE 3-BAND RECEIVER COVERING 550KHz TO 30MHz WITH A 455KHz IF. FEATURES INCLUDE BUILT-IN SPEAKER, BAND SPREAD, SPEAKER-PHONES AND STANDBY-RECEIVE SWITCH, ANL, AND BFO. THE EC-1A AND EC-1B ARE THE SAME RADIO AS THE S-41G OR S-41W WITH EXCEPTION OF THE STYLE OF KNOBS AND COLOR OF THE DIAL AND CASE. THEY ARE TOTALLY DIFFERENT FROM THE EC AND EC-1. TUBES USED: 12SA7 MIXER AND OSCILLATOR, 12SK7 IF, 12SQ7 DETECTOR AND 1st AUDIO, 12SQ7 BFO, 35L6 AUDIO OUTPUT, AND 35Z5 RECTIFIER. THE POWER SOURCE IS 120 VOLTS AC-DC.

EC-1A ECHOPHONE COMMERCIAL

EC-1B ECHOPHONE COMMERCIAL

EC-2   ECHOPHONE   1941-46 $29.95
        COMMERCIAL

EIGHT TUBES AND THREE BANDS COVERING 550KHz TO 30MHz WITH A 455KHz IF. FEATURES INCLUDE CALIBRATED BAND SPREAD, BFO, ANL, SPEAKER-PHONES AND STANDBY-RECEIVE SWITCE, AND A STAGE OF RF AMPLIFICATION. THE POWER SOURCE IS 120 OR 240 VOLTS AC-DC DEPENDING ON THE BALLAST TUBE. AN EXTERNAL SPEAKER IS NEEDED WITH THIS RADIO. TUBES USED: 6SG7 RF, 6K8 OSCILLATOR AND MIXER, 6SK7 IF, 6H6 DETECTOR AND ANL, 6SC7 BFO AND 1st AUDIO, 25L6 AUDIO OUTPUT, 25Z6 RECTIFIER, AND BK36 120 VOLT BALLAST TUBE.

EC-3   ECHOPHONE   1941-46 $49.95
        COMMERCIAL

NINE TUBES AND THREE BANDS COVERING 550KHz TO 30MHz WITH A 455KHz IF. FEATURES INCLUDE A CRYSTAL FILTER, VERIABLE SELECTIVITY, CRYSTAL PHASING CONTROL, CALIBRATED BAND SPREAD, ANL, BFO, RF AMPLIFIER AND SPEAKER-PHONES & STANDBY-RECEIVE SWITCH. THE POWER SOURCE IS 120-240 VOLTS AC-DC DEPENDING ON THE BALLAST TUBE. AN EXTERNAL SPEAKER IS REQUIRED. TUBES USED: 6SG7 RF, 6K8 MIXER & OSCILLATOR, 6SK7 1st IF, 6SK7 2nd IF, 6H6 DETECTOR & ANL, 6SC7 BFO, 25L6 AUDIO OUTPUT, 25Z6 RECTIFIER, AND BK29D 120-VOLT BALLAST TUBE.

EC-2 ECHOPHONE COMMERCIAL

EC-3 ECHOPHONE COMMERCIAL

EC-6   ECHOPHONE   1942-46   UNKNOWN
        COMMERCIAL

A 7-TUBE 3-BAND METAL-CASED PORTABLE RADIO COVERING 550KHz TO 19MHz WITH A 455KHz IF. FEATURES INCLUDE A 3-WAY POWER SOURCE OF 120 VOLTS AC-DC OR BATTERY POWER, BUILT-IN SPEAKER, AND BAND SPREAD. THE EC-6 IS IDENTICAL TO THE RE-1 "TROOP ENTERTAINMENT" RADIO. TUBES USED: 1R5 OSCILLATOR & MIXER, TWO 1N5s AS 1st & 2nd IF, 1H5 DETECTOR & 1st AUDIO, 5OL6 AUDIO OUTPUT FOR 120-VOLT USE, 3Q5 AUDIO OUTPUT FOR BATTERY USE, AND A 35Z5 RECTIFIER FOR 120-VOLT USE.

RE-1, EC-6 ECHOPHONE COMMERCIAL

EC-112   NONE   1948-53   UNKNOWN
EC-113
EC-114

SIX TUBES AND THREE BANDS COVERING 550KHz TO 22MHz WITH A 455KHz IF. WITH BAND SPREAD, BUILT-IN SPEAKER AND LOOP AN-TENNA. THE POWER SOURCE IS 120 VOLTS AC OR DC. TUBES USED: 12SA7 OSCILLATOR AND MIXER, TWO 12SK7s AS 1st AND 2nd IF, 12SQ7 DETECTOR AND 1st AUDIO, 35L6 AUDIO OUTPUT, AND 35Z5 RECTI-FIER. OTHER THAN THE TYPE OF CASE, THESE THREE RADIOS ARE IDEN-TICAL. THE EC-112 HAS A MOLDED, IVORY-COLORED PLASTIC CASE; THE EC-113 AND 114 HAVE WOODEN CASES, AS SHOWN.

EC-113

EC-114

EC-306   NONE   1948   UNKNOWN
EX-306

THIS 6-TUBE 3-BAND TABLETOP RADIO-PHONOGRAPH USES THE SAME CHASSIS AS THE EC-112 WITH THE ADDITION OF AUDIO & POWER CONNECTIONS FOR THE 78-RPM RECORD CHANGER & A 12SF7 DETEC-TOR & 1st AUDIO TUBE INSTEAD OF A 12SQ7. THE ONLY DIFFERENCE BETWEEN THE EC & EX-306 IS AUTOMATIC SHUT-OFF ON THE EX RECORD CHANGER AND MANUAL SHUT-OFF ON THE EC RECORD CHANGER.

EC-306

EC-306

EC-400	NONE	1947	$159.50–$479.50
EC-401			
EC-402			
EC-406			

A 12-TUBE 3-BAND RECEIVER COVERING THE STANDARD AM AND FM BROADCAST BANDS PLUS SHORT-WAVE FROM 5.8MHz TO 18MHz. THE POWER SOURCE IS 120 VOLTS AC. OTHER FEATURES INCLUDE SEPARATE BASS AND TREBEL TONE CONTROLS, SEPERATE AM AND FM TUNING CONTROLS, AND TEN TUNING PRESET PUSH-BUTTONS (5 AM AND 5 FM). THERE ARE SOME MINOR ELECTRICAL VARIATIONS AMOUNG THESE MODELS. THEY WERE SOLD AS A CHASSIS ONLY FOR CUSTOM INSTALLATION OR IN A CHOICE OF VARIOUS CONSOLE CABINET STYLES WITH A 12" SPEAKER AND 78-RPM RECORD CHANGER. TUBES USED: 6BA6 RF, 6BE6 MIXER, 6J6 OSCILLATOR, 6AL5 FM DETECTOR, TWO 6SG7 IF, 6SH7 IF, 6SQ7 AM DETECTOR AND 1st AUDIO, 6SQ7 PHASE INVERTER, TWO 6V6 PUSH-PULL AUDIO OUTPUT, AND A 5Y3 RECTIFIER. SELLING PRICE DEPENDED ON CABINET OPTIONS.

EC-400 CHASSIS

EC-403	NONE	1947-48	UNKNOWN
EC-404			

THESE 15-TUBE 5-BAND RECEIVERS USE THE S-47 CHASSIS IN CONSOLE CABINETS OF VARIOUS STYLES, WITH A 78-RPM RECORD CHANGER AND CHOICE OF TWO 10" SPEAKERS OR A SINGLE 15" SPEAKER. THE FREQUENCIES COVERED ARE THE STANDARD AM AND FM BROADCAST BANDS PLUS A GENERAL COVERAGE SHORT-WAVE BAND 5.8MHz TO 18MHz AND TWO SHORT-WAVE SPREAD BANDS COVERING 9MHz TO 12MHz AND 15MHz TO 18MHz. OTHER FEATURES INCLUDE FM AFC, SEPERATE BASS AND TREBLE TONE CONTROLS, SEPERATE AM AND FM TUNING CONTROLS, 5 AM AND 5 FM PRESET TUNING PUSH-BUTTONS, AND A PUSH-PULL 6V6 AUDIO OUTPUT. FOR OTHER SPECIFICATIONS SEE S-47. THE EC-403 IS SHOWN HERE.

EC-403

DETAIL OF THE EC-403 DIAL

EC-600

EC-600   NONE   1946   UNKNOWN

A 4-TUBE SINGLE-BAND BATTERY-OPERATED RECEIVER COVERING 540KHz TO 1680KHz. REQUIRES A 90-VOLT "B" AND A 1.5-VOLT "A" BATTERY. IT WAS INTENDED FOR USE IN RURAL AREAS OF THE COUNTRY THAT LACKED ELECTRICITY. TUBES USED: 1R5 OSCILLATOR AND MIXER, 1T4 IF, 1S5 DETECTOR, AVC, AND 1st AUDIO, AND 3Q4 AUDIO OUTPUT.

EX-102   NONE   1948-53   UNKNOWN
EX-103

A 5-TUBE 3-BAND TABLETOP RADIO COVERING 540KHz TO 22MHz. THE POWER SOURCE IS 120 OR 240 VOLTS AC-DC DEPENDING ON THE TYPE OF BALLAST TUBE USED. THESE RADIOS USE THE SAME CABINETS AS THE EC-112, 113, AND 114, AND THE OUTWARD APPEARANCE IS IDENTICAL. THE DIFFERENCE IS THE INTERCHANGABLE BALLAST TUBE, AND ONE LESS IF AMPLIFIER TUBE TO ACCOMODATE THE BALLAST TUBE ON THE CHASSIS. TUBES USED: 12SA7 MIXER AND OSCILLATOR, 12SK7 IF (455KHz), 12SQ7 DETECTOR AND 1st AUDIO, 35L6 AUDIO OUTPUT, AND 35Z5 RECTIFIER.

EX-102, EX-103

EX-104   NONE   1949-50   UNKNOWN
EX-106

SIX TUBES AND FOUR BANDS COVERING 540KHz TO 12MHz WITH A SLIDE-RULE DIAL AND TABLETOP WOOD CABINET SIMILAR TO THE EX-107. FEATURES INCLUDE AN EARPHONE JACK, AND 6" PM SPEAKER. THE EX-104 HAS A BUILT-IN LOOP ANTENNA AND A 120- 240-VOLT AC POWER SUPPLY, THE EX-103 HAS NO BUILT-IN ANTENNA AND HAS A 6-VOLT DC VIBRATOR POWER SUPPLY. TUBES USED: 6SA7 OSCILLATOR AND MIXER, TWO 6SK7s AS 1st AND 2nd IF (455KHz), 6SQ7 DETECTOR AND 1st AUDIO, 6K6 AUDIO OUTPUT, AND 5Y3 RECTIFIER (EX-104) OR 6X5 RECTIFIER (EX-103).

EX-107   NONE   1947   UNKNOWN

EIGHT TUBES AND FIVE BANDS COVERING 550KHz TO 1700KHz, 2 GENERAL COVERAGE SHORT-WAVE BANDS FROM 2.2MHz TO 22MHz, AND 2 SHORT-WAVE SPREAD BANDS FROM 9MHz TQ 12MHz, AND 15MHz TO 18MHz. THE IF IS 455KHz. FEATURES INCLUDE BUILT-IN LOOP ANTENNA, EARPHONE JACK, AUDIO INPUT & AC POWER JACKS FOR PHONOGRAPH ATTACHMENT, 8" PM SPEAKER, AND A UNIVERSAL POWER SUPPLY FOR 120 OR 240 VOLTS AC. TUBES USED: 6SG7 RF, 6SA7 OSCILLATOR & MIXER, 6SG7 1st IF, 6SQ7 2nd IF & DETECTOR, 6SQ7 PHASE INVERTER & 1st AUDIO, TWO 6K6's IN PUSH-PULL AUDIO OUTPUT, AND A 5Y3 RECTIFIER.

EX-107

T AND # SERIES TELEVISION RECEIVERS

The television model numbering system is somewhat confusing. Many of the different models used the same chassis; the differences were in the type and style of the cabinets, and in some cases, the size of the picture tube. Many of the photographs which follow were taken from Hallicrafters' advertising brochures, and from Howard W. Sams & Company's "Photofact" folders. The T-54 was the first television set to be produced by the company. It was also produced with varying cosmetic changes for large mail-order companies like Sears and Montgomery Wards, and bore those companies' names.

MODEL	NAME	DATE	PRICE
T-54	NONE	1947-48	$169.50

A 7" 22-TUBE 13-CHANNEL VHF SET WITH A PUSH-BUTTON TUNER THAT INCLUDES CHANNEL 1. FEATURING ELECTROSTATIC DEFLECTION, FM SOUND SYSTEM, AND A 7JP4 CRT. THE POWER SOURCE IS 120 VOLTS AC.

T-60	NONE	1947-48	$595.00
T-68			

A 16" x 22" REAR PROJECTION SCREEN, 12-CHANNEL PUSH-BUTTON TUNER, 24 TUBES, INSTALLED IN A TALL METAL RACK WITH THE ELECTRONICS ON THE BOTTOM AND THE PROJECTION SCREEN ON TOP. THE T-68 IS THE SAME UNIT IN A SLIGHTLY DIFFERENT CABINET. 120 VOLTS AC.

T-54

T-60

T-61	NONE	1947-48	$279.50

A 10" SCREEN, 23 TUBES, 12-CHANNEL PUSH-BUTTON TUNER, TWO-PIECE CHASSIS CONSISTING OF THE TUNER, IF, AND AUDIO ON ONE UNIT, AND THE POWER SUPPLY AND SWEEP CIRCUITS ON THE OTHER UNIT; ALL HOUSED IN A BLACK BAKELITE TABLETOP CASE, ELECTROMAGNETIC DEFLECTION, 120-VOLT AC.

T-64	NONE	1948-49	$199.50 for 12" model
			$179.50 for 10" model

CHOICE OF 10" OR 12" ROUND SCREEN, IN A WOOD CONSOLE OR TABLETOP CABINET, HAS ELECTROMAGNETIC DEFLECTION, 12-CHANNEL PUSH-BUTTON TUNER, 120-VOLT AC. USES THE SAME CHASSIS AS THE T-61.

T-67	NONE	1948-49	$279.50

A 10" SCREEN, 23 TUBES, USES THE SAME CHASSIS AS THE T-61. THE DIFFERENCE IS THE WOOD TABLETOP CABINET RATHER THAN BLACK BAKELITE. 120-VOLT AC.

T-69	NONE	1949	$259.50

A 15" ROUND SCREEN, 23 TUBES, 12-CHANNEL PUSH-BUTTON TUNER, USES THE SAME CHASSIS AS THE T-61 AND IS HOUSED IN A CONSOLE CABINET. 120-VOLT AC.

T-67

#505   NONE   1948 $189.50
#506

A 7" SCREEN, 22 TUBES, 13-CHANNEL PUSH-BUTTON TUNER. USES THE SAME CHASSIS AS THE T-54 AND IS HOUSED IN A WOOD TABLETOP CABINET. THERE IS A DIFFERENCE IN CABINET STYLING BETWEEN THE 505 AND 506, AND SOME OF THE 506s HAD THE CHANNEL 1 BUTTON OMITTED, MAKING IT A 12-CHANNEL SET.

#509   NONE   1948-49 $279.50
#510

A 10" SCREEN, 23 TUBES, 12-CHANNEL PUSH-BUTTON TUNER. USES THE SAME CHASSIS AS THE T-61. THE ONLY DIFFERENCE IS THE TYPE AND STYLE OF THE CABINET. 120 VOLTS AC.

#505

#506

#511

#511   NONE   1950   UNKNOWN

16" ROUND TUBE, 12-CHANNEL PUSH-BUTTON TUNER, 24 TUBES, 2-PIECE CASE WITH THE PICTURE TUBE, POWER SUPPLY AND HIGH VOLTAGE IN A LARGE CASE ON THE BOTTOM, THE TUNER AND AUDIO ON THE TOP IN A SMALLER CASE SIMILAR TO THE 506. THESE SECTIONS COULD ALSO HAVE BEEN ARRANGED SIDE-BY-SIDE. THIS SET USES THE SAME BASIC CHASSIS AS THE T-61 WITH AN ADDITIONAL TUBE AND OTHER CHANGES TO ACCOMODATE THE 16" PICTURE TUBE. 120 VOLTS AC.

512   NONE   1949   UNKNOWN
513

A 12" 23-TUBE 2-PIECE CHASSIS WITH A 12-CHANNEL ROTARY TUNER HOUSED IN A CONSOLE CABINET, NO DOORS. THIS SAME BASIC CHASSIS IS USED IN THE 515. THE DIFFERENCE IN MODELS IS THE COLOR AND STYLE OF THE CABINET, 120-VOLT AC.

514   NONE   1948 $189.50

A 7" SCREEN, 22 TUBES, AND A 12-CHANNEL PUSH-BUTTON TUNER. OTHER THAN THE OMISSION OF CHANNEL 1 AND THE CASE STYLE, THIS SET IS IDENTICAL TO THE T-54.

MODEL 512C

#512

#514

153

FINE TUNING
CHANNEL SELECTOR

VERTICAL HOLD
HORIZONTAL HOLD

PICTURE
CONTRAST

PICTURE
BRIGHTNESS

POWER- SOUND
VOLUME

92X745

#515

#515	NONE	1949	UNKNOWN

15" ROUND TUBE, 12-CHANNEL ROTARY TUNER, 23 TUBES, 2 PIECE CHASSIS, 8" DYNAMIC SPEAKER, WOOD CONSOLE CABINET, NO DOORS, VIRTICLE CHASSIS WITH CONTROLS TOP TO BOTTOM ALONG RIGHT FRONT OF CABINET. 120 VOLTS AC

#518, 519	NONE	1949-50	UNKNOWN

#520, 521
#600, 601
#602, 603, 604

ALL OF THESE SETS USED THE SAME 20-TUBE CHASSIS WITH A 12-CHANNEL ROTARY TUNER. THE DIFFERENCES WERE IN THE SIZE OF THE PICTURE TUBE, TYPE AND STYLE OF THE CABINET (VARIOUS CONSOLE AND TABLETOPS), AND THE SIZE OF THE SPEAKER. THE 518, 521, 601, AND 602 HAD 12" SCREENS, THE 600 HAD A 10" SCREEN, THE 519, 520, 603, AND 604 HAD 16" SCREENS. 120 VOLTS AC.

#605, 606	NONE	1950-51	UNKNOWN

MODEL #605 HAS A 19" ROUND CRT, 2-PIECE VERTICAL CHASSIS, ORIENTAL CHEST-STYLE MAHOGANY CONSOLE, HIGH LEGS WITH BOTTOM RAIL, FULL DOORS, 25 TUBES AND A DUAL-RANGE 12-CHANNEL TUNER, 120 VOLTS AC. #606 WAS THE SAME WITH FRUITWOOD OAK FINISH.

#680, 681	NONE	1950	UNKNOWN

 690

ALL OF THESE SETS USE THE SAME 20-TUBE CHASSIS WITH A 12-CHANNEL DUAL RANGE CONTINUOUS TUNER. THE 680 AND 681 HAVE A 10" CRT AND ARE HOUSED IN TABLE-TOP CABINETS, MADE OF MAHOGANY AND LIMED OAK RESPECTIVELY. THE 690 HAS A 12" CRT AND IS HOUSED IN A MAHOGANY CONSOLETTE. 120 VOLTS AC.

#715, 716	NONE	1950	UNKNOWN

#730, 731
#740, 741

THE SAME 20-TUBE CHASSIS IS USED FOR THESE MODELS AS IS USED ON THE 680. THE DIFFERENCE IS IN THE SIZE, TYPE, AND STYLE OF THE CABINETS. THEY ALL HAVE A 12" ROUND CRT. THE 715 HAS A BROWN BAKELITE TABLETOP CASE. THE 716 HAS A

TELEVISION RECEIVER MODEL 600

#600

MODEL 605

#605

LEATHERETTE COVERED WOOD TABLETOP CASE. THE 730 AND 731 ARE HOUSED IN A CONSOLE CABINET, MAHOGANY, AND LIMED OAK RESPECTIVELY, NO DOORS. THE 740 AND 741 WERE MAHOGANY AND LIMED OAK CONSOLES WITH HALF DOORS.

#745, 747	NONE	1950	UNKNOWN
748, 750,			
751, 760,			
761			

THE SAME 21-TUBE CHASSIS WITH A 16" RECTANGULAR CRT AND 12-CHANNEL DUAL RANGE CONTINUOUS TUNER WAS USED FOR THESE MODELS. THE DIFFERENCES BETWEEN MODELS IS THE TYPE AND SIZE OF THE CABINETS. THE 745 IS A MAHOGANY WOOD TABLETOP, THE 747 IS A TABLETOP COVERED IN MAHOGANY BROWN "PYROXYLIN" (DON'T ASK ME WHAT THAT IS!); THE 748 IS A TABLETOP COVERED IN BLONDE "PYROXYLIN"; THE 750 AND 751 ARE CONSOLES WITHOUT DOORS, OF MAHOGANY AND LIMED OAK RESPECTIVELY; THE 760 AND 761 ARE CONSOLES WITH HALF DOORS AND ARE MAHOGANY AND LIMED OAK RESPECTIVELY. THE TABLETOP UNITS HAVE A 5" SPEAKER, AND THE CONSOLES HAVE A 8" SPEAKER. THE POWER SOURCE IS 120 VOLTS AC.

#760

#715

#760

#716

#805

#770, 771	NONE	1950	UNKNOWN

THESE TWO CONSOLE MODELS USE THE SAME CHASSIS AND 16" RECTANGULAR CRT AS THE 745. IN ADDITION THEY HAVE A 3-SPEED WEBCORE AUTOMATIC RECORD CHANGER AND AN AM-FM RADIO RECEIVER BUILT INTO A PULL-OUT DRAWER AT THE BOTTOM OF THE CABINET. THE FINISH IS "CORDOVAN" MAHOGANY AND LIMED OAK RESPECTIVELY, NO DOORS. THE POWER SOURCE IS 120 VOLTS AC.

#805	NONE	1950-51	$289.95
806			$299.95
810			$239.95

USING A 16-TUBE CHASSIS WITH A 16" RECTANGULAR CRT AND A 12-CHANNEL TURRET TUNER THE 805 AND 806 ARE "50s MODERN"–STYLE CONSOLES FINISHED IN MAHOGANY AND LIMED OAK RESPECTIVELY. #810 IS A MAHOGANY WOOD TABLETOP. 120 VOLTS AC.

#811	NONE	1951	$279.95

A 24-TUBE CHASSIS WITH 16" RECTANGULAR CRT, 12-CHANNEL TURRET TUNER, AND A BUILT-IN AM RADIO RECEIVER ALL HOUSED IN A MAHOGANY VENEER TABLETOP CABINET. THIS SAME CHASSIS WAS ALSO USED IN THE 820, 821, 860, AND 861. 120 VOLTS AC.

#815	NONE	1950-51	$259.95

A 21-TUBE CHASSIS WITH 16" RECTANGULAR CRT AND 12-CHANNEL TURRET TUNER. HOUSED IN A MAHOGANY VENEER TABLETOP CABINET. THIS CHASSIS WAS ALSO USED FOR THE 822, 870, AND 871. 120 VOLTS AC.

#818	NONE	1950	$339.95

HOUSED IN A MAHOGANY VENEER CONSOLE CABINET WITHOUT DOORS. THE 818 USES THE SAME 24-TUBE CHASSIS AS THE 811 WITH A 16" ROUND CRT.

#810

#818

#811

#815

| #820, | NONE | 1950 | $359.95 |
| #821 | | | $389.95 |

THE 811 24-TUBE CHASSIS IS USED HERE WITH A 17" RECTANGULAR CRT AND IS HOUSED IN A CONSOLE CABINET WITH HALF DOORS. THE 820 IS MAHOGANY AND THE 821 IS "SANDSTONE OAK."

| #822 | NONE | 1950 | $319.95 |

THE 815 21-TUBE CHASSIS WITH A 16" ROUND CRT IS USED HERE AND IS HOUSED IN A "CONTEMPORARY-MODERN" MAHOGANY CONSOLE CABINET WITHOUT DOORS. 120 VOLTS AC.

| #832 | NONE | 1950 | $259.95 |

USES A 18-TUBE CHASSIS WITH A 16" ROUND CRT HOUSED IN A CONTEMPORARY-STYLE MAHOGANY CONSOLE WITHOUT DOORS. 120 VOLTS AC.

| #860, | NONE | 1951-52 | $459.50 |
| #861 | | | $499.50 |

A TV/AM RADIO/3-SPEED PHONOGRAPH COMBINATION USING THE 811 24-TUBE CHASSIS WITH A 17" RECTANGULAR CRT AND A 12" PM SPEAKER HOUSED IN A LARGE CONSOLE. THE 860 IS "OLD WORLD" MAHOGANY, AND THE 861 IS "SANDSTONE OAK." THERE WERE AT LEAST FIVE PRODUCTION RUNS OF THESE MODELS.

#832

#860

#820

#822

#861

| #870 | NONE | 1950 | $319.95 |
| #871 | | | $339.95 |

THESE TWO MODELS USE THE 815 21-TUBE CHASSIS WITH A 17" RECTANGULAR CRT AND AN 8" PM SPEAKER HOUSED IN A CONSOLE CABINET WITHOUT DOORS. THE 870 IS FINISHED IN MAHOGANY AND THE 871 IN LIMED OAK.

| #880 | NONE | 1950 | $399.95 |

USES A 21-TUBE 12-CHANNEL CHASSIS WITH A 19" ROUND CRT HOUSED IN A MAHOGANY-FINISHED CONSOLE CABINET WITHOUT DOORS. 120 VOLTS AC.

| #890, 894 | NONE | 1950-51 | $599.00 each |
| 898 | | | |

20" RECTANGULAR CRT, 12-CHANNEL TURRET TUNER, BUILT IN AM-FM RADIO, 3-SPEED PHONOGRAPH, AND 12" PM SPEAKER. ALL THREE HAD CONSOLE CABINETS WITH FULL DOORS. THE 890 WAS CALLED "PROVINCIAL" IN "HONEY MAPLE," THE 894 WAS CALLED "SHERATON" IN "OLD WORLD MAHOGANY," AND THE 898 WAS CALLED "MODERN" IN "BLONDE KORINA." THE RADIO CHASSIS IN THESE UNITS WAS SEPERATE FROM THE TV. 120 VOLTS AC.

#870

#890

#880

#894

#898

#1000

#1000   **NONE**   **1950-52**   **UNKNOWN**

THE 1000 HAS A 17" RECTANGULAR CRT ON A 21-TUBE CHASSIS WITH A 12-CHANNEL TURRET TUNER AND A 5" PM SPEAKER HOUSED IN A TABLETOP "MASONITE" CABINET WITH SIMULATED WOOD-GRAINED FINISH. 120 VOLTS AC.

#1001, 1002   **NONE**   **1950-52**   **UNKNOWN**

1003, 1004

1007

THESE MODELS USE THE SAME BASIC 21-TUBE CHASSIS AND 17" RECTANGULAR CRT AS THE 1000. THE DIFFERENCE IS THE TYPE, STYLING, AND FINISH OF THE VARIOUS TABLE-TOP AND CONSOLE CABINETS. THE 1002 IS IN A MAHOGANY-FINISHED WOOD TABLE-TOP CABINET. I HAVE NO INFORMATION ON THE OTHERS.

#1002

#1005, 1006   **NONE**   **1951-52**   **UNKNOWN**

THESE MODELS USE A 21-TUBE CHASSIS THAT IS SIMILAR TO THE 1000 WITH MODIFICA-TIONS IN SOME CIRCUITRY AND DIFFERENT CONTROL AND COMPONENT LAYOUT. A 17" RECTANGULAR CRT IS USED. I HAVE NO INFORMATION ON THE CABINETS BUT SUSPECT THEY ARE TABLETOP UNITS.

#1008   **NONE**   **1950-52**   **UNKNOWN**

THE 1000 21-TUBE CHASSIS WITH A 20" RECTANGULAR CRT AND AN 8" PM SPEAKER, HOUSED IN A VERY PLAIN CONSOLE CABINET WITHOUT DOORS.

#1008

#1010

#1015

| #1010, 1012 | NONE | 1952-53 | UNKNOWN |

1013

THESE MODELS USE A 18-TUBE CHASSIS WITH A 12-CHANNEL ROTARY TUNER AND A 17" OR 20" CRT HOUSED IN VARIOUS STYLES OF TABLETOP AND CONSOLE CABINETS. THE 1010 IS A 17" SET IN A TABLETOP CABINET. I HAVE NO INFORMATION ON THE OTHER CABINETS.

| #1015, 1016 | NONE | 1951-52 | UNKNOWN |

1017, 1018

1019

THE SAME 21-TUBE 12-CHANNEL CHASSIS AS THE 1005 IS USED HERE WITH A 20" OR 21" CRT DEPENDING ON THE CABINET. ALL ARE HOUSED IN VARIOUS STYLES OF CONSOLE CABINET. THE 1015 HAS A WOOD CONSOLE CABINET WITH FULL DOORS AND A 21" CRT. I HAVE NO INFORMATION ON THE STYLING OF THE OTHERS.

| #1021, 1022 | NONE | 1952-53 | UNKNOWN |

1026, 1027

THE SAME 18-TUBE CHASSIS AS THE 1010 WITH A 20" CRT HOUSED IN VARIOUS CONSOLE CABINETS. 120 VOLTS AC.

| #1025 | NONE | 1952-53 | UNKNOWN |

A 21-TUBE 12-CHANNEL SET WITH A 21" CRT AND BUILT-IN 3-SPEED RECORD CHANGER HOUSED IN A WOOD CONSOLE CABINET WITH FULL DOORS. THE RECORD CHANGER IS MOUNTED IN A PULL-OUT DRAWER IN THE SPEAKER COMPARTMENT.

| #1050, 1072, 1074, 1075, 1077 | 1953-54 | UNKNOWN |

1078, 1081, 1085, 1088, 1092

ALL THESE MODELS USE THE SAME 18-TUBE CHASSIS WITH A 12-CHANNEL ROTARY TUNER AND EITHER 17", 20", OR 21" RECTANGULAR CRT. THEY ARE HOUSED IN VARIOUS STYLES OF TABLETOP AND CONSOLE CABINETS. THE 1075 IS A 21" SET IN A COMPACT TABLETOP BAKELITE CABINET (DARK BROWN OR BLACK).

#1025

#1075

#14808

#1051, 1052, 1053   1953-54 UNKNOWN
1054, 1055, 1056
1060, 1061, 1062, 1063
ALL OF THESE MODELS USE THE SAME 18-TUBE CHASSIS AS THE 1010 WITH VARIOUS SIZE CRTS— FROM 17" TO 21"—AND ARE HOUSED IN CONSOLE AND TABLETOP CABINETS OF VARIOUS STYLES. I HAVE NO OTHER INFORMATION ON THESE MODELS.

#1082, 1086   1954-55 UNKNOWN
THESE TWO MODELS USE A 19-TUBE CHASSIS WHICH IS THE SAME BASIC CHASSIS USED IN THE 1050. THE ADDITIONAL TUBE IS FOR A UHF TUNER MAKING THESE SETS CAPABLE OF RECEIVING THE STANDARD 12 CHANNELS PLUS THE UHF CHANNELS 13 THROUGH 84. I HAVE NO OTHER INFORMATION.

#1111, 1113   1952-53 UNKNOWN
THESE MODELS USE THE SAME 18-TUBE 12-CHANNEL CHASSIS AS THE 1010. I HAVEN'T A CLUE AS TO THE DIFFERENCES EXCEPT TO SAY IT IS PROBABLY IN THE CRT SIZE AND CABINET STYLING.

#14808   1952-53 UNKNOWN
THIS MODEL USES A 21-TUBE CHASSIS WITH 12-CHANNEL TURRET TUNER AND A 14" RECTANGULAR CRT. THE CHASSIS IS VERY SIMILAR TO THE 1000. THE SET IS HOUSED IN A "LEATHERETTE" COVERED WOOD TABLETOP CABINET.

#1790P, 1790U   1958 UNKNOWN
7PT
THESE MODELS USE A 13-TUBE WRAP-AROUND VERTICAL CHASSIS WITH A 12-CHANNEL ROTARY TUNER AND 17" CRT HOUSED IN VARIOUS STYLES OF COMPACT METAL AND WOOD TABLETOP CABINETS. 120 VOLTS AC.

#1790P

#17838

#17804, 17812, 17813, 17814   1951-52   UNKNOWN
17815, 17819, 17824, 17825
17838, 17848, 17849, 17850
A 21-TUBE CHASSIS WITH 17" RECTANGULAR CRT, 12-CHANNEL TURRET TUNER, AND PHONOGRAPH INPUT JACK HOUSED IN VARIOUS STYLES OF TABLETOP AND CONSOLE CABINETS. THE 17814 IS A MAHOGANY-FINISHED TABLETOP CABINET, THE 17838 IS A MAHOGANY-FINISHED CONSOLE WITH HALF-DOORS. THE TABLETOP MODELS USE A 5" PM SPEAKER AND THE CONSOLES A 10" PM SPEAKER.

#17811, 17816, 17817   1951-52   UNKNOWN
17860, 17861
A 24-TUBE CHASSIS WITH 17" RECTANGULAR CRT, 12-CHANNEL TURRET TUNER WITH BUILT-IN AM RADIO. THE 17811 IS A TABLETOP "MASONITE" CABINET FINISHED IN SIMULATED MAHOGANY WOOD GRAIN. THE 17816 AND 17817 ARE WOOD TABLETOPS FINISHED IN MAHOGANY AND "GOLDEN OAK" RESPECTIVELY, AND THE 17860 AND 17861 ARE CONSOLES. THE TABLETOPS USED A 5" PM SPEAKER AND THE CONSOLES USED A 12" PM SPEAKER. 120 VOLTS AC.

17810, 17905   1951-52   UNKNOWN
A 16-TUBE CHASSIS WITH A 17" RECTANGULAR CRT AND A 12-CHANNEL TURRET TUNER. THE 905 IS ALSO IN A TABLETOP CABINET COVERED IN BROWN "LEATHERETTE," WITH A 5" PM SPEAKER. 120 VOLTS AC.

#17906, 17908, 17922, 17930   1951-52   UNKNOWN
17931, 17932, 17933, 17934
A 21-TUBE CHASSIS WITH 17" RECTANGULAR CRT AND 12-CHANNEL TURRET TUNER HOUSED IN VARIOUS STYLES OF TABLETOP AND CONSOLE CABINETS WITH 5", 8", OR 10" PM SPEAKERS DEPENDING ON THE CABINET. 120 VOLTS AC.

#20823   1952-53   UNKNOWN
THIS MODEL USES THE SAME 21-TUBE, 12-CHANNEL CHASSIS AS THE 14808, WITH A 20" RECTANGULAR CRT. I HAVE NO INFORMATION ON THE CABINET.

#17817

#17810

#20872	NONE	1951	UNKNOWN

A 14-TUBE CHASSIS WITH A 12-CHANNEL DUAL-RANGE CONTINUOUS TUNER, A 19"
ROUND (METAL) CRT, AND A 10" PM SPEAKER HOUSED IN A MAHOGANY WOOD CON-
SOLE CABINET WITHOUT DOORS. 120 VOLTA AC.

#20882	NONE	1951	UNKNOWN

THE SAME 21-TUBE 12-CHANNEL CHASSIS AS THE 17804 IS USED HERE WITH A 20" RECT-
ANGULAR CRT AND A 10" PM SPEAKER HOUSED IN A MAHOGANY WOOD CONSOLE
CABINET WITH HALF DOORS.

#20990, 20994		1951-52	UNKNOWN

THESE MODELS USE A 24-TUBE CHASSIS WITH A 12-CHANNEL TURRET TUNER, 20" RECT-
ANGULAR CRT, 12" PM SPEAKER, BUILT-IN AM RADIO, AND THREE-SPEED RECORD
CHANGER. THEY ARE HOUSED IN A LARGE CONSOLE CABINET WITH FULL DOORS. THE
20994 IS MAHOGANY. 120 VOLTS AC.

#21923, 21928		1951-52	UNKNOWN
21940, 21980

THESE MODELS USE A 21-TUBE CHASSIS WITH 12-CHANNEL TURRET TUNER AND A 20"
ROUND CRT HOUSED IN VARIOUS STYLES OF TABLETOP AND CONSOLE CABINETS. THE
21980 IS A MAHOGANY CONSOLE WITHOUT DOORS AND USES A 10" PM SPEAKER.

MODEL 20994

#20994

#20872

MODEL 21980

#21980

17T101

17T740

17T720

17TT700

17K110,17K111,17T100   1955-56   UNKNOWN
17T101,17T170,17T171

THESE MODELS USE A 20-TUBE CHASSIS WITH A 17" RECTANGULAR CRT AND BOTH VHF AND UHF TUNERS COVERING CHANNELS 2 THROUGH 83. THEY ARE HOUSED IN VARIOUS TYPES OF TABLETOP AND CONSOLE CABINETS AND A 5" OR 8" PM SPEAKER DEPENDING ON THE CABINET. 120 VOLTS AC.

17TS700, 710   1956   UNKNOWN
17TS720, 730

USING A 14-TUBE VERTICAL WRAP-AROUND CHASSIS WITH SIDE-MOUNTED CONTROLS, A 12-CHANNEL ROTARY SWITCH TUNER AND A 17" RECTANGULAR CRT. THESE MODELS ARE HOUSED IN VARIOUS COMPACT TABLETOP CABINETS. 120 VOLTS AC.

17TS740, 760,   1957-58   UNKNOWN
17TS780

THESE MODELS USE A 14-TUBE VERTICAL WRAP-AROUND CHASSIS WITH A 17" RECTANGULAR CRT AND BOTH UHF AND VHF TUNERS COVERING CHANNELS 2 THROUGH 83. SIDE-MOUNTED CONTROLS, HOUSED IN A COMPACT TABLETOP CASE, 120 VOLTS AC. THE DIFFERENCE IN MODELS IS THE COLOR OF CASE AND TRIM.

17TT700, 701, 710, 711   1956-57   UNKNOWN
17TT760, 761

THESE MODELS USE A 13-TUBE VERTICAL WRAP-AROUND CHASSIS WITH A 17" RECTANGULAR CRT, TOP MOUNTED CONTROLS, UHF AND VHF TUNERS, AND ARE HOUSED IN COMPACT TABLETOP CASES. THE DIFFERENCE AMOUNG MODELS IS THE COLOR OF THE CASE AND TRIM. 120 VOLTS AC.

1K140, 141, 150, 151   1955-56   UNKNOWN
1T120, 121, 160, 161

THE SAME 20-TUBE VHF-UHF CHASSIS AS THE 17K110, WITH A 21" RECTANGULAR CRT
HOUSED IN TABLETOP AND CONSOLE CABINETS OF VARIOUS STYLES.

1K200, 201, 210   1956   UNKNOWN
1K211, 220, 221
1K230, 231

A 26-TUBE CHASSIS WITH A 21" RECTANGULAR CRT AND BOTH VHF AND UHF TUNERS
COVERING CHANNELS 2 THROUGH 83 AND HOUSED IN VARIOUS STYLES OF CONSOLE
CABINETS WITH AN 8" PM SPEAKER. THE 21K211 IS A TRADITIONALLY-STYLED MAHOGANY
CONSOLE WITHOUT DOORS. 120 VOLTS AC.

1K330, 340   1955-56
1T320

A 15-TUBE WRAP-AROUND VERTICAL CHASSIS WITH 21" RECTANGULAR CRT, 12-
CHANNEL TURRET TUNER, SIDE-MOUNTED CONTROLS HOUSED IN VARIOUS COMPACT
TABLETOP AND CONSOLE CABINETS. SOME MODELS HAVE UHF AND VHF TUNERS.

21K340

21K211

21K330

21K331, 341   1955-56   UNKNOWN
21T321

THESE MODELS USE THE SAME CABINETS AND CHASSIS AS THE 21K330, BUT HAVE A UHF TUNER COVERING CHANNELS 14 THROUGH 83 AND EMPLOY AN ADDITIONAL TUBE (FOR A TOTAL OF 16).

21K370, 371   1956   UNKNOWN
21T360, 361

ALL THESE MODELS USE THE SAME 15-TUBE CHASSIS WITH A 21" CRT, AND BOTH VHF AND UHF TUNERS AND FRONT-MOUNTED CONTROLS. THEY ARE HOUSED IN VARIOUS STYLES OF CONSOLE AND COMPACT TABLETOP CABINETS. 120 VOLTS AC.

21KT520, 521   1956   UNKNOWN
21KT540, 541

THESE MODELS USE THE SAME 17-TUBE WRAP-AROUND VERTICAL CHASSIS, FRONT-MOUNTED CONTROLS, A 21" CRT, AND BOTH VHF AND UHF TUNERS COVERING CHANNELS 2 THROUGH 83. THEY ARE HOUSED IN VARIOUS STYLES OF CONSOLE AND COMPACT TABLETOP CABINETS. THE SPEAKER SIZE RANGES FROM 4" TO 8" DEPENDING ON THE CABINET. 120 VOLTS AC.

21KS335, 620, 621   1956   UNKNOWN
21KT640

A 15-TUBE VERTICAL WRAP-AROUND CHASSIS WITH 21" CRT AND BOTH VHF & UHF TUNERS COVERING CHANNELS 2 THROUGH 83. THE CONTROLS ARE SIDE-MOUNTED AND THE CABINETS ARE COMPACT TABLETOPS IN VARIOUS STYLES. 120 VOLTS AC.

21KT850, 851   1956   UNKNOWN
21KT854, 855

THESE MODELS USE THE SAME 13-TUBE ALL CHANNEL CHASSIS AS THE 17TT711 WITH A 21" RECTANGULAR CRT HOUSED IN A COMPACT TABLE TOP CASE. AGAIN THE DIFFERENCE IN MODELS IS THE COLOR OF THE CASE AND TRIM. 120 VOLTS AC

21T420,421   1956   UNKNOWN

THE SAME BASIC 15-TUBE VERTICAL WRAP-AROUND CHASSIS AS THE 21K330 WITH UHF AND VHF TUNERS AND 21" RECTANGULAR CRT HOUSED IN VARIOUS COMPACT TABLE TOP AND CONSOLETTE CABINETS.

TRADE NAME   Hallicrafters   HALLICRAFTERS MODEL 21T360M   MODELS   CHASSIS

21T360

21T321

21KT540

21T440,441   1956   **UNKNOWN**

A 15-TUBE VERTICAL WRAP-AROUND CHASSIS WITH A 21" CRT, UHF AND VHF TUNERS. SIDE-MOUNTED CONTROLS HOUSED IN A COMPACT TABLETOP CASE. 120 VOLTS AC.

21TS600,601   1956   **UNKNOWN**
21TT630

A 15-TUBE VERTICAL WRAP-AROUND CHASSIS WITH 21" RECTANGULAR CRT, SIDE-MOUNTED CONTROLS, "ALL CHANNEL" RECEPTION (VHF-UHF 2 THROUGH 83). HOUSED IN VARIOUS STYLES OF COMPACT TABLETOP CABINETS. 120 VOLTS AC.

#21TS751M   **NONE**   1956   **UNKNOWN**

A 15-TUBE VERTICAL WRAP-AROUND CHASSIS WITH A 21" RECTANGULAR CRT, TOP-MOUNTED CONTROLS, AND ALL CHANNEL TUNING (2 THROUGH 83). HOUSED IN A COMPACT TABLETOP CABINET WITH VARIEGATED MAROON AND BLACK PAINTED FINISH. 120 VOLTS AC.

21TT750,751   1956   **UNKNOWN**

A 13-TUBE VERTICAL WRAP-AROUND CHASSIS WITH A 21" RECTANGULAR CRT, UHF AND VHF TUNERS, AND TOP MOUNTED CONTROLS HOUSED IN A COMPACT TABLETOP CASE. 120 VOLTS AC. THE DIFFERENCE IN MODELS IS THE COLOR OF THE CASE.

24K240,241   1955-56   **UNKNOWN**

A 24-TUBE CHASSIS WITH A 24" RECTANGULAR CRT, ALL-CHANNEL TUNING (2 THROUGH 83), AND A 10" PM SPEAKER HOUSED IN A WOOD CONSOLE CABINET WITH FULL DOORS. THE FINISH WAS MAHOGANY OR BLOND OAK. 120 VOLTS AC.

24K380, 381   1955-56   **UNKNOWN**
24K480, 481

THESE MODELS USE THE SAME 15-TUBE ALL-CHANNEL CHASSIS AS THE 21K370 WITH A 24" CRT AND ARE HOUSED IN VARIOUS STYLES OF CONSOLE AND TABLETOP CABINETS. THE SPEAKER SIZE RANGES FROM 4" TO 8" DEPENDING ON THE CABINET.

24KT550,551   1955-56   **UNKNOWN**
24TT510,511

THESE MODELS USE THE SAME 17-TUBE ALL-CHANNEL CHASSIS AS THE 21KF520 WITH A 24" RECTANGULAR CRT HOUSED IN VARIOUS CONSOLE AND COMPACT TABLETOP CABINETS WITH A 4", 6", OR 8" PM SPEAKER DEPENDING ON THE CABINET.

21TS751M

21T440

24KT550

24T430, 431   1955-56   **UNKNOWN**

A 15-TUBE VERTICAL WRAP-AROUND CHASSIS WITH A 24" RECTANGULAR CRT AND VHF/UHF ALL-CHANNEL TUNING, SIDE-MOUNTED CONTROLS, 120 VOLTS AC. HOUSED IN CONSOLETTE CABINETS SIMILAR TO THE 21K340.

24T450, 451   1955-56   **UNKNOWN**

THESE MODELS USE THE SAME 15-TUBE CHASSIS AS THE 24T430 AND ARE HOUSED IN A COMPACT TABLETOP CABINET SIMILAR TO THE 21T440.

24TS601, 610, 611   1956   **UNKNOWN**

A 15-TUBE WRAP-AROUND VERTICAL CHASSIS WITH A 24" RECTANGULAR CRT, ALL CHANNEL TUNING, AND SIDE-MOUNTED CONTROLS HOUSED IN A COMPACT TABLETOP CABINET FINISHED IN SIMULATED MAHOGANY OR BLOND OAK, WITH A 4" PM SPEAKER. 120 VOLTS AC.

27K250, 251   1955-56   **UNKNOWN**

THESE MODELS USE THE SAME 24-TUBE ALL-CHANNEL CHASSIS AS THE 24K240 WITH A 27" RECTANGULAR CRT, HOUSED IN A WOOD CONSOLE CABINET WITH FULL DOORS. FINISHED IN MAHOGANY OR BLOND OAK, WITH A 10" PM SPEAKER.

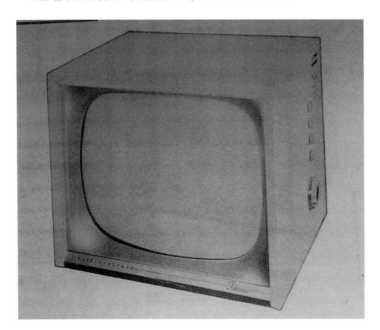

24TS610

21CK801   1955-56   **UNKNOWN**

THIS MODEL IS THE ONLY COLOR TELEVISION PRODUCED BY THE COMPANY THAT I AM AWARE OF. IT USES A 26-TUBE CHASSIS DESIGNED BY RCA (TYPE CTC4) WITH A 21" ROUND CRT (21AXP22), AND ALL-CHANNEL TUNING, HOUSED IN A HALLICRAFTERS-DESIGNED CONSOLE CABINET WITHOUT DOORS FINISHED IN MAHOGANY OR BLOND OAK. 120 VOLTS AC.

With the exception of the model 21CK801, all of these televisions are black and white sets. Before the 21CK801 color set was produced, there was an experimental 15" color set built. Although I have no proof, I believe that about ten of these experimental prototypes were produced and were then sent to some of the larger Hallicrafters distributers for demonstration purposes.

(This information was kindly relayed by "word of mouth" from Ed Reitan, a color t.v. historian.)

27K250

MISCELLANEOUS UNITS OF VARIOUS MODEL SERIES

MODEL	NAME	DATE	ORIGINAL PRICE
A-84	SUPER FIDELITY	1953-55	$99.50

A 5-TUBE 10-WATT HI-FI AUDIO AMPLIFIER. FEATURES INCLUDE A FREQUENCY RESPONSE OF 10Hz TO 100KHz, TOTAL HARMONIC DISTORTION OF LESS THAN 0.17% AT 10 WATTS OUTPUT, HUM AND NOISE LEVEL 80db AT 10 WATTS, SENSITIVITY IS 1.25 VOLTS RMS FOR A 10 WATT OUTPUT, OUTPUT IMPEDANCE OF 8 AND 16 OHMS. TUBES USED: 12AU7 PREAMP AND INVERTER, 12AU7 PUSH-PULL DRIVER, TWO KT-66s IN PUSH-PULL AUDIO OUTPUT, AND A 5V4 RECTIFIER. THE POWER SOURCE IS 120 VOLTS AC. THIS AMPLIFIER WAS DESIGNED FOR USE WITH THE ST-83 TUNER AND THE A-85 PRE-AMP FOR CUSTOM INSTALLATIONS. IT WAS ALSO USED WITH OTHER COMPONENTS IN THE 1621 AND 1622 CONSOLE SYSTEMS. THE CHASSIS IS CHROMED.

A-84 SUPER FIDELITY

A-85   NONE   1953-55 $69.50

THIS IS A SEPERATE PRE-AMPLIFIER DESIGNED FOR USE WITH THE A-84 POWER AMPLIFIER. I HAVE NO OTHER DATA ON THIS UNIT.

AT-1, 2, 3   ATOM   1953   UNKNOWN

A 4-TUBE 1-BAND TABLE RADIO COVERING 540KHz TO 1620KHz WITH BUILT-IN LOOP ANTENNA, PROVISION FOR EXTERNAL ANTENNA, AND A 455KHz IF FREQUENCY. THEY ARE HOUSED IN COMPACT PLASTIC CASES AND THERE WERE AT LEAST THREE PRODUCTION RUNS. THE ONLY DIFFERENCE BETWEEN MODELS IS THE COLOR OF THE CASE. THE POWER SOURCE IS 120 VOLTS AC-DC. TUBES USED: 12AU6 OSCILLATOR AND MIXER, 12AV6 IF AND 1st AUDIO, 50C5 AUDIO OUTPUT, AND 35W4 RECTIFIER. IT IS INTERESTING TO NOTE THAT THESE MODEL NUMBERS WERE USED TWICE: FOR THESE RADIOS AND FOR THE ANTENNA TUNERS ASSOCIATED WITH THE H-4 TRANSMITTER.

ATCL-5, 6   ATOM   1952-53   UNKNOWN
ATCL-7, 8
ATCL-9, 10, 11

A 5-TUBE 1-BAND CLOCK RADIO COVERING 535KHz TO 1620KHz WITH A 455KHz IF. FEATURES INCLUDE "POWER PRINT CIRCUITRY" (ONE OF THE FIRST COMMERCIAL PRODUCTS PRODUCED USING PRINTED CIRCUITRY), BUILT-IN LOOP ANTENNA, AND A TIMED APPLIANCE OUTLET. TUBES USED: 12BE6 OSCILLATOR AND MIXER, 12BA6 IF, 12AV6 DETECTOR, AVC, AND 1st AUDIO, 50C5 AUDIO OUTPUT, AND 35W4 RECTIFIER. THE MAJOR DIFFERENCE IN THE MODELS WAS THE COLOR OF THE BAKELITE CASE. THE ATCL-5 AND 9 WERE BROWN; ATCL-6 AND 10 WERE GREEN; ATCL-7 AND 11 WERE WHITE. THE ATCL-9, 10, AND 11 HAVE A TIMED APPLIANCE OUTLET; THE 5, 6, 7, AND 8 DO NOT. 120 VAC.

AT-1 ATOM (brown)

ATCL-5 ATOM (BROWN)

The AT-2

Another radio built by Hallicrafters for another firm was the Dewald company's model K-412, identical to Hallicrafters' AT-2. I am sure that there were other Hallicrafters radios produced for this company's lines, as well as for companies like Wards, Sears, CBS Columbia, and Delco.

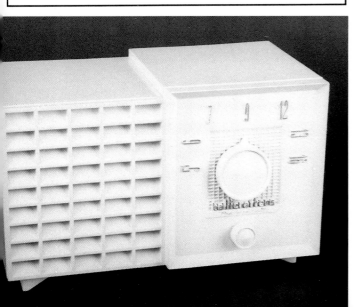

ATCL-7 ATOM (WHITE)

AT-2 ATOM (WHITE)

ATX-11,12   NONE   1953   UNKNOWN
ATX-13

A 5-TUBE 1-BAND RADIO COVERING THE STANDARD AM BROADCAST BAND WITH A 455KHz IF. THESE MODELS ALSO USE PRINTED CIRCUITRY AND HAVE A BUILT-IN LOOP ANTENNA. TUBES USED: 12BE6 OSCILLATOR AND MIXER, 12BA6 IF, 12AV6 DETECTOR, AVC, AND 1st AUDIO, 50C5 AUDIO OUTPUT, AND 35W4 RECTIFIER. THE ONLY DIFFERENCE AMONG MODELS IS THE COLOR OF THE COMPACT MOLDED PLASTIC CASE. 120 VOLTS AC-DC.

BC-441-A   1942   UNKNOWN

THE MILITARY VERSION OF THE HT-12 RADIO TELEPHONE. A SINGLE-BAND CRYSTAL-CONTROLLED TRANSMITTER WITH TUNABLE OR CRYSTAL-CONTROLLED RECEIVER COVERING 1700KHz TO 2800KHz WITH FOUR SWITCH SELECTABLE CRYSTAL POSITIONS. THE POWER SOURCE IS 120 VOLTS AC.

CA-2   SKYFONE   1947   UNKNOWN
CA-4

A 7-TUBE COMPACT AIRCRAFT TRANSCEIVER. THE TRANSMITTER IS A SINGLE CHANNEL CRYSTAL-CONTROLLED UNIT FOR USE ON ANY FREQUENCY BETWEEN 2MHz AND 7MHz, WITH A POWER OUTPUT OF 10 WATTS. THE RECEIVER IN THE CA-2 TUNES 195KHz TO 410KHz, AND 540KHz TO 1610KHz IN TWO BANDS WITH A 455KHz IF. THE RECEIVER IN THE CA-4 IS A SINGLE BAND UNIT COVERING 195KHz TO 410KHz; OTHERWISE THESE SETS ARE IDENTICAL. THE POWER SUPPLY IS A VIBRATOR TYPE WITH 12-VOLT DC INPUT. TUBES USED: 12BE6 RECEIVER OSCILLATOR AND MIXER, 12BA6 IF, 12AT6 RECEIVER DETECTOR, AVC, 1st AUDIO, AND TRANSMITTER SPEECH AMPLIFIER, A 6V6 RECEIVER AUDIO OUTPUT, A 6V6 TRANSMITTER POWER AMPLIFIER, A 6J5 TRANSMITTER OSCILLATOR, AND A 6X5 RECTIFIER.

CPCR-1*   NONE   1952   NONE

THIS UNUSUAL 5-TUBE CLOCK RADIO WAS NOT A PRODUCTION MODEL. IT IS BUILT INTO A CLEAR "LUCITE" CASE AND WAS SENT TO THE DISTRIBUTORS TO DEMONSTRATE THE COMPANY'S NEW PRINTED CIRUCIT TECHNOLOGY. IT IS ELECTRICALLY IDENTICAL TO THE ATCL SERIES OF CLOCK RADIOS. THE COMPANY DID NOT ISSUE A MODEL NUMBER FOR THIS SET SO I HAVE ISSUED THE NUMBER "CPCR-1" ("CLEAR PLASTIC CLOCK RADIO") FOR IDENTIFICATION.

BC-441-A

(LEFT TO RIGHT) CA-2, CA-4 SKYFONE

CPCR-1

CR-44 **RANGER** 1969-70 $129.95

CR-44A

A 16-TRANSISTOR 5-BAND PORTABLE RADIO COVERING THE STANDARD AM AND FM BROADCAST BANDS PLUS 185KHz TO 400KHz, 2MHz TO 5.2MHz, AND 152MHz TO 173MHz FM. FEATURES INCLUDE A FERRITE ROD ANTENNA BUILT INTO THE ROTATING HANDLE (WITH A COMPASS SO THE SET CAN BE USED AS A DIRECTION FINDER), TELESCOPING WHIP ANTENNA, BATTERY CONDITION AND S-METERS. THE IF FREQUENCIES ARE 455KHz AM AND 10.7MHz FM. THE POWER SOURCE IS 6 VOLTS DC FROM 4 "D" CELLS OR 120 VOLTS AC WITH OUTBOARD ADAPTOR. MADE IN JAPAN.

CR-50 **SEA AIR** 1969-70 $119.95

NEARLY IDENTICAL IN APPEARANCE, FEATURES, AND FUNCTIONS TO THE CR-44, THIS 13-TRANSISTOR 5-BAND PORTABLE RADIO COVERS THE STANDARD AM BROADCAST BAND PLUS 185KHz TO 400KHz, 2MHz TO 5.2MHz, 5.2MHz TO 15.5MHz, AND 108MHz TO 135MHz. THE IF FREQUENCIES ARE 455KHz AND 10.7MHz, THE POWER SOURCE IS 6 VOLTS DC OR 120 VOLTS AC WITH OUTBOARD ADAPTOR. MADE IN JAPAN.

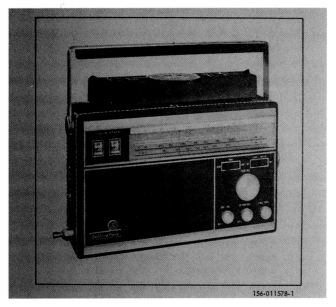

156-011578-1

CR-44 RANGER

CR-50 SEA AIR (FRONT VIEW)

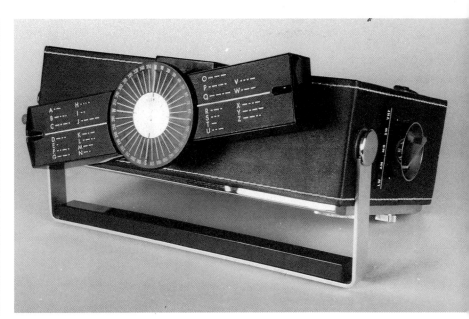

CR-50 SEA AIR (TOP VIEW)

CR-3000

CR-3000 **NONE** 1968-70 $229.95

A 6-BAND DELUXE AM/SW/FM STEREO RECEIVER WITH 33 TRANSISTORS AND 26 DIODES COVERING 190KHz TO 400KHz, 535KHz TO 1605KHz, 2MHz TO 4MHz, 5.85MHz TO 10.3MHz, 11.4MHz TO 18.2MHz, AND 88MHz TO 108MHz. A ROTATING DRUM DIAL DISPLAYS ONLY THE BAND IN USE. OTHER FEATURES INCLUDE A 10-WATT PER CHANNEL POWER OUTPUT, S-METER AND STEREO INDICATOR LIGHT, BUILT-IN FERRITE ROD AND LINE CORD ANTENNAS, MULTIPLE INPUTS FOR MAGNETIC AND CERAMIC PHONOGRAPH CARTRIDGE, TAPE RECORDER, AND AUXILIARY. THE POWER SOURCE IS 120 VOLTS AC, AND THE IF FREQUENCIES ARE 455KHz AND 10.7MHz. MADE IN JAPAN.

CSB-20-2   **COMMAND LINE**   **1964**   **UNKNOWN**
CSM-20-2

A 16-TUBE SINGLE-BAND SINGLE CHANNEL CRYSTAL-CONTROLLED TRANSCEIVER FOR NBFM USE IN THE 148MHz TO 174MHz BAND. THE TRANSMITTER POWER OUTPUT IS 20 WATTS FROM THE 7984 FINAL AMPLIFIER TUBE. OTHER FEATURES INCLUDE A CRYSTAL OVEN, DUAL CONVERSION RECEIVER WITH 8MHz & 455KHz IFs, SQUELCH CONTROL, BUILT-IN SPEAKER, POWER ON AND TRANSMITTER INDICATOR LIGHTS. THE CSM (MOBILE UNIT) USES 12 VOLTS DC WITH A TRANSISTORIZED DC TO DC CONVERTER, AND THE CSB (BASE UNIT) USES A 120-VOLT AC POWER SOURCE.

CSB-30-2   **COMMAND LINE**   **1969**   **UNKNOWN**
CSM-30-2

A 16-TUBE SINGLE-BAND SINGLE-CHANNEL (OPTIONAL DUAL CHANNEL) CRYSTAL-CONTROLLED TRANSCEIVER FOR NBFM USE IN THE 148MHz TO 174MHz BAND. THE TRANSMITTER OUTPUT IS 30 WATTS FROM THE 8150 FINAL AMPLIFIER TUBE. OTHER FEATURES INCLUDE A DUAL CONVERSION RECEIVER WITH 10.7MHz & 1.65MHz IFs, CRYSTAL OVEN, EIGHT-SECTION CRYSTAL-LATTICE FILTER, SQUELCH CONTROL, AND A DETACHABLE CONTROL HEAD THAT CAN BE ATTACHED TO THE RADIO OR CONNECTED BY CABLE. THE CSM (MOBILE UNIT) IS 12 VOLTS DC WITH A TRANSISTORIZED DC TO DC CONVERTER, AND THE CSB (BASE UNIT) HAS A BUILT-IN 120-VOLT AC POWER SUPPLY WITH SILICON RECTIFIERS.

CSB-20-2 COMMAND LINE

CSM-20-2 COMMAND LINE

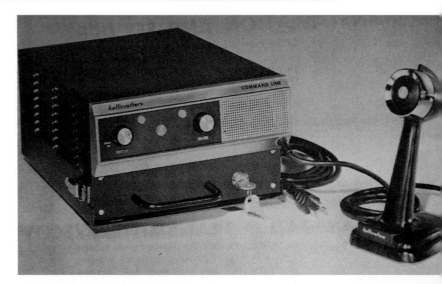

CSB-30-2 COMMAND LINE

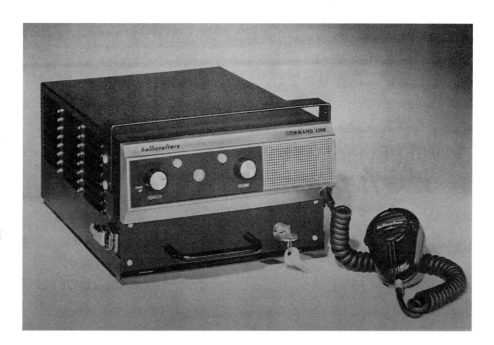

CSM-30-2 COMMAND LINE

CSB-100-2 COMMAND LINE

EP-132

CSB-100-2   **COMMAND LINE**   1968   **UNKNOWN**

AN 18-TUBE SINGLE-BAND SINGLE-CHANNEL (OPTIONAL DUAL CHANNEL) CRYSTAL-CON-TROLLED TRANSCEIVER FOR NBFM BASE USE IN THE 148MHz TO 174MHz BAND. THE TRANS-MITTER OUTPUT IS 100 WATTS FROM THE 7854 FINAL AMPLIFIER TUBE. THE ENTIRE UNIT IS HOUSED IN A STEEL CABINET OF DESKTOP HEIGHT WITH A GRAY LINEN-WEAVE FORMICA TOP. OTHER FEATURES INCLUDE CRYSTAL OVEN, DUAL CONVERSION RECEIVER WITH 10.7 MHz AND 1.65MHz IFs, CRYSTAL-LATTICE FILTER, SQUELCH, AND REMOTE OP-ERATION CAPABILITY. THE POWER SOURCE IS 120 VOLTS AC.

EP-132   **NONE**   1945   **UNKNOWN**

A 19-TUBE 2-BAND UHF-VHF RECEIVER COVERING 210MHz TO 400MHz. THIS RADIO FEA-TURES TWO SEPARATE PUSH-PULL RF AMPLIFIERS, MIXERS, AND OSCILLATORS USING THE ACORN STYLE TUBES, A TUNING CONTROL WITH CONCENTRIC VERNIER TUNING SHAFT AND A 100 TO 1 TUNING RATIO. OTHER FEATURES INCLUDE AN S-METER, ANL AND AU-DIO FILTERS. THE POWER SOURCE IS 120 VOLTS AC. THESE WERE BUILT FOR THE NAVY AS EXPERIMENTAL UNITS WITH THE NAVY DESIGNATION OF "CBPX." THEY ARE SIMILAR IN SIZE AND WEIGHT TO THE S-36.

FM-48

FM-46   NONE   1967 $49.95
FM-48

A 9-TRANSISTOR 11-DIODE 2-BAND TABLE RADIO COVERING THE STAN-DARD AM/FM BROADCAST BANDS, WITH IF FREQUENCIES OF 455KHz AND 10.7MHz. FEATURES INCLUDE FM AFC WITH DEFEAT SWITCH, BUILT-IN FERRITE ROD LOOP ANTENNA FOR AM AND FM LINE CORD AN-TENNA WITH PROVISION FOR EXTERNAL FM ANTENNA. THE POWER SOURCE IS 120 VOLTS AC. THE FM-48 IS HOUSED IN A WOOD CABINET FINISHED IN WALNUT BROWN. MADE IN JAPAN.

FM-52 PROTOTYPE, NO CLOCK

FM-52, 54, 56   NONE   1967 $59.95

THESE MODELS ARE AM/FM CLOCK RADIOS USING THE SAME CHASSIS AS THE FM-46 AND ARE HOUSED IN MOLDED PLASTIC TABLETOP CABINETS WITH A CLOCK MOUNTED ON THE LEFT SIDE OF THE CABINET. THE DIFFERENCE IN MODELS IS THE COLOR OF THE CABI-NET. THE FM-52 SHOWN HERE IS A PRE-PRODUCTION PROTOTYPE SAMPLE UNIT AND DOES NOT HAVE THE CLOCK. MADE IN JAPAN.

FM-66

FM-54

FM-66   NONE   1966   UNKNOWN

A 6-TUBE 2-BAND TABLE RADIO COVERING THE STANDARD AM/FM BROADCAST BANDS WITH IF FREQUENCIES OF 455KHz AND 10.7MHz. HOUSED IN A WOOD CABINET FINISHED IN WALNUT BROWN. FEA-TURES INCLUDE FM AFC WITH DEFEAT SWITCH, BUILT-IN FERRITE LOOP AM ANTENNA AND FM LINE CORD ANTENNA WITH PROVISION FOR EXTERNAL ANTENNA. THE CHASSIS USED IN THIS MODEL IS NEARLY IDENTICAL TO THE WR-700. 120 VOLTS AC. TUBES USED: 12DT8 FM RF AMP AND OSCILLATOR, 12BE6 AM OSCILLATOR AND MIXER, 12BA6 AM IF AND 1st FM IF, 12BA6 AM DETECTOR, AVC, FM 2nd IF, 12AV6 1st AU-DIO, 50C5 AUDIO OUTPUT, AND A SILICON DIODE RECTIFIER.

FM-1000

H2M-500

H2M-1000

H8PA SKY MASTER
Photograph courtesy of Dan Mertz, Richland WA.

| M-1000 | NONE | 1970 | $39.95 |

A 10-TRANSISTOR 2-BAND PORTABLE RADIO COVERING THE STANDARD AM/FM BROAD-
CAST BANDS. BUILT-IN FERRITE ROD AM LOOP ANTENNA AND TELESCOPING WHIP FM
ANTENNA. THE POWER SOURCE IS FOUR 1.5-VOLT "AA" CELLS OR 120 VOLTS AC WITH
BUILT-IN AC ADAPTOR. MADE IN JAPAN.

| H2M-500 | NONE | 1977 | $389.00 |

A SOLID-STATE FREQUENCY SYNTHESIZED 800 CHANNEL 2-METER FM TRANSCEIVER WITH
PLL DIGITAL FREQUENCY READ-OUT. FOR MOBILE USE IN THE 144MHz TO 148MHz AMA-
TEUR BAND. TUNING IS IN 5KHz STEPS AND THE TRANSMITTER POWER OUTPUT IS EI-
THER 1 OR 25 WATTS. OTHER FEATURES INCLUDE NOISE BLANKER AND REPEATER OFF-
SET FUNCTIONS. THE POWER SOURCE IS 12 VOLTS DC.

| H2M-1000 | NONE | 1977 | $749.00 |

A SOLID-STATE FREQUENCY SYNTHESIZED 800 CHANNEL 2-METER CW/FM/SSB TRANS-
CEIVER WITH PLL DIGITAL FREQUENCY READ-OUT. FOR BASE OR MOBILE USE IN THE
144MHz TO 148MHz AMATEUR BAND. TUNING IS IN 5KHz STEPS AND THE TRANSMITTER
POWER OUTPUT IS 12 WATTS. OTHER FEATURES INCLUDE A NOISE BLANKER, REPEATER
OFFSET, AND BUILT-IN 12-VOLT DC AND 120-VOLT AC POWER SUPPLIES.

| H8PA | SKY MASTER | 1936 | UNKNOWN |

A 8-TUBE 3-BAND RECEIVER COVERING 545KHz TO 17MHz WITH A 465KHz IF AND HOUSED

HC-100 HAND COMMAND, WITH CARRYING CASE

IN A TABLETOP STEEL CABINET WITH BLACK WRINKLE FINISH. FEATURES INCLUDE A BFO,
"MAGIC EYE" TUNING INDICATOR, VERNIER TUNING AND BOTH 500 AND 5000 OHM
SPEAKER OUTPUT CONNECTIONS. A EXTERNAL SPEAKER IS REQUIRED WITH THIS SET.
THE POWER SOURCE IS 120 VOLTS AC. TUBES USED: 6K7 RF, 6A7 MIXER AND OSCILLATOR,
6K7 IF, 6K7 BFO, 75 DETECTOR AND 1st AUDIO, 76 AUDIO OUTPUT, 6G5 TUNING INDICA-
TOR, AND 80 RECTIFIER.

| HC-100 | HAND COMMAND | 1968-71 | $375.00 |
| HC-100H | | | |

A SOLID-STATE 2-CHANNEL CRYSTAL-CONTROLLED HANDHELD 2-METER FM TRANSCEIVER
COVERING 148 TO 173MHz. DOUBLE CONVERSION RECEIVER, 6-SECTION LATTICE FILTER,
2-WATT OUTPUT, BATTERY CONDITION METER, TELESCOPING WHIP ANTENNA, BUILT-IN
SPEAKER-MICROPHONE, 26 TRANSISTORS. THE POWER SOURCE IS IS 12 VOLTS DC FROM
INTERNAL NI-CAD BATTERY OR EXTERNAL SOURCE. OPTIONAL ACCESSORIES INCLUDE
EXTERNAL PTT MICROPHONE AND EXTERNAL POWER CORD FOR MOBILE USE. THE UNIT
IS HOUSED IN A RUGGED ALUMINUM CASE COVERED WITH BLACK VINYL. THE HC-100H
IS THE SAME BASIC UNIT BUT COVERS 146 TO 148MHz.

HC-150 HAND COMMAND, WITH CARRYING CASE

HC-150   HAND COMMAND   1974   UNKNOWN

A SOLID-STATE CRYSTAL-CONTROLLED 2-METER FM HANDHELD TRANSCEIVER COVERING 132 TO 174MHz, WITH ONE TO SIX CHANNELS. IT HAS 23 TRANSISTORS, 3 ICs, AND 15 DIODES. FEATURES INCLUDE SQUELCH CONTROL, 2 WATTS OUTPUT, SIMPLEX OPERATION, BUILT-IN SPEAKER-MICROPHONE WITH PTT, JACKS FOR EXTERNAL MICROPHONE, SPEAKER, AND ANTENNA. THE POWER SOURCE IS FROM AN INTERNAL 12-VOLT NI-CAD BATTERY. THE NUMBER OF CHANNELS WAS A USER-SPECIFIED OPTION. THE UNIT SHOWN HERE IS THE ENGINEERING MODEL SHOP PRE-PREDUCTION PROTOTYPE. ACCESSORIES INCLUDE THE JR-150/15 MOBILE MOUNT WITH LINEAR POWER AMPLIFIER.

HC-170   NONE   1977   UNKNOWN

A SOLID-STATE ONE-TO-SIX–CHANNEL CRYSTAL-CONTROLLED 2-METER HANDHELD FM TRANSCEIVER COVERING 132 TO 174MHz. THE RECEIVER IS SINGLE CONVERSION WITH "DUAL PHASE LOCK LOOP" CIRCUITRY. OTHER FEATURES INCLUDE SIMPLEX OPERATION, MODULAR CONSTRUCTION, TRANSMITTER OUTPUT OF 2 OR 5 WATTS, TONE CODED SQUELCH, ENCODE BURST TONE, BUILT-IN SPEAKER-MICROPHONE WITH PTT, PROVISION FOR REMOTE AND MOBILE OPERATION. THE POWER SOURCE IS FROM AN INTERNAL 12-VOLT NI-CAD BATTERY. THE NUMBER OF CHANNELS IS A USER-SPECIFIED OPTION. DURING THIS TIME THE COMPANY WAS OWNED BY THE BRAKER CORPORATION AND THE NAME WAS CHANGED TO "HALLICRAFTERS INTERNATIONAL INC." THESE UNITS WERE BUILT IN TEXAS.

HC-400   HAND COMMAND   1970-75   UNKNOWN
HC-405

A SOLID-STATE CRYSTAL-CONTROLLED HANDHELD FM TRANSCEIVER COVERING 450 TO 512MHz. FEATURES INCLUDE A DUAL CONVERSION RECEIVER, SQUELCH, BUILT-IN SPEAKER-MICROPHONE WITH PTT, PROVISION FOR CONTINUOUS TONE SQUELCH FOR SELECTIVE RECEIVING WITH THE CTS-4 ACCESSORY, TRANSMITTER POWER OUTPUT OF 2 WATTS, AND JACKS FOR CONNECTING EXTERNAL SPEAKER, MICROPHONE, PTT, AND ANTENNA. THE UNIT CONTAINS 20 TRANSISTORS, 4 ICs, AND 16 DIODES. THE POWER SOURCE IS A 12-VOLT NI-CAD BATTERY. THERE WERE THREE VERSIONS OF THIS UNIT AVAILABLE: THE "STANDARD" WITH PROVISION FOR 1 OR 2 CHANNELS AND A LIGHT DUTY BATTERY; THE "EXTENDED" WITH PROVISION FOR 1 OR 2 CHANNELS; AND THE "DELUXE" WITH PROVISION FOR 1 TO 4 CHANNELS AND A HEAVY DUTY BATTERY. THE NUMBER OF CHANNELS WAS A USER-SPECIFIED OPTION. ACCESSORIES INCLUDE THE JR-430 MOBILE MOUNTING RACK WITH LINIER POWER AMPLIFIER.

HC-170

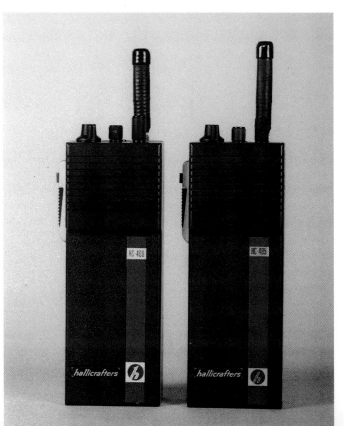

HC-400, HC-405 HAND COMMAND

HC-450	NONE	1977	UNKNOWN

THE HC-450 HAS THE SAME FUNCTIONS, FEATURES, APPEARANCE, AND SPECIFICATIONS AS THE HC-170 EXCEPT FOR ITS FREQUENCY COVERAGE, WHICH IS EITHER 405 TO 420MHz OR 450 TO 512MHz (USER-SPECIFIED) AND A POWER OUTPUT OF 2 OR 4 WATTS.

HC-500	NONE	1977	UNKNOWN

THIS UNIT IS SIMILAR TO THE HC-170, CAN HAVE FROM ONE TO SIX CHANNELS, AND IS FOR USE IN THE 450 TO 470MHz BAND. THE TRANSMITTER OUTPUT POWER IS SELECTABLE AND CAN BE 0.2, 0.4, 1.0, 2.0, OR 4.0 WATTS. THE POWER SOURCE IS 12 VOLTS FROM STANDARD OR RECHARGABLE "AA" CELLS.

HCM-260	NONE	1977	UNKNOWN

A 23-CHANNEL SOLID-STATE CITIZENS BAND TRANSCEIVER FEATURING A COMBINATION OF OUTPUT AND S-METER, RIT, SQUELCH, PA OR CB SWITCH, ANL, AND TRANSMIT AND RECEIVE INDICATOR LIGHTS. FOR 12-VOLT DC MOBILE OPERATION. THE TRANSMITTER OUTPUT POWER IS 5 WATTS, MADE IN JAPAN.

HT-1E	VILLAGE RADIO	1967	UNKNOWN

A SOLID-STATE CRYSTAL-CONTROLED SINGLE-CHANNEL PORTABLE HANDHELD TRANSCEIVER SIMILAR IN APPEARANCE TO THE OPS/FM-1 SERIES. IT IS FOR AM TRANSMISSION IN THE 30 TO 40MHz BAND WITH A POWER OUTPUT OF 1/2-WATT. THE RECEIVER IS DUAL CONVERSION. OTHER FEATURES INCLUDE ANL, SQUELCH, AND A RUGGED WEATHERPROOF ALUMINUM CASE. THE POWER SOURCE IS 12 VOLTS FROM 8 INTERNAL "D" CELLS OR EXTERNAL POWER SOURCE. 12 TRANSISTORS AND 5 DIODES. THESE UNITS WERE USED IN CONJUNCTION WITH THE TR-20 BASE UNIT AND HAVE NO CONNECTION WITH THE ORIGINAL HT LINE OF TRANSMITTERS.

HT-2	VILLAGE RADIO	1969-70	UNKNOWN
HT-2A			

A 19-TRANSISTOR 4-DIODE 2-CHANNEL CRYSTAL CONTROLLED PORTABLE HANDHELD FM TRANSCEIVOR FOR GROUND-TO-GROUND AND AIR-TO-GROUND USE IN THE 30 TO 40MHz BAND AND 115 TO 135MHz BAND. THE TRANSMITTER POWER OUTPUT IS 1/2 WATT AND THE RECEIVER IS DUAL CONVERSION. OTHER FEATURES INCLUDE SQUELCH AND WEATHERPROOF ALUMINUM CASE SIMILAR TO THE HT-1E AND OPS/FM-1 SERIES. THERE ARE MINOR DIFFERENCES BETWEEN THE HT-2 & 2A, BUT NO CONNECTION TO THE ORIGINAL HT LINE OF TRANSMITTERS.

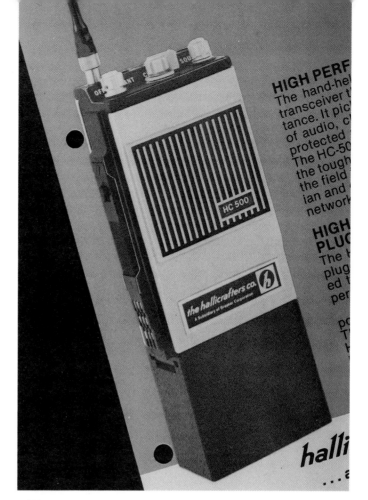

HC-450

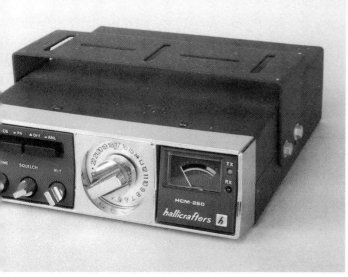

HCM-260

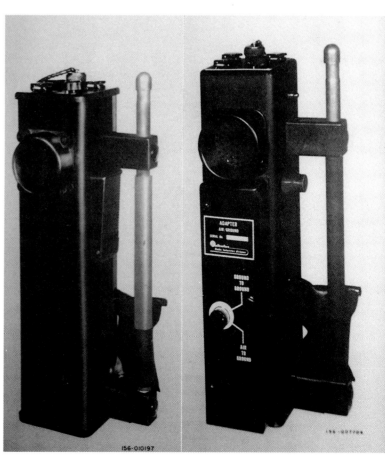

HT-1E VILLAGE RADIO   HT-2 VILLAGE RADIO

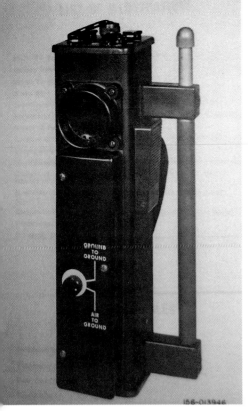

HT-2A VILLAGE RADIO

HTR-262 (TOP VIEW)

HTR-262 (FRONT VIEW)

JR-430 WITH HC-400

| HTR-262 | NONE | 1960 | UNKNOWN |

A TRANSISTOR PORTABLE RADIO COVERING 540KHz TO 1620KHz. FEATURING 6 PLUG-IN TRANSISTORS, A PUSH-PULL AUDIO OUTPUT DRIVING A 6" x 9" PM SPEAKER, TOP-MOUNTED CONTROLS, A MAHOGANY WOOD CASE WITH BRASS TRIM THAT LOOKS THE SAME FROM FRONT OR BACK, AND A UNUSUAL DIAL SYSTEM WITH TRANSVERSE MOVING POINTERS THAT CAN BE READ CORRECTLY WHEN VIEWED FROM FRONT OR REAR. THE IF FREQUENCY IS 455KHz AND THE POWER SOURCE IS 9 VOLTS FROM TWO 4.5-VOLT LANTERN BATTERIES. THESE UNITS WERE BUILT BY HALLICRAFTERS CANADA LTD.

HTR-262

In 1959, Hallicrafters built the CBS Columbia model TR-260, which was the same as the Hallicrafters HTR-262. I am sure there are other models built for this company, as well as for firms like Wards, Sears, Delco, and Dewald.

| JR-150/15 | NONE | 1974 | UNKNOWN |

THIS IS THE MOBILE MOUNTING SYSTEM FOR USE WITH THE HC-150 HANDHELD TRANSCEIVER. IT CONSISTS OF THE MOBILE MOUNTING RACK WITH BUILT-IN 30-WATT LINEAR POWER AMPLIFIER (MODEL PA-150), RA-45 MICROPHONE, PS-5 MOBILE SPEAKER (SIMILAR TO THE R-47), THE A-81 MOBILE WHIP ANTENNA AND VARIOUS MOUNTING HARDWARE. THE AMPLIFIER REQUIRES A DRIVE POWER OF 5 WATTS AND HAS A FREQUENCY RANGE OF 148 TO 164MHz. THE UNIT ALSO HAS A BUILT-IN BATTERY CHARGER TO RECHARGE THE INTERNAL BATTERY OF THE TRANSCEIVER. A KEY LOCK IS PROVIDED SO THE HANDHELD CAN'T BE REMOVED BY UNAUTHORIZED PERSONAL. THE SYSTEM USES THE VEHICLES' 12-VOLT DC POWER SOURCE.

| JR-400 | NONE | 1970-75 | UNKNOWN |
| JR-430 | | | |

THE JR-430 IS THE MOBILE MOUNTING SYSTEM FOR THE HC-400 SERIES HANDHELD TRANSCEIVERS AND HAS THE SAME APPEARANCE, FUNCTIONS, ACCESSORIES, AND SPECIFICATIONS AS THEIR JR-150/15 WITH EXCEPTION OF THE POWER AMPLIFIER (MODEL PA-430), WHICH REQUIRES A DRIVE POWER OF 2 WATTS AND OPERATES IN 450 TO 470MHz FREQUENCY BAND. THE JR-400 IS THE SAME SYSTEM BUT WITHOUT THE POWER AMPLIFIER.

LA-500 NONE 1964-65 UNKNOWN

A CW/SSB/AM LINEAR AMPLIFIER REQUIRING 7 TO 25 WATTS DRIVE POWER FOR 240 WATTS PEP OUTPUT SSB, 200 WATTS CW, AND 60 WATTS CARRIER ON AM. FEATURES INCLUDE 6 PRE-TUNED CHANNELS FOR ANY FREQUENCY BETWEEN 2 & 18MHz, AND A FULL FUNCTION METER TO MONITOR INTERNAL CIRCUITS AND RF OUTPUT. FOUR 7984 TUBES ARE USED FOR THE FINAL RF AMPLIFIER, AND THE SEPERATE POWER SUPPLY (MODEL P-500) USES SILICON DIODE RECTIFIERS. THIS UNIT WAS DESIGNED FOR USE WITH THE SBT-20 SERIES TRANSCEIVERS AND REQUIRES A POWER SOURCE OF 120 OR 240 VOLTS AC. IT WAS BUILT BY THE RADIO INDUSTRIES DIVISION.

MHS-140A NONE 1964 UNKNOWN

A LABORATORY STANDARD FREQUENCY SYNTHESIZER COVERING A SINGLE RANGE OF FREQUENCIES FROM 2.4550MHz TO 3.4550MHz IN 100Hz INCREMENTS WITH A FREQUENCY STABILITY OF 1 PART IN 10^8 PER DAY. FEATURING A MECHANICAL DIGITAL READ-OUT, 100KHz AND 1MHz MARKER OUTPUTS AS WELL AS THE VARIABLE FREQUENCY OUTPUT. THE UNIT CAN BE USED AS A SIGNAL AND MARKER GENERATOR OR RECEIVER AND TRANSMITTER VFO WHERE EXTREEM FREQUENCY ACCURACY IS NEEDED. THE UNIT USES HYBRID CIRCUITRY CONSISTING OF 7 AND 9 PIN MINIATURE TUBES, PENCIL TUBES, TRANSISTORS, AND SILICON DIODES. THE POWER SOURCE IS 120 VOLTS AC.

MHS-400 NONE 1964 UNKNOWN
MHS-402

THESE ARE LABORATORY STANDARD FREQUENCY SYNTHESIZERS SIMILAR IN APPEARANCE, FUNCTION, AND SPECIFICATIONS TO THE MHS-140A. THE FREQUENCY COVERAGE IS FROM 2MHz TO 34MHz IN 4 BANDS. THE POWER SOURCE OF THE MHS-400 IS 120 VOLTS AC, AND THE POWER SOURCE OF THE MHS-402 IS 240 VOLTS AC. THESE INSTRUMENTS AND THE MHS-140A WERE DESIGNED AND BUILT BY THE MANSON LABORATORIES DIVISION OF HALLICRAFTERS.

LA-500 WITH P-500 POWER SUPPLY

MHS-140A

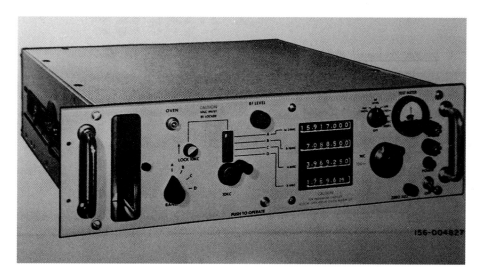

MHS-402

NVD-117	NONE	1977	$3,362.00	
NVD-201			$3,545.00	

THESE ARE "NIGHT VISION DEVICES" DESIGNED TO BE USED BY POLICE DEPARTMENTS AND THE MILITARY. THEIR PRIMARY PURPOSE IS THAT OF A WEAPONS SIGHT THAT COULD BE EASILY ATTACHED TO MOST ASALT TYPE RIFLES. THEY WERE ALSO AVAILABLE WITH A PISTOL GRIP FOR GENERAL NIGHT VIEWING (NVD-201), AND AS AN ATTACHMENT TO VARIOUS TYPES OF CAMERAS. THE POWER SOURCE IS TWO 2.8-VOLT MERCURY BATTERIES, THE OBJECTIVE LENS IS 75mm f/1.4, FIELD OF VIEW IS 48m @ 200m RANGE 36mm f.9, AND THE RESOLUTION (L.P./MM) IS 36.

ALL OF THE "OPS" UNITS WHICH FOLLOW WERE BUILT FOR THE US Office of Public Safety AND WERE INTENDED FOR PARAMILITARY AND POLICE USE. MOST OF THESE MODELS WERE USED TO CREATE LARGER INTEGRATED SYSTEMS, FOR EXAMPLE THE OPS/FM-1A WAS DESIGNED AS A PORTABLE POINT-TO-POINT FIELD TRANSCEIVER WITH THE OPS/FM-5 AS THE BASE UNIT.

OPS/AU-40	NONE	1969	UNKNOWN

A ADAPTOR KIT FOR MOUNTING THE OPS/FM-5 & FM-10 SERIES TRANSCEIVERS ON A MOTORCYCLE, CONSISTING OF A REMOTE CONTROL HEAD WITH MICROPHONE AND AMPLIFIED SPEAKER, AND VARIOUS MOUNTING BRACKETS.

OPS/FM-1A	NONE	1967	UNKNOWN

A 26-TRANSISTOR HANDHELD 2-CHANNEL CRYSTAL-CONTROLLED FM TRANSCEIVER FOR USE IN THE 148 TO 174MHz BAND. BUILT-IN SPEAKER-MICROPHONE, SQUELCH, DUAL CONVERSION RECEIVER AND TRANSMITTER OUTPUT POWER OF 1.5 WATTS. PROVISION FOR EXTERNAL ANTENNA, SPEAKER-MICROPHONE AND POWER. THE POWER SOURCE IS 12 VOLTS DC FROM EIGHT INTERNAL "D" CELLS. THE UNIT IS HOUSED IN A RUGGED WEATHERPROOF EXTRUDED ALUMINUM CASE MEASURING 11.5" TALL BY 2 7/8" SQUARE, AND WEIGHING 4.35 lbs WITH BATTERIES.

Hallicrafters NVD-117 Night Weapons Sight

NVD-117

Hallicrafters Hand-held Night Viewing Instrument

NVD-201

OPS/FM-1A (SIDE VIEW)

OPS/FM-1A (TOP VIEW)

OPS/FM-1B	NONE	1968	UNKNOWN
OPS/FM-1C		1974	
OPS/FM-1H		1971	

THE OPS/FM-1B AND FM-1H HAVE THE SAME FUNCTIONS, SPECIFICA-TION AND APPEARANCE AS THE FM-1A WITH MINOR COSMETIC AND COMPONENT DIFFERENCES. THE FM-1C HAS TWO MORE TRANSISTORS THAN THE OTHERS WITH A TOTAL OF 28. THERE IS A RE- CHARGABLE NI-CAD BATTERY PACK THAT COULD BE USED WITH ALL THESE MOD-ELS IN PLACE OF THE EIGHT "D" CELLS, AND THERE WAS A USER-SPECI-FIED OPTION FOR EITHER NARROW OR WIDE BAND OPERATION.

| OPS/FM-2L | NONE | 1974-77 | UNKNOWN |

THE OPS/FM-2L IS SIMILAR IN APPEARANCE AND FUNCTION TO THE FM-1 SERIES. IT IS FOR FM USE IN THE 30 TO 42MHz BAND, HAS 31 TRAN-SISTORS, PROVISION FOR NARROW OR WIDE BAND OPERATION, A DUAL CONVERSION RECEIVER, SQUELCH, 2-CHANNEL CRYSTAL-CON-TROLLED RECEIVE AND TRANSMIT, AND A TRANSMITTER POWER OUT-PUT OF 2 WATTS. OPTIONAL ACCESSORY ITEMS INCLUDE THE OPS/BS-25 MI-CAD BATTERY (REPLACES THE EIGHT "D" CELLS), BC-13 BATTERY CHARGER, OPS/HS-1 HEADSET, AND VARIOUS   CARRYING CASES.

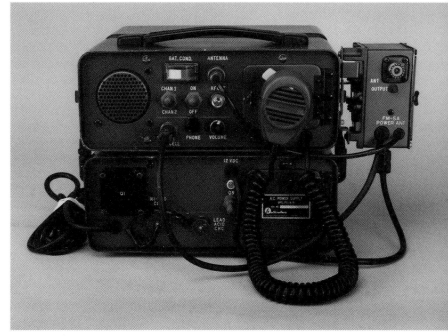

OPS/FM-5 (A-G MODELS) WITH OPS/PS-A16 POWER SUPPLY AND OPS/PA-20 POWER AMPLIFIER

OPS/FM-5 CARRYING BAG

| OPS/FM-5 | NONE | 1969-74 | UNKNOWN |
| (A-G) | | | |

SIMILAR IN PURPOSE TO THE FM-1 SERIES, THIS UNIT IS A 2-CHANNEL CRYSTAL-CONTROLLED FM TRANSCEIVER FOR USE IN THE 146 TO 172MHz BAND. IT CAN BE USED IN PORTABLE, MOBILE, OR BASE STATION OPERATION DEPENDING ON THE ACCESSORIES USED. FEA-TURES INCLUDE A DUAL CONVERSION RECEIVER, CHOICE OF NARROW OR WIDE BAND OPERATION, A TRANSMITTER POWER OUTPUT OF 8 WATTS, AND SQUELCH. THE POWER SOURCE IS 12 VOLTS DC FROM A SEPARATE NI-CAD BATTERY PACK (OPS/BS-25), 120 VOLTS AC FROM THE OPS/PS/A-16 AC POWER SUPPLY, OR 12 VOLTS DC FROM THE OPS/PS-25 DC TO DC CONVERTER FOR MOBILE USE. OTHER ACCESSORIES INCLUDE VARIOUS CAR-RYING CASES, ANTENNAS, MICROPHONES, MOUNTING BRACKETS, AND THE PA-20 POWER AMPLIFIER. THERE ARE RELATIVELY MINOR COSMETIC AND COMPONENT LAYOUT DIFFER-ENCES BETWEEN THE "A" AND "G" MODELS, AND THE NUMBER OF TRANSISTORS USED IS 28 IN THE "A" MODEL AS OPPOSED TO 32 IN THE "G" MODEL. THEY ARE ALL HOUSED IN WEATHERPROOF ALUMINUM CASES.

OPS/FM-7 (A-L)   NONE   1970-74   UNKNOWN

THE OPS/FM-7 HAS THE SAME APPEARANCE, FUNCTIONS, AND GENERAL SPECIFICATIONS AND USES THE SAME ACCESSORIES AS THE FM-5 SERIES EXCEPT IT IS FOR USE IN THE 30 TO 42MHz BAND AND THE TRANSMITTER POWER OUTPUT IS 6 WATTS. IT HAS 31 TRANSISTORS.

OPS/FM-10   NONE   1970   UNKNOWN

THE OPS/FM-10 IS SIMILAR IN APPEARANCE, FUNCTION, AND GENERAL SPECIFICATIONS TO THE FM-5 SERIES AND USES THE SAME ACCESSORIES. THE DIFFERENCES ARE THAT IT IS A 2-BAND UNIT COVERING 132 TO 150 MHz AND 148 TO 172 MHz AND THE OUTPUT POWER OF THE TRANSMITTER IS 10 WATTS.

OPS/FM-10A   NONE   1978   UNKNOWN

WITH MINOR DIFFERENCES THIS UNIT IS THE SAME AS THE FM-10. IT WAS BUILT IN GRAND PRAIRIE, TEXAS AFTER NORTHROP SOLD THE HALLICRAFTERS DIVISION TO THE BRAKER CORPORATION.

OPS/PA-20   NONE   1969-74   UNKNOWN

A 20-WATT SOLID-STATE FM AND CW RF POWER AMPLIFIER FOR USE WITH FM-5 SERIES TRANSCEIVERS. THE FREQUENCY RANGE IS 146 TO 170MHz AND THE POWER SOURCE IS 12 VOLTS DC. THE UNIT HAS THREE TRANSISTORS AND ITS OWN WEATHERPROOF ALUMINUM CASE THAT CAN BE ATTACHED TO THE TRANSCEIVER WITH CLIPS.

OPS/PS-A16   NONE   1969-74   UNKNOWN

THE BASE STATION POWER SUPPLY FOR THE FM-5 AND FM-7 SERIES TRANSCEIVERS WITH OR WITHOUT THE PA-20 POWER AMP. THE INPUT VOLTAGE IS 100 TO 250 VOLTS AC, AND THE OUTPUT VOLTAGE IS 13.6 VOLTS DC AT 5.2 AMPS REGULATED. THE UNIT MAY ALSO BE USED AS A BATTERY CHARGER FOR LEAD-ACID AND NI-CAD BATTERY PACKS. IT IS PACKAGED IN ITS OWN WEATHERPROOF ALUMINUM CASE THAT CAN BE ATTACHED TO THE TRANSCEIVER. IT HAS THREE TRANSISTORS AND SEVERAL DIODES.

OPS/RU-5A   NONE   1969-74   UNKNOWN

THIS IS AN ALL-SOLID-STATE "BACK-TO-BACK" ONE-WAY REPEATER FOR USE WITH THE FM-1 SERIES TRANSCEIVERS. RECEIVES ON 148MC AND TRANSMITS ON 170MC, HAS A THREE-MINUTE TIMER, USES THE FM-1 AS A POWER SOURCE, AND REQUIRES TWO FM-1 UNITS FOR ITS OPERATION—ONE TO RECEIVE AND ONE TO TRANSMIT. IT HAS NINE TRANSISTORS AND SEVERAL DIODES.

OPS/RU-6A   NONE   1969-74   UNKNOWN

A BACK-TO-BACK REPEATER FOR USE WITH THE FM-5 SERIES TRANSCEIVERS. THE UNIT DERIVES ITS POWER FROM THE FM-5 AND REQUIRES TWO FM-5 UNITS FOR A COMPLETE SET-UP. IT HAS EIGHTEEN TRANSISTORS AND SEVERAL DIODES.

PA-120   NONE   1977 $209.00

A SOLID-STATE 120-WATT FM POWER AMPLIFIER REQUIRING AN INPUT DRIVE POWER OF 20 TO 40 WATTS FOR AN OUTPUT POWER OF 80 TO 120 WATTS. THE POWER SOURCE IS 13.8 VOLTS DC. THIS AMPLIFIER WAS DESIGNED AS THE COMPANION FOR THE H2M-500 TRANSCEIVER.

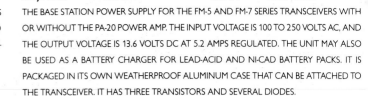

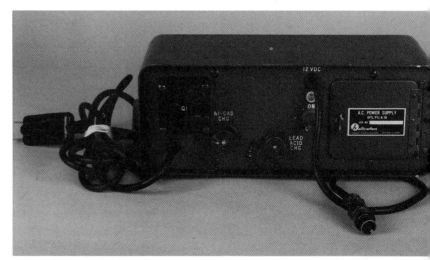

OPS/FM-7L

OPS/PS-A16

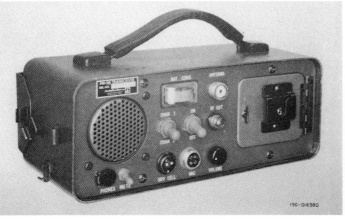

OPS/FM-10

OPS/RU-6A

PA-250L   NONE   1977 $379.00

A SOLID-STATE 250-WATT BROADBAND 2-METER POWER AMPLIFIER FOR FM AND AM/SSB OPERATION. INPUT DRIVE POWER REQUIRED IS 2 TO 15 WATTS FOR 130 TO 250 WATTS FM OUTPUT, AND 150 TO 300 WATTS PEP SSB. THE POWER SOURCE IS 13.8 VOLTS DC. THIS UNIT WAS DESIGNED FOR USE WITH THE H2M-1000 TRANSCEIVER.

PC-210   PORTA COMMAND   1970-72   UNKNOWN

A SOLID-STATE 2-CHANNEL FM TRANSCEIVER FOR USE IN THE 132 TO 150MHz AND 148 TO 174MHz BANDS. FOR PORTABLE, MOBILE, OR BASE USE. THE POWER OUTPUT IS SWITCH-SELECTABLE FOR 2 OR 10 WATTS. BY USING THE MO-12 ADAPTER (MASTER OSCILLATOR) THE NUMBER OF CHANNELS CAN BE INCREASED TO TWELVE. OPTIONAL ACCESSORY ITEMS INCLUDE THE PT-200 120/240-VOLT AC POWER SUPPLY, THE PS-4 10-WATT AMPLIFIED SPEAKER, THE BN-2 BATTERY CASE FOR TWO BS-25 NI-CAD BATTERYS OR EIGHT STANDARD "D" CELLS, THE BC-13 NI-CAD BATTERY CHARGER, THE MR-2B MOBILE MOUNTING RACK, THE RA-45 MOBILE MICROPHONE, THE RA-56 DESK MICROPHONE, THE RA-62 TELEPHONE HANDSET, THE A-79 AND A-80 ANTENNAS, AND THE BG-24 BACKPACK CARRYING CASE. THE POWER SOURCE IS 12 VOLTS DC.

PC-210F   PORTA COMMAND   1790-1972   UNKNOWN

A SOLID-STATE 2-CHANNEL FM TRANSCEIVER SIMILAR IN APPEERENCE TO THE PC-210 AND COVERING A FREQUENCY RANGE OF 160 TO 174MHz. IT IS FOR PORTABLE USE ONLY WITH A POWER OUTPUT OF 5 WATTS. THE POWER SOURCE IS 18 VOLTS DC FROM TWELVE INDUSTRIAL "D" CELLS. OPTIONS INCLUDE THE MO-4 ADAPTOR FOR 4-CHANNEL OPERATION, BN-3 BATTERY CASE, RA-45 MICROPHONE, RA-62 HANDSET, BG-25 OR BG-25HV (HI-VISIBILITY) CARRYING BAG, AND VARIOUS ANTENNAS.

PC-230   PORTA COMMAND   1970-72   UNKNOWN

A SOLID-STATE 2-CHANNEL FM TRANSCEIVER WITH THE SAME APPEARANCE, FUNCTIONS, ACCESSORIES AND SPECIFICATIONS OF THE PC-210 WITH THE FOLLOWING EXCEPTIONS. IT IS FOR MOBILE OR BASE USE ONLY, HAS A POWER OUTPUT OF 30 WATTS, AND USES THE A-82 MOBILE ANTENNA, OR THE A-83, 84, 0R 85 BASE ANTENNA.

PC-210 PORTA COMMAND WITH MO-12 OPTION

PC-230 PORTA COMMAND (STANDARD TWO-CHANNEL)

PC-210F PORTA COMMAND

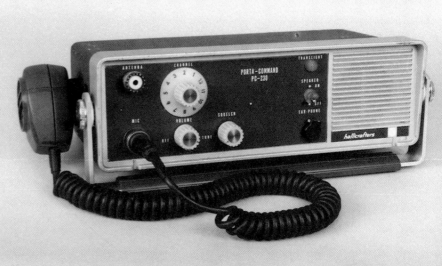

PC-230 PORTA COMMAND (WITH MO-12 OPTION)

PT-200

R-44/ARR-5

R-19/TRC-1

R-45/ARR-7 WITH TUNING MOTOR AND SHOCK MOUNT

PT-200   **NONE**   **1970-72**   **UNKNOWN**

THE BASE STATION POWER SUPPLY FOR THE PC-200 SERIES TRANSCEIVERS. THE INPUT VOLTAGE IS 100 TO 250 VOLTS AC AND THE OUTPUT VOLTAGE IS VARIABLE FROM 12 TO 15 VOLTS DC, AND REGULATED PLUS OR MINUS 1.5 VOLTS FROM 8 MA TO 6 AMPS.

R-19/TRC-1   **1944**   **UNKNOWN**

A 17-TUBE CRYSTAL-CONTROLLED SINGLE-FREQUENCY FM RECEIVER USED IN TELEPHONE COMMUNICATIONS IN THE 39MHz FREQUENCY RANGE. THE POWER SOURCE IS 120 VOLTS AC. FEATURES INCLUDE SQUELCH, ANTENNA TRIMMER, MULTI-FUNCTION METER, BUILT-IN SPEAKER, AND REMOTE CONTROL CAPABILITIES.

R-44/ARR-5   **NONE**   **1944**   **UNKNOWN**

A 14-TUBE 3-BAND RECEIVER COVERING 28 TO 145MHz WITH RECEPTION MODES OF AM, FM, OR CW. THE IF FREQUENCY IS 5.25MHz. FEATURES INCLUDE MOTOR DRIVEN TUNING WITH AUTO REVERSE AND ADJUSTABLE STOPS, ANL, BFO, AN IF OUTPUT JACK FOR CONNECTION OF A PAN-ADAPTOR, AND S-METER. POWER IS SUPPLIED BY AN OUTBOARD 28-VOLT "DYNA-MOTOR." THE UNIT WAS DESIGNED FOR INSTALLATION IN MILITARY AIRCRAFT. IT IS VERY SIMILAR TO THE S-36 ELECTRICALLY BUT IS RADICALLY DIFFERENT PHYSICALLY. TUBES USED: 955 OSCILLATOR, 956 RF AMPLIFIER, 954 MIXER, 6AC7 1st IF, 6AB7 2nd

IF, 6AC7 3rd IF, 6H6 AM 2nd DETECTOR, 6J5 BFO, 6H6 FM DISCRIMINATOR, 6SK7 FM LIMITER, 6SQ7 1st AUDIO, 6V6 AUDIO OUTPUT, OD3/VR-150 VOLTAGE REGULATOR, AND 956 "RADIATION SUPPRESSOR." THE AUDIO OUTPUT IS FOR HEADPHONES ONLY.

R-45/ARR-7   **NONE**   **1944**   **UNKNOWN**

A 12-TUBE 6-BAND RECEIVER COVERING 550KHz TO 42MHz WITH RECEPTION MODES OF AM OR CW. THE IF FREQUENCY IS 455KHz. FEATURES INCLUDE MOTOR-DRIVEN TUNING WITH AUTO REVERSE AND ADJUSTABLE STOPS, ANL, BFO, CRYSTAL FILTER, S-METER, AND AN IF OUTPUT JACK FOR CONNECTION OF A PAN-ADAPTOR. THE POWER SOURCE IS A SEPARATE 28-VOLT "DYNA-MOTOR," AND LIKE THE R-44 THE R-45 WAS DESIGNED FOR INSTALLATION IN MILITARY AIRCRAFT. ELECTRICALLY THIS SET IS VERY SIMILAR TO THE SX-28 ALTHOUGH IT IS PHYSICALLY RADICALLY DIFFERENT. TUBES USED: 6SA7 OSCILLATOR, 6AB7 1st RF, 6SK7 2nd RF, 6SK7 MIXER, 6SA7 1st IF, 6SK7 2nd IF, 6SK7 3rd IF, 6H6 DETECTOR, 6J5 BFO, 6SQ7 1st AUDIO, 6V6 AUDIO OUTPUT, AND OD3/VR-150 VOLTAGE REGULATOR. THE AUDIO OUTPUT IS FOR HEADPHONES ONLY. WHILE BOTH THE R-44 AND R-45 ARE RELATIVELY COMMON IT IS DIFFICULT AND UNUSUAL TO FIND EITHER WITH THE TUNING MOTOR ASSEMBLY INTACT. THE R-45 SHOWN HERE HAS THE MOTOR ASSEMBLY, THE R-44 DOES NOT.

R-274/FRR, R-274D/FRR   1952 $975.00

SEE MODEL SX-73. R-274/FRR IS THE MILITARY NUMBER FOR THE SX-73 AND THERE ARE NO APPRECIABLE DIFFERENCES BETWEEN THE UNITS.

R-649/UR   NONE   1954   UNKNOWN

A 15-TUBE 5-BAND RECEIVER COVERING 200KHz TO 18MHz. RECEPTION MODES ARE AM, CW, AND MCW OVER THE ENTIRE RANGE. FEATURES INCLUDE BFO, ANL, AND BUILT-IN SPEAKER. THE POWER SOURCE IS 120 VOLTS AC OR DC. THE DIAL AND KNOBS ARE SIMILAR TO THE R-274D (SX-73). THESE UNITS WERE BUILT FOR THE TREASURY DEPARTMENT AND USED AS MONITORS BY THE COAST GUARD. THEY ARE OF HEAVY STEEL CONSTRUCTION, RACK MOUNTABLE, AND WEIGH 84 POUNDS.

RBK-13   NONE   1942 $307.50

SEE MODEL S-36. RBK-13 IS THE MILITARY MUMBER FOR THE S-36 AND THERE ARE NO APPRECIABLE DIFFERENCES BETWEEN THE UNITS.

RBK-15   NONE   1944 $307.50

SEE MODEL S-36A. RBK-15 IS THE MILITARY NUMBER FOR THE S-36A. THE ONLY APPRECIABLE DIFFERENCE IS THE ADDITION OF A 16th TUBE, A TYPE 956 USED AS A "RADIATION SUPPRESSOR" BETWEEN THE ANTENNA AND THE RF AMPLIFIER.

R-45/ARR-7 SHOCK MOUNT

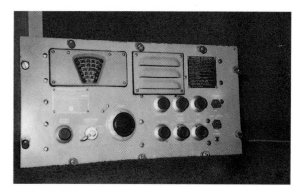

R-649/UR (FRONT VIEW)
Photograph courtesy of David Sampson, Dewitt NY.

R-649/UR (TOP VIEW)
Photograph courtesy of David Sampson, Dewitt NY.

R-274/FRR, R-274D/FRR

RBK-16   NONE   1952   UNKNOWN

THIS 16-TUBE 3-BAND RECEIVER IS VERY SIMILAR TO THE RBK-15 AND S-36A. THE COMPONENT LAYOUT, TUBES USED, FREQUENCY COVERAGES AND RECEPTION MODES ARE IDENTICAL. THE DIFFERENCES: THE PANEL IS GRAY RATHER THAN BLACK, SOME OF THE TRANSFORMERS AND LARGE CAPACITORS ARE A DIFFERENT STYLE, THERE IS NO CIVILIAN MODEL NUMBER ON THE DIAL ESCUTCHEON, MOST OF THE SMALL CAPACITORS ARE CERAMIC DISC TYPE RATHER THAN PAPER AND WAX OR MICA, AND THE WIRING IS ALL TEFLON-COATED RATHER THAN COTTON OR RUBBER.

RBK-16, IN S-36 CABINET

RC-10   NONE   1965   UNKNOWN

A SOLID-STATE 4-CHANNEL CRYSTAL-CONTROLLED BATTERY-OPERATED SINGLE CONVERSION RECEIVER FOR THE RECEPTION OF AM SIGNALS IN THE 3 TO 12MHz FREQUENCY BAND. THE IF FREQUENCY IS 455KHz, AND THE SELECTIVITY IS 5.5KHz MINIMUM AT 6 DB DOWN. THE POWER SOURCE IS 9 VOLTS DC FROM SIX "D" CELLS. EIGHT TRANSISTORS AND TWO DIODES, WITH BUILT-IN SPEAKER AND ANTENNA TRIMMER. BUILT BY THE "RADIO INDUSTRIES" DIVISION.

RC-10

RE-1   SKY COURIER   1942   UNKNOWN

A 7-TUBE 3-BAND PORTABLE RECEIVER COVERING 540KHz TO 19MHz WITH A 455KHz IF. FEATURES INCLUDE BUILT-IN SPEAKER, BAND SPREAD, AND A THREE-WAY POWER SOURCE OF 120 VOLTS AC OR DC, AND BATTERY POWER. TUBES USED: 1R5 OSCILLATOR AND MIXER, TWO 1N5s AS 1st AND 2nd IF, 1H5 DETECTOR AND 1st AUDIO, 50L6 AUDIO OUTPUT FOR 120-VOLT USE, 3Q5 AUDIO OUTPUT FOR BATTERY USE, AND 35Z5 AS RECTIFIER FOR 120-VOLT AC USE. THESE RADIOS WERE USED AS TROOP ENTERTAINMENT AND MORALE-BOOSTERS DURING WORLD WAR II.

RSC-1   NONE   1941 $450.00

THE RSC-1 IS AN ALL-WAVE ALL-MODE RECEIVING SYSTEM COVERING 110KHz TO 143MHz. IT CONSISTS OF THE S-22R, S-27, AND SX-28 MOUNTED IN A TABLETOP RACK CABINET WITH SWITCHING CONTROLS.

RSC-2   NONE   1941 $140.00

THE RSC-2 IS A AM/FM BROADCAST RECEIVING STATION COVERING 540KHz TO 1.6MHz AND 40MHz TO 55MHz (THE OLD COMMERCIAL FM BAND). IT CONSISTS OF THE S-31 AM/FM TUNER, THE S-31A 25-WATT AUDIO AMPLIFIER, AND AN 8" SPEAKER, ALL MOUNTED IN A TABLETOP RACK CABINET.

RSC-2

RE-1 SKY COURIER

RTV-51   1975 $2,855.00
RTV-51-ML $1,870–$2,880 with options

THE RTV-51 IS A RURAL SUBSCRIBER RADIO TELEPHONE SYSTEM TO PROVIDE TELEPHONE SERVICE IN AREAS DISTANT FROM THE CENTRAL OFFICE, WHERE STANDARD TELEPHONE, CABLE, AND HIGH-DENSITY RADIO COMMUNICATIONS ARE NOT FEASIBLE. THE RTV-51 CAN HANDLE UP TO TEN PARTY LINE NUMBERS, AND THE RTV-51-ML CAN HANDLE UP TO TWENTY PRIVATE LINES. THIS IS ACCOMPLISHED OVER A SINGLE PAIR OF VHF FREQUENCIES IN THE 132 TO 174MHz BAND OR UHF IN THE 450 TO 470MHz BAND. EACH SYSTEM HAS A CENTRAL OFFICE TERMINAL AND A SUBSCRIBER TERMINAL, EACH CONSISTING OF RECEIVING AND TRANSMITTING UNITS, VARIOUS SWITCHING AND DIALING UNITS AND POWER SUPPLIES. THE SELLING PRICE VARIED DEPENDING ON THE FREQUENCIES AND OPTIONS DESIRED.

RTV-51, RTV-51-M, A FRONT VIEW OF CONTROL PANEL

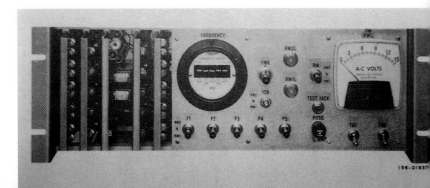

SBT-20   NONE   1964   UNKNOWN

A 6-CHANNEL TUBE-TYPE CRYSTAL-CONTROLLED SSB TRANSCEIVER FOR USE IN THE 2 TO 12MHz BAND. THE TRANSMITTER POWER OUTPUT IS 20 WATTS. THE UNIT USES A EXTERNAL POWER SUPPLY.

SBT-20A   1966   UNKNOWN
SBT-20B   1967

A MOSTLY SOLID-STATE VERSION OF THE SBT-20, THIS 6-CHANNEL CRYSTAL- CONTROLLED SSB/AM TRANSCEIVER OPERATES IN THE 2 TO 12MHz BAND. THE TRANSMITTER POWER OUTPUT IS 20 WATTS PEP SSB AND 5 WATTS AM. IT IS EQUIPPED FROM THE FACTORY FOR UPPER SIDBAND USE. THE POWER SOURCE IS 12 VOLTS DC. OPTIONAL ACCESSORIES INCLUDE THE RA-5 SELECTABLE SIDEBAND MODULE ALLOWING THE USE OF BOTH UPPER AND LOWER SIDEBAND, THE RA-7C MODULE ALLOWING CW AND VOX TRANSMISSION, P-20A 120/240 VOLT AC POWER SUPPLY, BA-4 12-VOLT NI-CAD BATTERY, AND BC-1C BATTERY CASE AND CHARGER. WITH ALL OPTIONS INSTALLED THE UNIT HAS 26 TRANSISTORS, 23 DIODES, AND ONE 8042 TUBE AS THE FINAL RF AMPLIFIER. THERE ARE MINOR COSMETIC AND ELECTRICAL DIFFERENCES BETWEEN THE A & B MODELS. THESE UNITS WERE BUILT BY THE RADIO INDUSTRIES DIVISION IN CHICAGO.

SBT-22-18   NONE   1972-77 $1,067.00–$1,400.00

THE SBT-22-18 IS SIMILAR IN APPEARANCE AND FUNCTION TO THE SBT-22 WITH THE SAME FREQUENCY COVERAGE AND POWER OUTPUT. THE DIFFERENCE IS IN THE NUMBER OF CHANNELS AVAILABLE TO THE USER. IT HAS THE BASIC SIX CHANNELS OF THE SBT-22, WITH EACH MAIN CHANNEL HAVING THREE SUB-CHANNELS, FOR A TOTAL OF EIGHTEEN. THE UNIT HAS 47 TRANSISTORS AND 58 DIODES. IT USES THE SAME OPTIONAL ACCESSORY ITEMS AS THE SBT-22 PLUS THE PS-25 DC TO DC CONVERTER AND HC-6 HAND CRANK GENERATOR. THE UNIT SHOWN HERE HAS THE AT-22 ANTENNA TUNER INSTALLED. PRICE VARIED DEPENDING ON EMISSION MODES AND NUMBER OF CHANNELS INSTALLED.

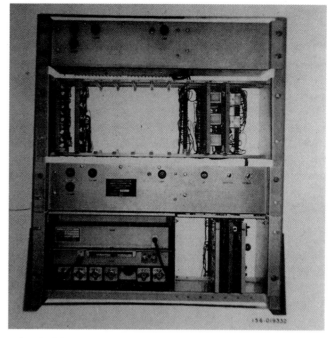

RTV-51, RTV-51-M, RELAY RACK

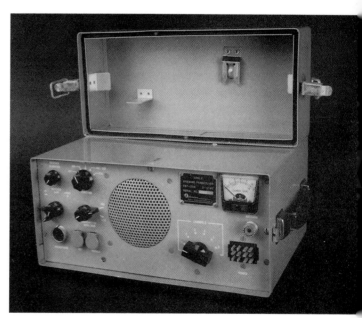

SBT-20A

SBT-22

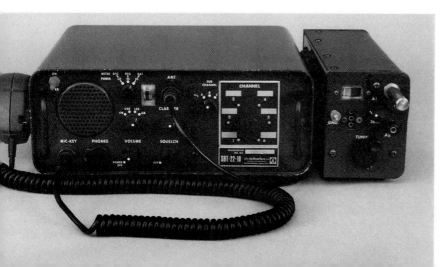

SBT-22   NONE   1969-72   UNKNOWN

A SOLID-STATE 6-CHANNEL CRYSTAL-CONTROLLED TRANSCEIVER COVERING THE 2 TO 18MHz BAND. THE STANDARD OUTPUT MODES ARE CW AND UPPER SIDEBAND. THE POWER OUTPUT OF THE TRANSMITTER IS 20 WATTS SSB AND 5 WATTS AM ON HIGH POWER SETTING, OR 5 WATTS ON LOW POWER SETTING. THE UNIT CAN BE USED IN MOBILE, PORTABLE, OR BASE STATION OPERATION. OPTIONAL ACCESSORIES INCLUDE THE AM AND LOWER SIDEBAND MODULE, PAC-5 120/240-VOLT AC POWER SUPPLY, BA-22 NI-CAD BATTERY, BC-9 BATTERY CHARGER, RA-48 AND RA-62M HANDSETS, RA-45 MICROPHONE, AT-22 ANTENNA TUNER, THE LA-500 LINEAR AMPLIFIER, AND VARIOUS CARRYING CASES AND ANTENNAS. WITHOUT OPTIONS THE UNIT HAS 43 TRANSISTORS AND 55 DIODES AND WAS DESIGNED FOR PARA-MILITARY USE.

SBT-22-18, SHOWN WITH AT-22 ANTENNA TUNER

SBT-100   NONE   1969-77 $1,439.00–$1,750.00

THE SBT-100 IS A MOSTLY SOLD-STATE 6-CHANNEL CRYSTAL-CONTROLLED TRANSCEIVER OPERATING IN THE 2 TO 18 MHz BAND WITH A POWER OUTPUT OF 100 WATTS. THE STANDARD OUTPUT MODES ARE CW AND UPPER SIDEBAND AND CAN BE EXTENDED TO AM AND LOWER SIDEBAND WITH OPTIONAL MODULE. THE BUILT-IN POWER SUPPLY ALLOWS BASE OPERATION FROM A 120 OR 240-VOLT AC SOURCE OR MOBILE OPERATION FROM A 12-VOLT DC SOURCE. THE UNIT HAS 45 TRANSISTORS, 63 DIODES, AND USES TWO 7984 TUBES AS THE FINAL RF AMPLIFIER. OPTIONAL ACCESSORIES INCLUDE THE MR-100 MOBILE RACK, AT-23 AND 24 ANTENNA TUNERS, RCM AND RCB REMOTE CONTROL HEADS, TS-22 TEST SET, OPS/RU-6 REPEATER, AND VARIOUS MICROPHONES, ANTENNAS AND CONNECTING CABLES. PRICE VARIED DEPENDING ON CHOICE OF EMISSION OPTIONS AND NUMBER OF CHANNELS INSTALLED.

SBT-100

STB-1102   NONE   1969   UNKNOWN

A FREQUENCY STABILIZER UNIT FOR USE WITH THE MHS-140A FREQUENCY SYNTHESIZER. ITS PURPOSE WAS TO INCREASE THE STABILITY OF THE MHS-140A ABOVE 1 PART IN 10^8 PER DAY. ALSO MADE BY MANSION LABORATORIES DIVISION.

STB-1102

ST-74   NONE   1950-51   UNKNOWN

A 7-TUBE HI-FI AM/FM TUNER WITH AUDIO PRE-AMP INTENDED FOR CUSTOM INSTALLATION IN THE USER'S CABINET. SOLD AS A CHASSIS ONLY WITH KNOBS AND DIAL ESCUTCHEON. THE IF FREQUENCIES ARE 455KHz AM AND 10.7MHz FM. A SEPARATE AUDIO POWER AMPLIFIER IS REQUIRED. THE POWER SOURCE IS 120 VOLTS AC. TUBES USED: 6AU6 FM RF AMP, 6BE6 AM AND FM OSCILLATOR AND MIXER, 6BA6 1st FM IF & AM, 68A8 2nd FN IF & AM DETECTOR, 12AL5 RATION DETECTOR, 6J5 1st AUDIO, AND 5Y3 RECTIFIER.

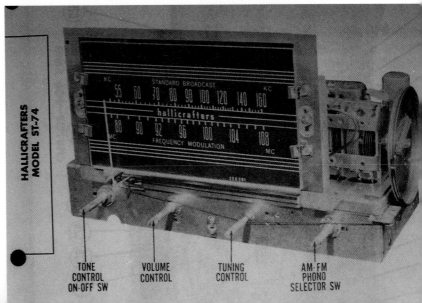

ST-74

ST-83   NONE   1954-55 $129.95

A 12-TUBE DELUXE HI-FI AN/FM TUNER WITH AUDIO PRE-AMP DE-
SIGNED FOR CUSTOM INSTALLATIONS, SOLD WITH COMPLETE FRONT
PANEL AND DUST COVERS. CHROME-PLATED CHASSIS. 455KHz AM IF,
10.7MHz FM IF, WITH AFC, SEPERATE BASS AND TREBLE TONE CONTROLS,
SEPARATE INPUTS FOR TAPE RECORDER, CRYSTAL OR MAGNETIC PHO-
NOGRAPHS WITH BUILT-IN MAGNETIC PHONOGRAPH PRE-AMP, ONE
AUXILLIARY INPUT, TWO SWITCHED AC OUTLETS, AND FERRITE ROD
AM ANTENNA. THE UNIT WAS DESIGNED FOR USE WITH THE A-84
AUDIO POWER AMPLIFIER. POWER SOURCE IS 120 VOLTS AC. TUBES
USED: 6CB6 FM RF AMP, 12AT7 FM OSCILLATOR AND MIXER, TWO 6BA6
AS 1st AND 2nd FM IF, 6BA6 3rd FM IF AND 1st AM IF, 6BD6 AM RF AMP,
6AL5 RATIO DETECTOR, 6BE6 AM OSCILLATOR AND MIXER, 6AV6 AM
DETECTOR, AVC, AND 1st AUDIO, 12AU7 CATHODE FOLLOWER, 12AU7
TONE AMP, AND 6AX5 RECTIFIER.

ST-83

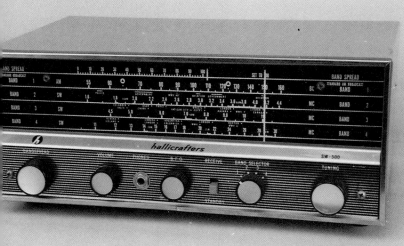

SW-500

SW-500   NONE   1961 $69.95

A 4-TUBE 4-BAND GENERAL COVERAGE RECEIVER IDENTICAL IN EVERY
WAY TO THE S-120 EXCEPT FOR THE COLOR OF THE LOWER PORTION
OF THE FRONT PANEL. FOR MORE TECHNICAL DATA SEE MODEL S-120.

SWE

SWE   NONE   1960   UNKNOWN

SWE IS THE MILITARY (USAF) MODEL NUMBER FOR THE SX-116. FOR TECHNICAL DETAILS
SEE MODEL NUMBER SX-116.

T900   NONE   1951   UNKNOWN

A "COLOR TRANSCENDER" FOR USE WITH THE 800 SERIES BLACK & WHITE TV SETS. THE
PURPOSE OF THIS ACCESSORY IS TO CONVERT THE SWEEP CIRCUITS OF THE TV FROM 525
LINES USED IN STANDARD BLACK & WHITE TRANSMISSIONS TO 405 LINES USED IN THE
PROPOSED NEW COLOR TRANSMISSION SYSTEM. ONCE INSTALLED, SWITCHING BETWEEN
THE TWO SWEEP SYSTEMS IS DONE AUTOMATICALLY BY THE TRANSCENDER. THE COLOR
PICTURE RECEIVED WOULD STILL BE IN BLACK & WHITE, BUT IT WOULD NOT BE VIEW-
ABLE AT ALL WITHOUT THE TRANSCENDER. THE UNIT CONSISTS OF ONE TUBE (6CD6)
AND MANY RESISTORS, CAPACITORS, COILS, AND ADJUSTING CONTROLS. SOLD AS A KIT
TO BE MOUNTED ON THE REAR APRON OF THE TV CHASSIS. IT DERIVES ITS POWER FROM
THE TV's POWER SUPPLY.

T900

TG-10F   NONE   1945   UNKNOWN

A CODE PRACTICE PAPER TAPE KEYER DESIGNED TO TRAIN MILITARY RADIO OPERATORS IN RECEIVING MORSE CODE. IT CONSISTS OF A VARIABLE-SPEED PAPER PUNCHED TAPE PLAYER AND 15-WATT AUDIO AMPLIFIER WITH PROVISION FOR SIMULTAINIOUS USE OF UP TO 300 HEADPHONE SETS, AND INPUTS FOR PHONOGRAPH AND MICROPHONE.

TG-10F

TR-5A,B,C HAMLET RADIO   1966-69   UNKNOWN

DESIGNED BY THE RADIO INDUSTRIES DIVISION FOR PARAMILITARY USE, THIS SINGLE-CHANNEL CRYSTAL-CONTROLLED AM TRANSCEIVER OPERATES IN THE 30 TO 40MHz BAND. THE RECEIVER IS A SOLID-STATE DUAL CONVERSION TYPE WITH IF FREQUENCIES OF 455KHz AND 10.455MHz AND A SENSITIVITY OF 1 MICROVOLT. THE 4-WATT TRANSMITTER IS MOSTLY SOLID-STATE WITH TWO 7905 TUBES AS OSCILLATOR AND POWER AMPLIFIER. THERE ARE A TOTAL OF 17 TRANSISTORS, 12 DIODES, AND 2 TUBES. THE PURPOSE OF THE UNIT IS POINT-TO-POINT COMMUNICATIONS AND RADIO NETS WITH THE TR-20 AS THE NET CONTROL STATION. THE POWER SOURCE IS 12 VOLTS DC. THERE ARE MINOR COSMETIC AND ELECTRICAL DIFFERENCES BETWEEN THE A, B, & C UNITS.

TR-5A HAMLET RADIO

TR-9   NONE   1969   UNKNOWN

A SOLID-STATE 3-BAND 10-WATT VFO CONTROLLED AM/CW TRANSCEIVER COVERING 2 TO 12MHz. THE RECEIVER AND TRANSMITTER EACH HAVE THEIR OWN SEPARATE CALLIBRATED VFO AND BUILT-IN ANTENNA TUNERS ALLOWING USE OF THE SAME OR DIFFERENT RECEIVE AND TRANSMIT FREQUENCIES OVER THE ENTIRE TUNING RANGE OF THE UNIT. IN ADDITION THERE ARE SIX SWITCH-SELECTABLE FIXED-FREQUENCY CRYSTAL POSITIONS PROVIDED. WITH A POWER SOURCE OF 12 VOLTS DC, THE UNIT CAN BE USED IN PORTABLE, MOBILE, OR BASE OPERATION DEPENDING ON THE OPTIONAL POWER SUPPLIES. THERE ARE 27 TRANSISTORS INCLUDING SEVERAL FETs, AND NUMEROUS DIODES.

TR-9

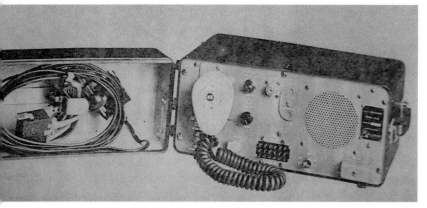

TR-20 VILLAGE RADIO

TR-20   VILLAGE RADIO   1966-69   UNKNOWN

THE TR-20 IS A SINGLE-CHANNEL CRYSTAL-CONTROLLED AM TRANCEIVER FOR USE IN THE 30 TO 40MHz BAND. VERY SIMILAR TO THE TR-5 WITH ITS SOLID-STATE DUAL CONVERSION RECEIVER AND HYBRID TRANSMITTER. THE DIFFERENCES ARE THE 20-WATT POWER OUTPUT OF THE TRANSMITTER AND DUAL POWER SUPPLY (12-VOLT DC & 120-VOLT AC). THE PURPOSE OF THE UNIT IS TO BE THE NET CONTROL OR BASE STATION FOR USE WITH THE TR-5 FIELD UNITS AND THE HT-1 SERIES HANDHELDS. IT WAS BUILT BY THE RADIO INDUSTRIES DIVISION.

TR-35,A   NONE   1966   UNKNOWN

A 4-CHANNEL CRYSTAL-CONTROLLED AM/CW TRANSCEIVER FOR USE IN THE 2 TO 9MHz BAND. THE UNIT FEATURES A SOLID-STATE SINGLE CONVERSION RECEIVER WITH A 455KHz IF, AND A HYBRID TRANSMITTER WITH A POWER OUTPUT OF 35 WATTS. IT HAS A DUAL POWER SUPPLY (12 VOLTS DC & 120 VOLTS AC) ALLOWING IT TO BE USED IN MOBILE OR BASE STATION OPERATIONS. THIS RADIO HAS 17 TRANSISTORS, 18 DIODES, AND 2 TUBES, A 7905 AS THE TRANSMITTER OSCILLATOR AND A 4604 AS THE FINAL RF AMPLIFIER. BUILT BY THE RADIO INDUSTRIES DIVISION.

TR-35, A

TR-88

TR-88   NONE   1955-57   UNKNOWN

A SINGLE BAND PORTABLE RADIO WITH SIX PLUG-IN TRANSISTORS, COVERING THE AM STANDARD BROADCAST BAND. HOUSED IN A LEATHER CASE AND USING 4 "D" CELLS AS A POWER SOURCE, THIS IS ONE OF THE FIRST COMMERCIAL TRANSISTOR RADIOS.

UPN-1   NONE   1943   UNKNOWN

HAVE NO INFORMATION ON THIS UNIT OTHER THAN HEARSAY THAT T IS A MILITARY RADIO RECEIVER FOR USE IN THE 3000MHz FREQUENCY RANGE.

2F   SKY ELITE   1975   UNKNOWN

A SOLID-STATE CRYSTAL-CONTROLLED 12-CHANNEL 2-METER FM TRANS-CEIVER. FEATURES INCLUDE SQUELCH, COMBINATION RF OUTPUT AND S-METER, BUILT-IN SPEAKER, EAR-PHONE JACK, AND PTT MICROPHONE. THE POWER SOURCE IS 12 VOLTS DC.

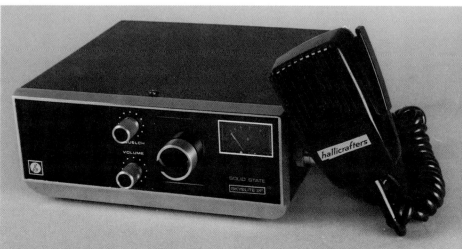

2F SKY ELITE

3HFP-1, 3HFP-2 (FRONT VIEW)

6HFP-1 VIRTUOSO

3HFP-1, 3HFP-2 (TOP VIEW)

51C1A

| 3HFP-1 | NONE | 1956 | UNKNOWN |
| 3HFP-2 | | | |

A 3-SPEED DUAL-SPEAKER HI-FI PHONOGRAPH HOUSED IN A WOOD TABLETOP CABINET. FEATURES INCLUDE A WEBCORE THREE-SPEED AUTOMATIC RECORD CHANGER, 8" WOOFER, AND 3" TWEETER. THE 3HP-1 IS MAHOGANY AND THE 3HP-2 IS LIMED OAK. THE POWER SOURCE IS 120 VOLTS AC. TUBES USED: 12AX7 PRE-AMP AND DRIVER, AND TWO 35C5 IN PUSH-PULL AUDIO OUTPUT. THE RECTIFIER IS A SILICON DIODE.

6HFP-1	VIRTUOSO	1956	UNKNOWN
6HFP-2			
8HFP-1			
8HFP-2			

A 6-TUBE 3-SPEED DUAL-SPEAKER HI-FI PHONOGRAPH HOUSED IN A WOOD TABLETOP CABINET SUPPORTED BY U-SHAPED WROUGHT-IRON LEGS. FEATURES INCLUDE SEPARATE BASS AND TREBLE TONE CONTROLS, A FIVE-POSITION AUDIO COMPENSATOR SWITCH, 8" WOOFER, 3" TWEETER, AND A WEBCORE THREE-SPEED AUTOMATIC RECORD CHANGER. THE 6HFP-1 AND 8HFP-1 ARE MAHOGANY, AND THE 6HFP-2 AND 8HFP-2 ARE LIMED OAK. ELECTRONICALLY THE 6 AND 8 SERIES ARE THE SAME; THE DIFFERENCES ARE IN THE STYLE OF CABINETS, AND THE RECORD CHANGER. THE POWER SOURCE IS 120 VOLTS AC. TUBES USED: 6AT6 1st AUDIO, 12AX7 2nd AND 3rd AUDIO, 6SN7 4th AUDIO AND PHASE IN-VERTER, TWO 6V6GT IN PUSH-PULL AUDIO OUTPUT, AND 5Y3GT RECTIFIER.

51C2A

400

329

400

| 51C1, A | NONE | 1954 | UNKNOWN |
| 51C2, A | | | |

A 5-TUBE 1-BAND TABLETOP CLOCK RADIO COVERING THE AM STANDARD BROADCAST BAND. FEATURES INCLUDE DUAL TOP-MOUNTED 3" SPEAKERS, SIDE-MOUNTED CONTROLS, A LARGE EASY-TO-READ FULL-FRONT CLOCK DIAL, AND A TIMED APPLIANCE OUTLET. THE POWER SOURCE IS 120 VOLTS AC. HOUSED IN WOOD CABINETS, THE 51C1 IS MAHOGANY AND THE 51C2 IS A GRAY-BLOND. THERE ARE MINOR COSMETIC DIFFERENCES IN THE A MODELS. TUBES USED: 12BE6 OSCILLATOR AND MIXER, 12BD6 IF, 12AV6 1st AUDIO AND DETECTOR, 50C5 AUDIO OUTPUT, AND 35W4 RECTIFIER. THE IF FREQUENCY IS 455KHz.

| 51C1B | NONE | 1956 | UNKNOWN |
| 51C2B | | | |

THE 51C1B AND 51C2B ARE BASICALLY THE SAME RADIO AS THE A SERIES, WITH MINOR COSMETIC AND ELECTRONIC DIFFERENCES INCLUDING A SINGLE TOP-MOUNTED SPEAKER. THE 51C1B IS MAHOGANY AND THE 51C2B IS GRAY-BLOND.

| 329 | NONE | 1979 | UNKNOWN |

A SOLID-STATE 3-BAND PORTABLE RECEIVER COVERING THE AM AND FM STANDARD BROADCAST BANDS AND ALL 40 CB CHANNELS. FEATURES INCLUDE A BUILT-IN FERRITE ROD LOOP ANTENNA FOR AM, A TELESCOPING WHIP ANTENNA FOR THE FM AND CB BAND, EARPHONE JACK, A DUAL POWER SUPPLY FOR BATTERY OR 120-VOLT AC OPERATION, AND THAT "MILITARY LOOK" SO POPULAR AT THE TIME. MADE IN HONG KONG.

| 400 | NONE | 1947 | $479.50 |

A 12-TUBE 3-BAND RECEIVER COVERING THE AM AND FM STANDARD BROADCAST BANDS AND SHORT-WAVE FROM 5.8MHz TO 18MHz, HOUSED IN A CONSOLE CABINET. FOR MORE TECHNICAL INFORMATION SEE MODEL EC-400.

611	NONE	1954	UNKNOWN
612			

A 6-TUBE 1-BAND TABLE RADIO COVERING THE AM STANDARD BROADCAST BAND AND HOUSED IN A PLASTIC CASE. BUILT-IN 4" x 6" PM SPEAKER AND LOOP ANTENNA. THE IF IS 455KHz AND THE POWER SOURCE IS 120 VOLTS AC/DC. TUBES USED: 12BA6 RF AMP, 12BE6 OSCILLATOR AND MIXER, 12BA6 IF, 12AV6 DETECTOR, AVC, AND 1st AUDIO, 35C5 AUDIO OUTPUT, AND 35W4 RECTIFIER. THE ONLY DIFFERENCE BETWEEN THE 611 AND THE 612 IS THE COLOR OF THE CASE, WHICH IS ALSO THE SAME CASE USED ON THE 621 AND THE 622.

621	NONE	1955	UNKNOWN
622			

THE 621 AND THE 622 ARE COSMETICALLY AND ELECTRONICALLY SIMILAR TO THE 611 AND THE 612. THESE MODELS COVER TWO BANDS, THE STANDARD AM BROADCAST BAND AND SHORT-WAVE FROM 5.9MHz TO 18MHz. BUILT-IN FERRITE ROD LOOP ANTENNA FOR THE BROADCAST BAND AND PROVISION FOR EXTERNAL ANTENNA FOR SHORT-WAVE. TUBES USED AND OTHER SPECIFICATIONS ARE THE SAME AS FOR THE 611 AND 612, AND AGAIN THE DIFFERENCE BETWEEN THE 621 AND THE 622 IS THE COLOR OF THE CASE.

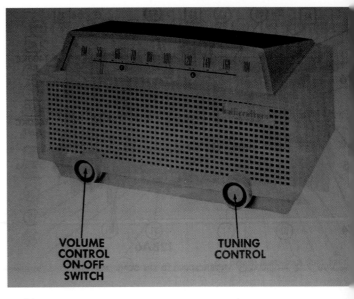

VOLUME CONTROL ON-OFF SWITCH   TUNING CONTROL

611

621

Model 1621 (Mahogany)
Model 1622 (Maple)

1621 SUPER FIDELITY

7002

1621	SUPER FIDELITY	1954	UNKNOWN
1622			

A HIGH-FIDELITY COMPONENT SYSTEM HOUSED IN A WOOD CONSOLE CABINET AND CONSISTING OF THE ST-83 AM/FM TUNER/PREAMP, THE A-84 TRIODE AMPLIFIER, A GARRARD MODEL RC-80 THREE-SPEED AUTOMATIC RECORD CHANGER, A 15" BASS SPEAKER, A HORN-TYPE TWEETER, AND CROSS-OVER NETWORKS. THE CABINET OF THE 1621 IS MAHOGANY, AND THE 1622 IS MAPLE; OTHERWISE THESE MODELS ARE IDENTICAL. THE SYSTEM HAS A TOTAL OF 17 TUBES. FOR MORE TECHNICAL SPECIFICATIONS SEE THE INDIVIDUAL COMPONENT MODELS.

7002	NONE	1973	UNKNOWN

A SOLID-STATE AM-FM TABLETOP CLOCK RADIO FEATURING A RED L.E.D. DIGITAL DISPLAY, SLEEP TIMER, EARPHONE JACK, BRIGHT OR DIM DISPLAY SWITCH, AND CHOICE OF MUSIC OR ALARM FOR WAKING. THE POWER SOURCE IS 120 VOLTS AC. MADE IN HONG KONG.

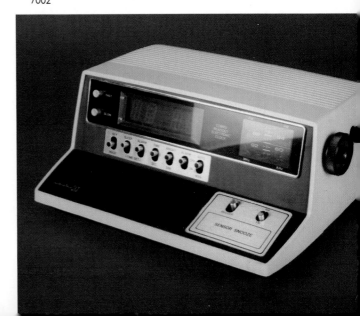

MISCELLANEOUS COMPLETE RECEIVING
AND TRANSMITTING STATIONS

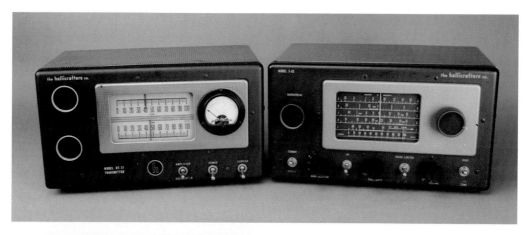

The HT-17 and S-53, circa 1948-50.

The HT-18 and S-53A, circa 1950.

The HT-40 and SX-140, circa 1961-64.

The HT-46 and SX-146, circa 1965-69.

The SR-42, HA-26, and SR-46, circa 1964.

The SR-42A, HA-26, and SR-46A, circa 1965-69.

The HT-44 and SX-117 with the PS-150-120 power supply, HA-10 and HA-8, circa 1962.

The SR-2000 with P-2000 power supply and HA-20 VFO, circa 1965-72.

MISCELLANEOUS ITEMS
WITHOUT MODEL NUMBERS

A few Hallicrafters brand tubes, which were used in all equipment shipped from the factory.

A Hallicrafters desk microphone with PTT and lock-on features, circa late 1950s.

This one-of-a-kind unit is a model 101 R.F. Coil Comparator, a test unit built by the in-house test equipment laboratory. Its purpose was to check RF coils supplied by vendors to find "matched pairs" to be installed in the production equipment, circa 1940s. There wasn't time before the photo shoot to restore this unit, but that project is scheduled soon!

Tuning units and coils for the HT-6 with original boxes, circa 1939-45.

A carbon-type desk microphone with PTT for use with the HT-1 through the HT-9, circa 1939-44.

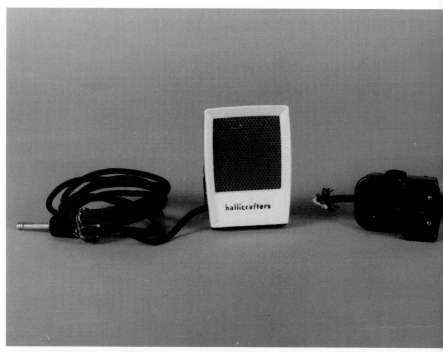

Two examples of Hallicrafters handheld microphones, one from the mid-1940s and the other from the late 1950s.

A model shop mock-up of a unknown six-channel transceiver consisting of a cardboard panel with controls and labels sitting in a steel frame, circa 1970s, from the plant in El Paso, Texas.

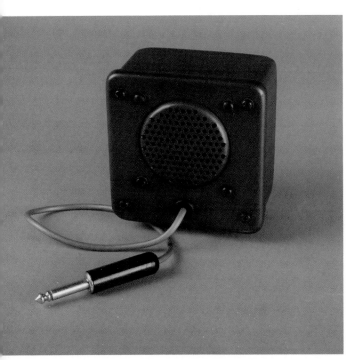

An extension speaker for use with the FM-5 series paramillitary transceivers.

A 2-1/2" by 3" panel meter made by the Simpson Meter Co. for Bill Halligan as a promotional sample, with the hopes that Bill would chose the Simpson Co. to produce meters for Hallicrafters equipment. It dates to about 1960.

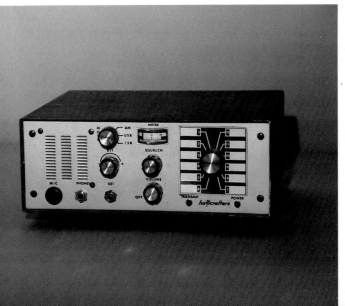

A model shop mock-up of a unknown twelve-channel transceiver consisting of a aluminum panel with controls and labels mounted on a aluminum case, circa 1970s, from the plant in El Paso, Texas.

Employee Incentives, Small Promotional Items, and Jewelry

A tie clip issued for three years of service to the company, circa 1950s.

A tie-tac from the 1960s, reason for issue unknown.

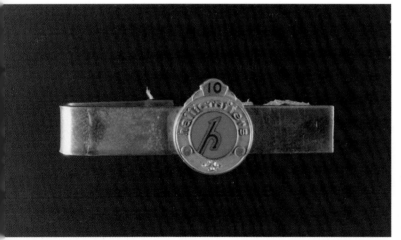

A tie clip issued for ten years of service to the company, circa 1960s.

The Hallicrafters Co. was a non-union shop. This button was issued by the company during a time when the union was trying to organize the employees. Its purpose was to let the union organizers know that the employee wearing the button did not want the union and would "rather fight than switch" from a non-union shop to a union shop! From the mid-1960s.

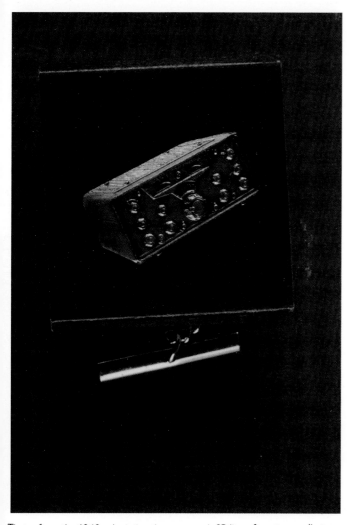

Tie-tac from the 1960s, depicting the company's SR line of amateur radio transceivers.

A TV penny bank, advertising Hallicrafters TVs and again given away by the distributors, circa 1950s.

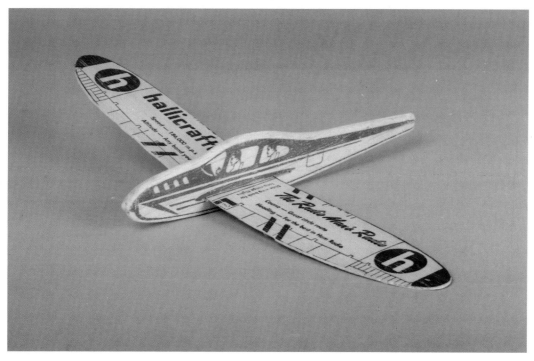

A balsa wood glider advertising Hallicrafters products. Items like this would be given away by distributors to attract customers, circa 1940s.

The front and back of a box of kitchen matches advertising Hallicrafters receivers of the 1960s.

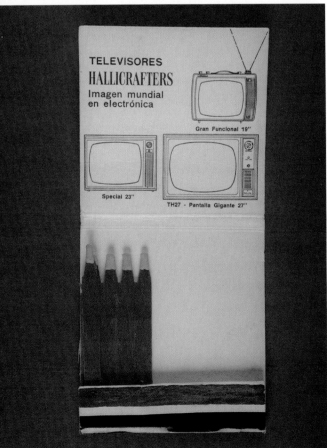

A matchbook advertising Hallicrafters TVs, another give-a-way item, from a dealer in Buenos Aires.

A stick pin depicting the famous SCR-299 WWII military communications truck which housed the BC-610 (HT-4) and other Hallicrafters-designed radio equipment, circa 1944.

A 45 rpm promotional record, narrated by Alex Dreier, which plays examples of how short-wave radio is used and some of the exciting events of the day that could be received by short-wave radio. Circa 1959.

Cloth arm patches depicting the Hallicrafters logo, circa 1960s.

This is a sterling silver belt buckle measuring 1.5" by 3", depicting the company's second logo of the mid- and late 1930s. I had it made for me in the late 1970s.

An anouncement of the Armed Forces Communication Association meeting in 1952. This meeting was called to discuss the use of the new printed circuit technology. The unusual thing about this announcement is that it is etched on printed circuit matterial.

the hallicrafters ★
MIDGET CW TRANSMITTER
OUTPUT—2 Lung Power
OPERATING RANGE—How hard
can you blow?
FREQUENCY—Let your conscience
be your guide!
the hallicrafters, inc.
2611 Indiana Ave.   CHICAGO, U. S. A.
WORLD'S LARGEST BUILDERS OF AMATEUR
COMMUNICATIONS RECEIVERS

The front and back of a wooden whistle depicting the HT-1 transmitter. This was a distributor give-away to announce the company's new transmitter product line, circa 1939.

A 65-page credit card–size book explaining how short-wave radio transmissions work including frequency skip, propagation, etc.. It also serves as advertising for the receiver product line, with descriptions and photos of many of the company's receivers of the mid-1950s.

Signs, Dealer Displays, and Packaging

A hand-painted clear plexiglass window sign for Hallicrafters TVs.

A bottom-lighted display sign built of plywood. The letters in the word Hallicrafters are individually cut from wood and are from 2.5" to 5" tall and 3/4" thick. The light source is a single 24" florescent tube. Circa mid-1950s.

A back-lighted window sign with the single word Hallicrafters. The backdrop is a slab of mahogany wood with holes cut in the shape of the letters. The letters themselves are individually cut from 3/8" clear plexiglass and placed over the corrosponding holes in the wood. The letter size is from 2.5" to 5". The light source is a single 24" florescent tube. Circa mid-1950s. This sign hangs in my office and is often used as a night light!

A Hallicrafters neon window sign in blue and green, from the mid-1950s.

A display sign for Hallicrafters TVs, painted on a steel panel approximately 2' by 3', circa mid-1950s.

A television sign on poster board, approximately 2' by 2'.

Red cloth display room banner, 1950s.

Green cloth display room banner, 1960s

The original shipping box for the HT-17 is typical of 1940s packaging.

The original boxes for the HT-17 tuning units, circa 1947.

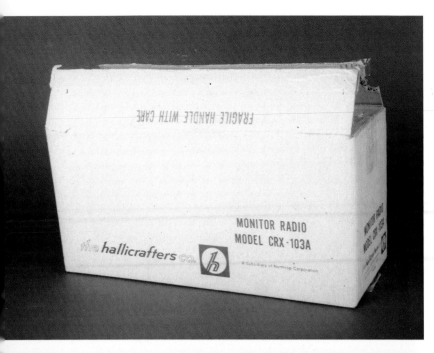

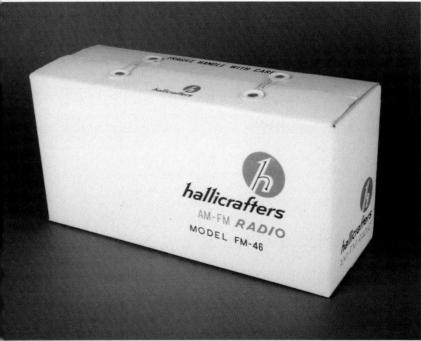

The original shipping boxes for the CRX-103A and FM-46, typical of the 1960s.

Small parts boxes (these are for crystals) typical of the 1960s.

Miscellaneous Advertising Brochures and Items

A cover shot of product catalogue #36, dated 1944-45.

A cover shot of product catalogue #P-38, dated 1946.

A cover shot of the 1970 price list.

The cover of the company's monthly in-house newsletter of the 1940s, "The Tuner."

the "COMMUNICATOR"

Published for the benefit of *hallicrafters* employees

VOL. II, NO. 9   May 1, 1969

QUARTERLY FILING DEADLINE MAY 2 FOR SALARIED SAVINGS PLAN

All Hallicrafters salaried personnel are reminded that the deadline for filing an application or notice of change in the Salaried Savings Plan is this Friday, May 2. Changes and entries become effective Monday, May 5.

The filing period for this quarter is called particularly to the attention of salaried employees who received a pay increase recently. You must file a notice of change if you wish to increase your contribution during this quarter.

"An increase in salary does not automatically raise the contribution to the Salaried Savings Plan," it was emphasized by Clete Wiot, Manager of Employee Relations and Services. "In authorizing the amount he wants de-

is earning $200 per week and authorizes the contribution of 5% of his base salary. This amounts to $10 per week. If he gets a salary increase to $220 per week, we do not automatically deduct 5% of $220, which is $11, we continue to deduct $10 per week until the employee authorizes us to increase the contribution."

If you are a salaried employee who recently received an increase in pay you are now eligible to make a larger contribution to the Salaried Savings Plan. To make the increase effective this quarter you must file a notice of change by this Friday, May 2.

Non-participating, eligible employees are encouraged to take advantage of this opportunity because new applications will not be accepted again until

and must have completed 90 days of continuous employment with the Company.

Participating employees have three investment options:

    Option 1 - 100% in Bond Fund

    Option 2 - 50% in Bond Fund
                      50% in Stock Fund

    Option 3 - 100% in Stock Fund

Participants must invest at least 2%, but not more than 5% of their weekly base salary (limited to even dollars) based on their salary of May 1, 1969. However, when salaried employees have continuously participated in the plan for at least three years, they may make a maximum contribution of 8% of their weekly base salary.

The cover of the company's monthly in-house newsletter of the 1960s, "The Communicator."

The cover of an amateur radio station log book, circa 1960s, usually given out by distributors as promotional material.

An early 1960s form used by distributors to order advertising, displays, and promotional material.

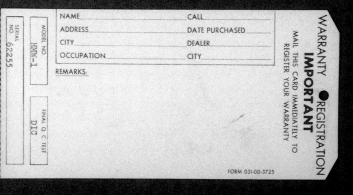

A product warantee registration card, circa 1950s and early 1960s.

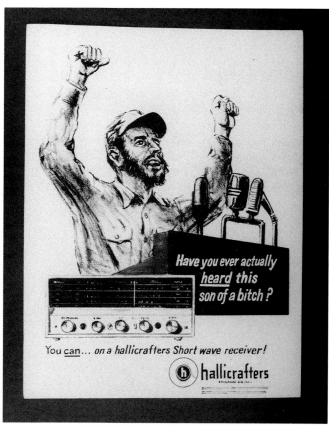

This advertisement from 1960-61 provides a glimpse into national sentiments about Castro and Cuba.

A late 1930s postcard for requesting information on the company's products.

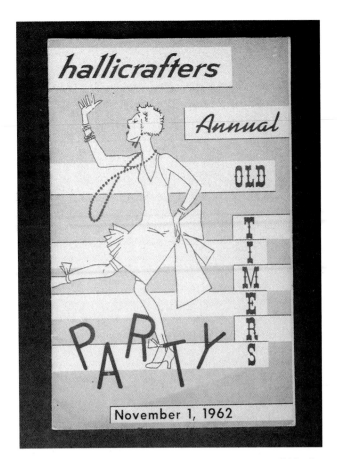

The 1962 "Old Timers Party" invitation booklet. Inside are pictures and names of Hallicrafters employees being honored for their years of service (spanning anywhere from one year to thirty), and details of the banquet. This was an annual event.

This advertisment stresses the importance of genuine Hallicrafters service personnel, circa 1940s.

Some examples of the scope of the company's distributor advertising program.

Miscellaneous advertising from the 1960s

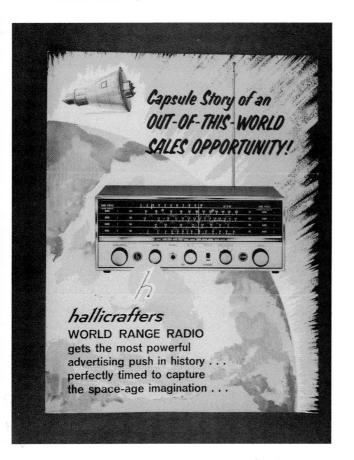

A stand-up cardboard dealer display advertising the T-54 television. This ad was also published in *The Saterday Evening Post.*

Display cards about Hallicrafters radio in several different languages, circa late 1960s and early 1970s.

A typical FCC license notice appearing on 1940s and 1950s radio equipment.

Part of a page from the 1934 Silver Marshall/Hallicrafters catalogue showing the "NRA" stamp. This stamp indicates that Hallicrafters contributed to Franklin D. Roosevelt's National Recovery Act, which had been implemented to pull the United States out of the Depression.

NOTICE
This equipment is licensed by the Federal Communications Commission, Washington, D.C. Tampering with or otherwise molesting this apparatus is punishable by fine or imprisonment or both.

the hallicrafters co. Chicago, Illinois

094-902895

MEET YOUR NEW NEIGHBOR...

The people of Rio will be new radio neighbors as soon as the job of winning the war and the peace is done. Doing that job well is the most important thing today in the eyes of the people of Hallicrafters. After the war only, will they turn their post-war plans into reality and bring to you the results of their full time war efforts to open a new post-war chapter in the history of Radio.

Waging a winning war on world wide fronts calls for the utmost in research engineering and production to turn out the finest equipment for our armed forces. Hallicrafters is doing just that: producing receivers and transmitters that are helping to speed the day when you will meet and know your South American neighbor simply by turning the dial of *your* Hallicrafters Radio.

HALLICRAFTERS - Builders of the Army's SCR-299 radio communications truck . . . this high powered mobile GIANT OF MILITARY RADIO fights on all battlefronts helping to knock out the enemy by directing the fire of land, sea and air forces. The SCR-299 forges tightly the links in the chain of communications. It "gets the message through!" THE HALLICRAFTERS CO., MANUFACTURERS OF RADIO AND ELECTRONIC EQUIPMENT, CHICAGO 16, U.S.A.

BUY A WAR BOND TODAY!

hallicrafters RADIO

An advertisment on the rear cover of "Radio News" (June 1944) with a patriotic message about buying war bonds. The SCR-299 is shown.

The following photographs show a stand-up dealer display sandwich board advertising the new line of Hallicrafters TVs. The pages provided potential customers with some of the company's history, the radio products, the plants, and the production line, circa early 1950s.

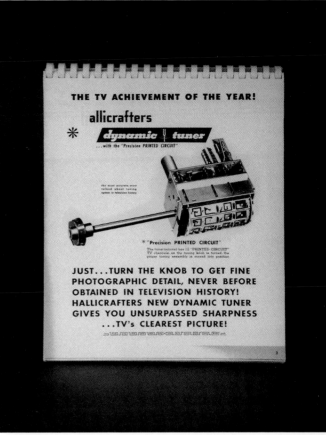

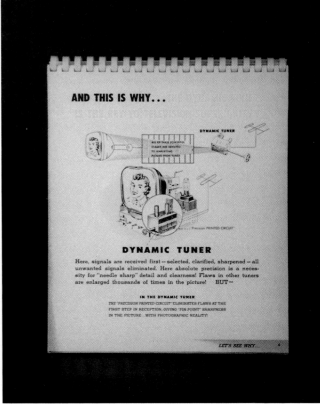

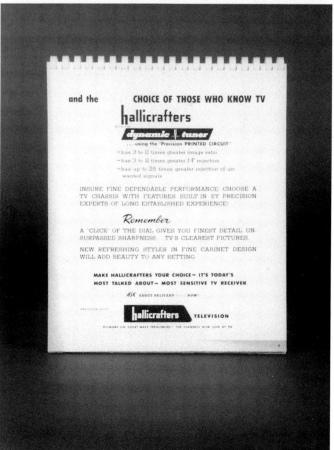

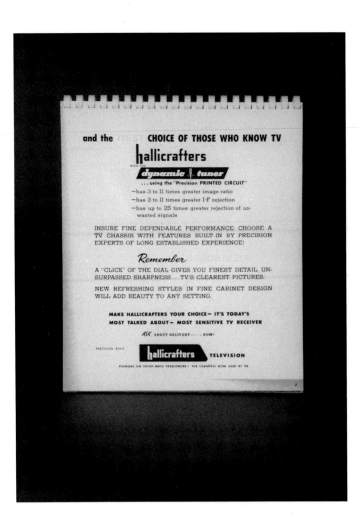

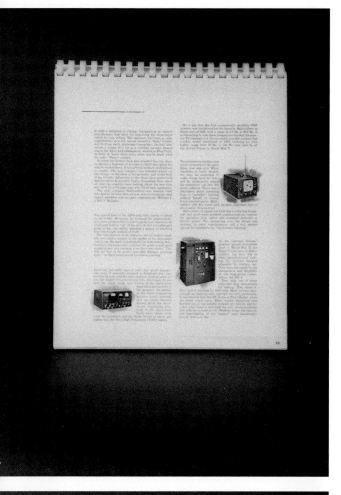

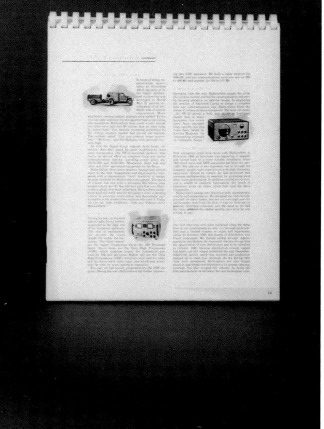

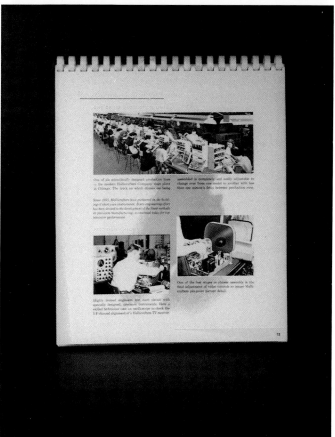

One of six scientifically designed production lines in the modern Hallicrafters Company main plant in Chicago. The track on which chassis are being assembled is completely and easily adjustable to change over from one model to another with less than one minute's delay between production runs.

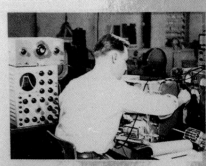

Highly trained engineers test each circuit with specially designed, precision instruments. Here a skilled technician uses an oscilloscope to check the I-F channel alignment of a Hallicrafters TV receiver.

One of the last stages in chassis assembly is the final adjustment of video controls to insure Hallicrafters pin-point picture detail.

The world's largest exclusive manufacturer of short wave radio communications equipment.

Plant No. 1 .. Occupying four entire floors at 2600 Indiana Avenue in Chicago.

Plant No. 2 .. Devoted to the fabrication of steel chassis — another Hallicrafters progressive expansion

the **hallicrafters** co.
2611 Indiana Ave., CHICAGO, U.S.A.
Cable Address, HALLICRAFT, CHICAGO

Index and Price Guide

The following chart provides current value ranges for Hallicrafters products, and serves as an index for where these items can be found in this book. All values here are solely my own opinion, averages based on many years of buying radio products, and seeing them for sale at swap meets. They represent "general retail" sales, often from auctions or private sales (like estate sales or garage sales). A serious collector who needs a particular model may be willing to go higher—depending on how long it has taken to locate the piece! Keep in mind that values vary in different geographical locations, and that the values of vintage communications equipment are very volatile; in recent years they have increased at an astonishing rate. When there was not enough information available to make a reasonable estimate, I have not provided a value.

Words like "mint," "good," and "average" can be defined differently by each collector or dealer. All values here are for items that are complete, not cosmetically or electronically modified, in good cosmetic condition; they may or may not be in good operating condition. Good cosmetic condition, for Hallicrafters equipment, means that the item is clean, with no rust or corrosion, and no degradation of the painted and lettered surfaces.

Items within this list are arranged in alphabetical and numerical order, and values are in U. S. dollars. For items that were sold either "factory wired" or in a kit form, I have provided values for the factory wired editions; those sold as kits were assembled by the customers, and their electronic merits are variable. The listing here for the kit version will refer you to the model number of the factory wired version, with an asterisk (*). The values of some items include the power source unit; these prices include the note "w.p.s." (with power source).

Model	Name	Page	Price
#822		157	$75-90
#832		157	$75-90
#860, 861		157	$100-150
#870, 871		158	$75-90
#880		158	$75-90
#890, 894, 898		158	$100-150
#1000		159	$75-90
#1001-#1004, 1007		159	$75-90
#1005, 1006		159	$75-90
#1008		159	$75-90
#1010, 1012, 1013		160	$50-80
#1015-#1019		160	$75-90
#1021, 1022, 1026, 1027		160	$75-90
#1025		160	$75-90
#1050		161	$50-80
#1051-#1056		160	$50-80
#1060-#1063		160	$50-80
#1072-#1078		161	$50-80
#1081, 1082		161	$50-80
#1085, 1086		161	$50-80
#1088		161	$50-80
#1092		161	$50-80
#1111		161	$50-80
#1113		161	$50-80
1621, 1622	Super Fidelity	194	$150-250
7002		194	$15-30
#14808		161	$50-80
#17804		162	$50-80
#17810, 17811		162	$50-80
#17812-#17815		162	$50-80
#17816, 17817		162	$50-80
#17819		162	$50-80
#17824, 17825		162	$50-80
#17838		162	$50-80
#17848-#17850		162	$50-80
#17860, 17861		162	$50-80
#17905, 17906		162	$50-80
#17908		162	$50-80
#1790P, 1790U		161	$35-60
#17922		162	$50-80
#17930-#17934		162	$50-80
#20823		162	$50-80
#20872		163	$50-80
#20882		163	$50-80
#20990, 20994		163	$100-150
#21923		163	$50-80
#21928		163	$50-80
#21940		163	$50-80
#21980		163	$50-80
A-80C		104	
A-82		104	
A-84	Super Fidelity	168	$60-80
A-85		169	
AN/GRR2			see SX-28
AT-1, 2, 3	Atom	169	$25-35
AT-3		104	$150-200
AT2	(antenna tuner)	104	
ATCL-5 through 11	Atom	169	$35-45
ATX-11, 12, 13		170	$25-35
B-42		104	
BA-100		104	
BA-101		104	
BC-13		105	
BC-441-A		170	$60-90
BC-610, A through F			see HT-4
BC-614, A through F			see HT-5
BC-669, 669A			see HT-14
BC-939			see AT-3
BL-20		105	
CA-2, CA-4	Skyfone	170	$60-80
CB-1	Little Fone	116	$40-60
CB-2	Little Fone	117	$40-60
CB-3, CB-3A	Little Fone	117	$40-60
CB-4	Little Fone	117	$20-40
CB-5	Little Fone	118	$40-60
CB-6	Little Fone	118	$20-40
CB-7	Little Fone	118	$40-60
CB-8	Little Fone	118	$20-40
CB-9	Little Fone	119	$40-60
CB-10		119	$30-50
CB-11, 11A	Little Fone	119	$30-50/pr.
CB-12		120	$30-50
CB-14		120	$40-60
CB-15		120	$20-40
CB-17		120	$40-60
CB-18		121	$20-40
CB-19		121	$40-60
CB-20		121	$20-40
CB-21	Reacter II	121	$20-40
CB-24		122	$20-40
CB-181		122	$20-40
CN-1		105	
CPCR-1		170	$100-150
CR-44, CR-44A	Ranger	171	$20-40
CR-50	Sea Air	171	$20-40
CR-3000		171	$75-100
CRX-1		108	$30-50
CRX-2, CRX-2A		109	$30-50
CRX-3		109	$30-50
CRX-4	Civic Patrol	109	$30-50
CRX-5	Civic Patrol	110	$30-50
CRX-100, 101, 102	Portamon	110	$20-40
CRX-103, 103A	Civic Monitor	110	$20-40
CRX-105, 105A	Civic Monitor	110	$20-40
CRX-106, 107	Portamon	110	$20-40
CSB-20-2	Command Line	172	
CSB-30-2	Command Line	172	
CSB-100-2	Command Line	173	
CSM-20-2	Command Line	172	
CSM-30-2	Command Line	172	
CTS-2, 4		105	
DD-1	Skyrider Diversity	33	$4000-6000 w/DD-A, DD-P
DD-A	Audio Power Amp	33	see DD-1
DD-CS		111	
DD-P	Tuner Power Supply	33	see DD-1
EC, EC-1	Echophone Commercial	146	$40-60
EC-1, B	Echophone Commercial	146	$45-65
EC-2	Echophone Commercial	147	$50-75
EC-3	Echophone Commercial	147	$55-80
EC-6	Echophone Commercial	147	$45-65
EC-112, 113, 114		148	$45-65
EC-306		148	$50-75
EC-400, 401, 402, 406		149	$35-65 w/only chassis; $95-200 w/cabinets
EC-403, 404		149	$150-350
EC-600		150	$45-65
EP-132		173	
EX-102, 103		150	$45-65
EX-104, 106		150	$50-70
EX-107		150	$60-80
EX-306		148	$50-75
FM-46, FM-48		174	$20-40
FM-52, 54, 56		174	$25-45
FM-66		174	$30-50
FM-1000		175	$20-40
FPM-200		97	$800-1000
FPM-300		98	$175-300
FPM-300 Mark II Safari		98	$175-300
H-3		105	
H-5, H-6, H-7	Handcraft	140	
H-8, H-10	Handcraft	141	
H-12	Handcraft	142	
H-13	Round the World	142	
H2M-500, H2M-1000		175	
H8PA	Sky Master	175	
HA-1, 1A	T.O. Keyer	99	$40-60
HA-2		99	$175-250 w.p.s.
HA-3, 3A		100	
HA-4	T.O. Keyer	100	$40-60
HA-5		100	$45-65
HA-6		99	$175-250 w.p.s.
HA-7		101	
HA-8	Splatter Guard	101	$40-60
HA-9		101	
HA-10		101	$40-60
HA-11		101	
HA-12, 12A		101	
HA-13		102	
HA-14, HA-15, HA-16		102	
HA-18, 18A		102	$25-35

Model	Name	Page	Price
HA-19		103	
HA-20		103	$90-150
HA-26		103	$25-40
HA-32		103	
HA-36		103	
HA-60		103	
HA-700, 800, 900		103	
HA-985		103	
HC-1		123	see HCW-1*
HC-100, 100H	Hand Command	175	
HC-150	Hand Command	176	
HC-170		176	
HC-400, 405	Hand Command	176	
HC-450		177	
HC-500		177	
HCG-3, 5		105	
HCM-260		177	$20-40
HCW-1		123	$30-50
HD-1		123	see HDW-1*
HD-2		124	see HDW-2*
HDW-1		123	$15-20
HDW-2		124	$15-30
HG-1		124	see HGW-1*
HGW-1		124	$30-60
HM-1		124	see HMW-1*
HMW-1		124	$30-60
HO-1		125	see HOW-1*
HOW-1		125	$30-60
HP-1		125	see HPW-1*
HPW-1		125	$30-60
HT-1		77	
HT-1E	Village Radio	177	
HT-2, HT-2A	Village Radio	177	
HT-2		77	
HT-3		77	
HT-4, A through F		78	$150-450
HT-5, A through F		78	$45-95
HT-6		79	$75-125
HT-7		79	$25-50
HT-8	The Cruising	80	
HT-9		80	$150-250
HT-11, A through E	The Ensign	81	
HT-12		81	
HT-14	The Commodore	82	$95-175
HT-17		82	$50-70
HT-18		82	$60-90
HT-19		83	$145-195
HT-20		83	$300-450
HT-21 LDS, LWS, HWS	Little Fone	84	
HT-22 LDS, LWS, HWS	Little Fone	84	
HT-23, HT-24	Little Fone	84	
HT-25, HT-26	Little Fone	85	
HT-30		85	$75-150
HT-31		85	$175-275
HT-32		86	$100-150
HT-32A		86	$175-225
HT-32B		86	$175-250
HT-33		87	$225-325
HT-33A		87	$375-500
HT-33B		87	$450-650
HT-36		88	
HT-37		88	$90-145
HT-40, 40K, MARK-1		89	$30-60
HT-41		89	$250-450
HT-44		90	$175-225 w.p.s.
HT-45		90	$350-450 w.p.s.
HT-46		91	$145-195
HT-86		86	$100-150
HTR-262		178	
HV	Handcraft	141	
HW	Handcraft	141	
J	Airflight	144	
JR-150/15		178	
JR-400		178	
JR-430		178	
K	Airflight	145	
LA-500		179	
————	Loudenboomer	90	$350-450 w.p.s.
MC-1		105	
MC-401S		105	
MC-412S, 412SR		105	
MHS-140A		179	
NVD-117		180	
NVD-201		180	
OPS/AU-40		180	
OPS/FM-10, 10A		182	
OPS/FM-1A, B, C		180-181	
OPS/FM-1H		181	
OPS/FM-2L		181	
OPS/FM-5 (A through G)		181	
OPS/FM-7 (A through L)		182	
OPS/PA-20		182	
OPS/PS-A16		182	
OPS/RU-5A		182	
OPS/RU-6A		182	
OPS/TS-20		106	
P-10		106	
P-20A		106	
PA-120		182	
PC-210	Porta Command	183	
PC-210F	Porta Command	183	
PC-230	Porta Command	183	
PM-12-M		112	$60-80
PM-12-S		111	$50-80
PM-23		112	$50-70
PM-8-S		111	$40-60
PS-20		106	
PS-5		114	
PT-200		184	
R-8		111	
R-8-T		111	$40-60
R-12		111	
R-12-T		111	$50-80
R-19/TRC-1		184	
R-42	Reproducer	112	$40-60
R-44		112	$30-50
R-44/ARR-5		184	$50-90
R-44B		113	$30-50
R-45	Reproducer	113	
R-45/ARR-7		184	$50-90
R-46, A, B		113	$30-50
R-47		114	$20-40
R-48, R-48A		114	$30-50
R-49		114	
R-50		115	$20-40
R-51		115	$40-60
R-75		115	
R-80		115	also see S-39
R-85		116	
R-274/FRR, R274D/FRR also see SX-73		185	$250-450
R649/UR		185	
RA-45		106	
RA-48		114	$40-50
RBK-13, RBK-15	also see S-36	185	$50-95
RBK-16		185	$50-95
RC-10		186	
RCB-100		106	
RCM-100		106	
R-CBS-1		116	
RE-1	Sky Courier	186	$45-65
R-EC2-3		116	
RM-10		106	
RSC-1, RSC-2		186	
RSP-1		116	
RTV-51, RTV-51-ML		186	
S-1	Skyrider	25	
S-2	Skyrider	26	
S-3	Skyrider	26	
S-4, 5, 6	Super Skyrider	27	$200-300
S-7	Super Skyrider	28	
S-8A		28	
S-9	Super Skyrider	28	$175-250
S-10	Ultra Skyrider	30	$250-300
S-11	Super Skyrider	30	$220-300
S-12	Skyrider Commercial	31	$250-300
S-14	Skychief	31	$100-150
S-15	Sky Challenger	31	$100-150
S-16	Super Skyrider	32	$175-225
S-17	Super Skyrider	32	$175-225
S-18	Sky Challenger II	35	$145-195
S-19	Sky Buddy	35	
S-19R	Sky Buddy	35	$75-125

Model	Name	Page	Price
S-20	Sky Champion	36	$125-145
S-20R	Sky Champion	37	$60-90
S-21	Skyrider 5-10	37	$100-125
S-22	Skyrider Marine	38	$100-125
S-22R	Skyrider Marine	38	$60-90
S-26F		40	
S-27, 27B, 27D, 27-FCC		41	$50-95
S-29	Sky Traveler	42	$45-75
S-30	Radio Compass	43	
S-31		43	
S-31A		44	
S-33	Sky Trainer	44	
S-35		45	
S-36, 36A		45	$50-95
S-37		46	$75-150
S-38		46	$75-90
S-38A, B, C, D, E, EM, EB		47-48	$40-60
S-39	Sky Ranger	49	$50-80
S-40, U, A, AU, B, BU		49-50	$50-75
S-41G, W	Skyrider Jr.	51	$45-65
S-47		53	$75-125
S-48		53	
S-49		54	
S-51, 52		54	$75-95
S-53, 53U		55	$65-85
S-53A, 53AU		56	$65-85
S-55, 56		56	$40-60
S-58, 59		57	$40-60
S-72, 72R, 72L		58	$50-75
S-76, 76U		60	$100-175
S-77		60	$45-65
S-77A		61	$45-65
S-78, S-78A		61	$40-60
S-80	Defender	62	$45-65
S-81, S-82	Civic Patrol	62	$25-50
S-85, 85U		63	$50-75
S-86		63	$50-75
S-93	Worldwide	64	$40-60
S-94, S-95	Civic Patrol	65	$25-50
S-102		67	$25-50
S-103	Continental	67	$25-40
S-106		68	$25-50
S-107		69	$45-75
S-108, S-109		69	$55-80
S-118		71	$45-65
S-119, 199K	Skybuddy II	72	$35-65
S-120		72	$25-50
S-120A		72	$25-50
S-125	Star Quest	73	$25-50
S-129		73	$60-90
S-200	Legionnaire	75	$25-50
S-210		75	$25-50
S-214		76	$30-60
S-240		76	$30-60
SBT-20, 20A, 20B		187	
SBT-22		187	
SBT-22-18		187	
SBT-100		~~199~~ 188	
SM-20, 21, 22		107	
SM-40		107	
SP-44	Skyrider Panoramic	107	$90-150
SR-34		91	$75-100
SR-34AC		91	$60-80
SR-42, 42A		92	$30-60
SR-46, 46A		93	$20-60
SR-75		93	$75-150
SR-150		94	$150-200 w.p.s.
SR-160		94	$95-125 w.p.s.
SR-400	Cyclone	95	$350-450 w.p.s.
SR-400A	Cyclone III.	95	$400-500 w.p.s.
SR-500	Console	96	
SR-500	Tornado	96	$150-200 w.p.s.
SR-540		96	
SR-750	Cyclone	97	
SR-2000	Hurricane	97	$500-700 w.p.s.
ST-74		188	
ST-83		189	$50-75
STB-1102		188	
———	Super Seven	28	
SW-500		189	$25-50
SWE		189	also see SX-116
SX-4, 5, 6	Super Skyrider	27	$200-300
SX-7	Super Skyrider	28	
SX-9	Super Skyrider	28	$175-250
SX-10	Ultra Skyrider	30	$250-300
SX-11	Super Skyrider	30	$220-300
SX-12	Skyrider Commercial	31	$250-300
SX-15	Sky Challenger	31	$100-150
SX-16	Super Skyrider	32	$175-225
SX-17	Super Skyrider	32	$175-225
SX-17-F	Super Skyrider	32	
SX-18	Sky Challenger II	35	$145-195
SX-23	Skyrider 23	39	$150-250
SX-24	Skyrider Defiant	39	$100-125
SX-25	Super Defiant	40	$125-175
SX-28	Super Skyrider	41	$125-250
SX-28, 28A, 28-FCC	Super Skyrider	42	$125-250
SX-32	Skyrider 32	44	$100-150
SX-38		49	
SX-42, 42U		51	$175-225
SX-43, 43U		52	$75-125
SX-46		53	
SX-62, 62U		57	$125-175
SX-62A, 62AU		58	$125-175
SX-62B, 62BU		58	$125-175
SX-71, 71U		58	$95-145
SX-73		59	$250-450
SX-88		63	$800-1200
SX-96		65	$125-175
SX-99, 99U		66	$75-100
SX-100		66	$200-250
SX-101, 101A		66	$90-135
SX-104		68	$25-50
SX-105		68	$25-50
SX-110		69	$75-100
SX-111		70	$125-175
SX-112		70	
SX-115		70	$350-450
SX-116		71	
SX-117		71	$145-175
SX-122R		72	
SX-122, 122A		73	$175-225
SX-130		74	$85-125
SX-133		74	$140-190
SX-140, 140K		74	$35-60
SX-146		75	$145-195
SX-1000A		76	
T-54		151	$100-150
T-60		151	
T-61, 64, 67		151	$100-150
T-68		151	
T-69		151	$80-100
T900		189	
TG-10F		190	
TR-5A, B, C	Hamlet Radio	190	
TR-9		190	
TR-20	Village Radio	191	
TR-35, TR-35A		191	
TR-88		191	
TS-1		108	
TS-22		108	
TS-201A		108	
TW-24		130	$25-45
TW-55		130	$25-35
TW-100, 101, 102		130	$25-35
TW-200A, 201A, 202A, 203A		131	$25-35
TW-500, 600	World-wide	131	$40-65
TW-1000 (A)	Worldwide	132	$60-90
TW-1200		133	
TW-2000	Worldwide	132	$60-90
UPN-1		191	
VP-2		107	
WR-600, 700, 800, 1000		125-126	$25-50
WR-1500, 2000, 2500		127	$45-65
WR-3000		128	$30-60
WR-3100		128	$20-40
WR-3200		129	$20-40
WR-4000		129	$40-70
Z-10	Round the World	143	
Z-13	Round the World	144	
Z-De Luxe	All Wave	144	